Finland
Daughter of the Sea

STUDIES IN HISTORICAL GEOGRAPHY

Also published in this series

Southern Africa
A J CHRISTOPHER

**Rural Settlement
in Britain**
BRIAN K ROBERTS

STUDIES IN HISTORICAL GEOGRAPHY

Finland
Daughter of the Sea

MICHAEL JONES

DAWSON · ARCHON BOOKS

First published in 1977

© Michael Jones 1977

Wm Dawson & Sons Ltd, Cannon House
Folkestone, Kent, England

Archon Books, The Shoe String Press, Inc
995 Sherman Avenue, Hamden, Connecticut 06514 USA

British Library Cataloguing in Publication Data

Jones, Michael
    Finland: daughter of the sea
    (Studies in historical geography)
    Bibl. – Index
    ISBN 0 7129 0695 9
    ISBN 0 208 01623 6 (Archon Books)
    ISSN 0308 6607
    1. Title
    301.34'09471   GF602.F/   LC 76-030001
    Man – Influence of environment
    Anthropo-geography – Finland
    Geology, Structural

Printed in Great Britain
by W & J Mackay Limited, Chatham
by photo-litho

Contents

Illustrations

Tables

Preface

ANYBODY WRITING ON Finland is faced with the problem of place names. Finland has two official languages, Finnish and Swedish. The latter is spoken by 6·5 per cent of the country's population, concentrated in the archipelago and coastal belts of the south and west. The country is officially divided into Finnish-speaking, Swedish-speaking and bilingual communes (local administrative units). Where placenames differ in the two languages, official usage employs the majority language first and the minority language second. This system has been adopted in the present work, using the 1970 population census as reference. In direct quotations, the form employed in the original is used. The name in the minority language is given in brackets at the first time of use.

A second linguistic problem arises with terminology. The Finnish system of legal rights is derived from the Swedish — a heritage of Finland's history until 1809 as a part of the Swedish realm — and, consequently, the majority of legal and land-survey terms were originally Swedish. For this reason, and because there is less uncertainty in definition than with the Finnish equivalents, Swedish land-survey terms are used where no corresponding English terms could be found. The terms are translated into English as far as possible, with the Swedish and Finnish forms given in brackets at the first time of use.

This book is based on a thesis entitled 'Some responses in human geography to land uplift in the Vasa area, Finland', which was undertaken for London University between 1966 and 1972. An introduction to land uplift and its human consequences was given by the late Professor Helmer Smeds, of the Department of Geography at Helsinki (Helsingfors) University, who showed an active interest in the early stages of the research before his death in 1967. Numerous friends and institutions have helped with practical matters and in the collection of information. It is impossible to mention them all by name. However, thanks are due especially to the archivists at the National Board of Land Survey in Helsinki and at the Vaasa (Vasa) County Land Survey Office, without whose help the study would not have been possible. A large part of the reading for the study was undertaken in Helsinki University Library. Part of the work was financed by a Hayter Award for three years (1966–9) from the Department of Education and Science in London, and part by a Research Scholarship for Finnish Studies for four months (autumn 1971) from the Ministry of Education in Helsinki. Special thanks are due to Professor W. R. Mead, of the Department of Geography, University College London, to Professor Stig Jaatinen, of the Department of Geography, Helsinki University, and to Professor Lauri Heikinheimo, of the Department of Forest Economics, Finnish Forest Research Institute, for their valuable advice and for the practical and financial assistance provided by their respective departments. The maps were drawn by T. R. Allen, M. Hayward, C. Hill and T. Odle at the Department of Geography, University College London, and K. Dikert, E. Laakso and E. Lahtinen at the Department of Geography, Helsinki University.

MICHAEL JONES

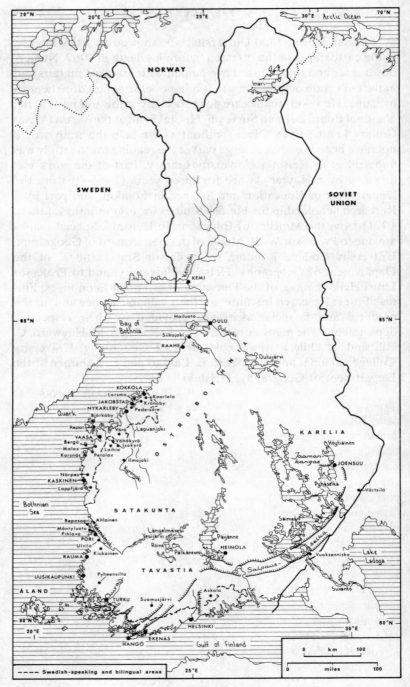

Fig 1   Finland

1

Finland, Daughter of the Sea

MOST LANDSCAPES are the product of two interacting sets of forces: physical processes and human activity. Traditionally, however, human activity tends to be investigated against the background of a physical environment which is tacitly assumed to be more or less static (if meteorological phenomena are ignored). 'Environment tends to be seen as a backdrop against which technology and society evolve and which, barring minute fluctuations of climate and the localized problem of soil erosion, is essentially static.'[1] This is because the speed of change resulting from physical processes is of a different order from changes resulting from human activity. Most physical processes proceed imperceptibly; on occasions, they occur catastrophically, as in earthquakes and floods; rarely do they occur constantly and perceptibly at the same time. In certain circumstances, none the less, physical processes of a continuous, long-term nature have special significance for human activity. Sea-level change and secular crustal movements are examples which have a particular impact on flat, low-lying coastlands. A basic theme in the historical geography of the Netherlands, for example, is the human response to a slowly rising sea level combined with land subsidence: the need for concerted water defence and its logical extension in land reclamation led to distinctive forms of local and central organization which have left their stamp on the Dutch landscape.[2] Land uplift is another phenomenon which is of long-term significance for human activity in certain parts of the world, most notably on the Bothnian shores of Finland and Sweden, where the land is rising by up to one metre every hundred years. Besides having significant effects in physical geography, especially on hydrology, shore development and vegetation, land uplift has a variety of consequences for human geography. Agriculture is provided with new land, fishing-waters disappear, harbours must be periodically moved, and navigation channels are affected. Land uplift and human responses to it form a fundamental theme in the region's historical geography, beginning with prehistoric settlement on successively emerging shorelines in the post-glacial period. Patterns of settlement, land use and land tenure, particularly along the coast, all show the influence of land uplift, both in the past and in the present.

Land uplift is a phenomenon associated especially with northern latitudes. The land has risen in all areas that were covered by continental ice sheets: North America, the islands of the Arctic, the northern fringes of Siberia and Northern Europe. The phenomenon is thought to be caused primarily by the isostatic readjustment of the Earth's crust after being depressed by the weight of the ice sheet during the last glaciation, although other tectonic factors must be taken into consideration. The impact of land uplift on human geography is not, however, of equal significance in all the areas affected. In northern Canada, shoreline displacement has entered Eskimo and Indian folklore[3] and has a place in the history of European colonization: harbours have had to be abandoned and ship channels have become dry, while remains of Eskimo beach dwellings and old fish traps have been found high above present sea level.[4] The areas most affected, around Hudson Bay and in the Arctic archipelago, have uplift rates reaching 1·3 m a century, but they are sparsely inhabited, and human responses to land uplift have not stimulated extensive investigation. In Norway and Scotland, human evidence of land uplift is furnished by archeological remains on raised beaches. However, these countries are characterized by steep shores, powerful coastal erosion and strong tides, so that uplift does not produce the spectacular emergence of land which typifies northern Sweden and, in particular, Finland. A high rate of uplift, low shores and a virtually tideless inland sea are here juxtaposed with old-established settlement of relatively high population density for the latitude: more than one-third of the world's population living north of 60° N is found in Finland, with an average density of fourteen persons per sq km; no other country situated so far north has a comparable population density.[5] Human adjustments to land uplift assume greater topicality in Finland than elsewhere and are correspondingly better documented.

Post-glacial land uplift is causing Finland to rise by approximately 30 cm a century in the Helsinki (Helsingfors) area and up to 90 cm a century along the shores of the Gulf of Bothnia. Finland's area is increasing every hundred years by about 1,000 sq km, of which two-thirds can be attributed to land uplift and the remainder to sedimentation and colonization by vegetation. Over half of this increase occurs on the west coast in Ostrobothnia, where the natural topography is particularly flat and the rate of uplift approaches its maximum.[6] Zachris Topelius, the nineteenth-century Finnish poet, writer, historian and geographer, described the result as 'a new province which every generation appears out of the sea, and every century gives Finland a new principality'.[7] The physical and human evidence of land emergence led him to call Finland 'Daughter of the Sea'. In the Finnish national epic, *Kalevala*, Finland is the creation of the Water Mother.[8]

The comparative rapidity with which the Earth's crust is rising in Finland offers an historical geographer a rare opportunity to examine in detail man's response to a constantly changing natural environment. There are three elements to be considered: the nature of the physical phenomenon; the types of social organization and cultural behaviour which influence the response; and the historical perspective. There is a trend among physical geographers towards studying the physical environment from the viewpoint of its human significance, which is seen as one means of usefully integrating physical geography with other branches of geography. Human geography, conversely, is concerned with patterns and distributions which are the spatial expression of man's impact on his environment; contemporary emphasis is on organization and behaviour as processes by which patterns are generated. A genetic interpretation of existing geographical conditions introduces the historical dimension, which is invaluable for understanding processes of change. The present study adopts an historical approach to explain past and present responses in Finland to the physical phenomenon of land uplift.

Human responses to land uplift are manifest in widely varied fields of activity: science, economic life, landscape, literature, even art. The geographical problem consists of two parts: what is the spatial expression of the responses to uplift, and how has it come about? An important theme is the way in which emergent land is integrated into the normal patterns of land use and tenure. The negative effects on fishing and navigation resulting from the constantly altering coastline and emerging sea bottom leave residual features in the landscape, both in the form of relict features such as abandoned harbours, and in a more indirect form such as former fishing-water boundaries reflected in the landscape of emerged areas as visible property boundaries. Negative effects on land directly result from changes in the level of the water-table. Land emergence affords problems to map-makers, who are faced with a constantly changing coastline and constantly changing depths at sea; contours in time become out of date, and land uplift must be considered in calculations of mean sea level along the Finnish coast. Areal measurements of land and water assume greater uncertainty in Finland than elsewhere. The effects of land uplift in the physical landscape are unusual in that, although occurring rapidly by the geological time scale, they can be largely predicted. This in turn has allowed laws and customs to develop, regulating to some extent the human responses. The way in which the emergent land is partitioned among landowners and the rights of use prior to partition depend on a combination of laws and customs. Their operation in practice depends first on the power of tradition, and second on economic and social factors, which vary historically and influence the rigidity with which the laws and customs are applied. Human responses to uplift reflect also the changing character and needs of society. Population changes, technological advances, increasing knowledge, varying economic conditions, shifting popular attitudes and changing government policies lead to ever-changing assessments by society of the potential uses and value of emergent land.

Finnish geographers and other scientists have mostly contented themselves with studying the physical aspects of land upheaval. The rate of uplift has been measured, using water-level records and data from repeated levellings, and influences of land uplift on physical geography have been investigated. While the influence of land uplift on human geography can be inferred from local and general historical studies, the question of how the new land is partitioned among landowners has been left largely to the legal profession and to land-surveyors, who have written on the theory, but rarely, if at all, on the practice and its influence on the landscape. One of the few detailed human-geographical contributions was made by H. Smeds, whose doctoral thesis, published in 1935, showed the influence of land uplift, among other factors, on the evolution of rural settlement in Malax (Maalahti), situated on the west coast of Finland south of the town of Vaasa (Nasa). In 1950, he discussed land uplift as a significant factor in assessing the economic geography of the Replot (Raippaluoto) skerry guard, north-west of Vaasa, and the physical and human consequences of uplift along the Ostrobothnian coast formed the main theme of his inaugural lecture at Helsinki University the same year. The theme appeared in various contexts in articles both before and after this date – for the last time in his book *Svenska Österbotten,* published in 1953, which contained numerous references to the influence of land uplift on the historical development and economy of the coastal and archipelago communities of the Vaasa area.[9]

A wealth of primary source material is available. Most important are the cartographic material and land-survey records in the archives of the National Board of Land Survey in Helsinki and the county land-survey offices. Supplementary are legal records of disputes over emergent land, while information on the day-to-day use of emergent land is provided by village records. For historical reasons, particularly extensive collections of land-survey documents and village records are found for Ostrobothnia, where land emergence makes its most significant human impact owing to the coincidence of the maximum rate of uplift in Finland with minimum bedrock slope and, along much of the coast, an extensive archipelago.

2

The Physical Phenomenon

The Observation and Measurement of Land Uplift

THE EARLIEST PUBLISHED reference to land uplift in Finland is in a
sermon of 1621 by Ericus Erici (Eerik Sorolainen), Bishop of
Turku (Åbo), who saw the evidence as heralding the approach of
the day of judgment:[1]

> In many places the water level has fallen, so that rocks and boulders,
> which before were under water and which nobody knew of, are now
> visible and stand high above water; and where earlier there was water,
> there are now meadows and sands; and where earlier there were rapids,
> there is now dry land, while new rapids have appeared where there were
> none before; all this proves that the last day is near.

Some consider that the bishop was referring in part to the
emergence of land along the coasts of Finland, but it is more
probable that the sermon was referring to the sudden formation in
1604 of a new outlet for lakes Pälkänevesi, Längelmävesi and
Vesijärvi in Tavastia, an event which lowered their levels and
caused their old outlet at the Sarsa rapids to dry up.[2] Tilting of the
surface as a result of land uplift was the probable cause.

An earlier reference to the effects of land uplift is contained in an
unpublished tax record of 1572, which refers to the destruction of a
fishing-place because of land emergence at the mouth of the Vörå å
(Vöyrinjoki), a river north-east of Vaasa; the fishing of bream and
ide had been recorded there a decade before.[3] The place today lies
some 7 km inland from the present river mouth. The disappearance
of another fishing-place was noted in the annual accounts of Korsholm (Mustassaari) crown farm, which from 1611 recorded the
emergence of a former sound known as 'Risö sund', in which the
inhabitants of Vaasa had fishing-rights by their town charter.[4]

18

From the seventeenth century onwards, lawsuits over disputed emergent land testify to the problems of ownership and use which arose from the continual appearance of new land. Scientific investigation of the shifting coastline in Sweden and Finland (until 1809 a single kingdom) began at the end of that century, and the story of its development is as interesting as the phenomenon itself.[5] The first systematic collection of detailed evidence was published by Urban Hiärne in 1702 and 1706 in the form of replies received to an enquiry concerning natural phenomena, which he had sent in 1694 to State and Church officials.[6] Ideas of a falling sea level, the water-diminution theories, were put forward by Hiärne, Emanuel Swedenborg (Swedberg), Anders Celsius and Carl von Linné (Linnaeus).[7] Olof Dalin investigated Sweden's past in the light of these theories in his *Svea Rikes Historia* published in 1747, and concluded that Sweden was originally an archipelago. Water-diminution theories came into conflict with the Church and were declared false by the Diet in 1747. An alternative explanation of the moving shoreline was advanced in 1765 by the Ostrobothnian land-surveyor, E. O. Runeberg, the first to argue that the land was rising while the level of the sea remained more or less constant.[8] The ensuing arguments between the Neptunists, who supported the water-diminution theory, and the Vulcanists, who put forward the idea of land upheaval, continued into the mid-nineteenth century, when Topelius discussed them in his geography lectures at the University of Helsinki. His lectures contained the most scientific and comprehensive presentation of the phenomenon up to that time.[9]

Theories of the causes and nature of land uplift were inseparable from the problems and techniques of measurement. Swedenborg estimated in 1719 that the sea level was falling by 4 or 5 Swedish ells (nearly 3 m) a century. Celsius, putting forward a different theory of water decrease in 1743, estimated that the level was falling by about 4½ Swedish feet (1·3 m) a century. His theory was ridiculed in 1755 by the Bishop of Turku, Johan Browallius, who cited among other facts the height of Turku Castle, which had been measured a few years before; the castle gates were less than 7½ Swedish feet (2·2 m) above mean sea level, which meant, if the calculations of Celsius were correct, that Duke Johan, who lived in the castle 190 years earlier, could only have entered dryshod by using a punt. The early calculations of a fall in sea level were based on occasional, isolated observations. When further observations indicated that the rate of sea-level change varied in different places, water-diminution theories came under increasing criticism and the way was open for theories of land upheaval.

Increasingly accurate observations of the changes in the relative levels of land and sea were made by sea-level marks cut in rocks, water scales (earlier referred to, inaccurately in the Finnish context, as 'tide poles') and mareographs (earlier referred to as 'tide gauges'). The oldest sea-level marks in Finland were cut in 1755 by the land-surveyor Eric Klingius on Bergö and Rönnskären, in the southern Vaasa archipelago. Occasional observations were made with water scales in Finland from 1852 and daily ones from 1888. The first mareograph was established at Hangö (Hanko) on the south coast in 1887, followed by one at Helsinki in 1904 and others around the coast in the 1920s and 1930s. The regular observation of changes in water level enabled a clearer picture to be obtained of the long-term variations (as opposed to short-term variations due to meteorological and other phenomena) and of their spatial pattern. A. Moberg was the first to work systematically on water-level data obtained from water scales.[10] The first map of land-uplift values around the shores of Sweden and Finland was produced by R. Sieger in 1893,[11] although it was based on inaccurate data.[12] Increasing precision in measuring water-level variations, combined with better understanding of the factors causing temporary changes in level, led to more accurate computations of land-uplift values. R. Witting attempted to take into account short-term phenomena that disturb annual sea-level means in the Baltic, in particular wind direction and strength, changes in air pressure, and the flow of water through the Danish straits.[13] Maps showing uplift values in the Baltic have been produced both within and outside Finland, including maps for the Finnish coast prepared at the Institute of Marine Research in Helsinki (Fig 2).

Table 1 shows calculations of the secular variation of sea level at ports along the Finnish coast, computed from daily sea-level observations, together with E. Kääriäinen's figures based on precise levellings. Differences between the figures of different authors arise because meteorological factors (precipitation and evaporation and especially air pressure and wind), hydrographic factors (water density and currents) and hydrological factors (river discharge) vary considerably from year to year and between different groups of years, affecting the mean sea-level values on which the computations of the secular variations are based (the minus value for Helsinki obtained by J. R. Rossiter in his earlier calculation, for example, is clearly erroneous). Numerical divergences result from the use

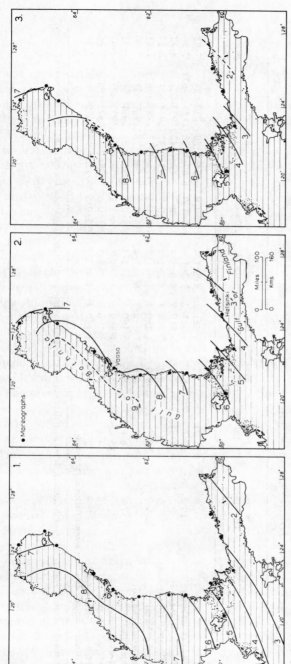

Fig 2 Land uplift along the Finnish coast according to different authorities: (1) the rate of secular variation in sea level in mm per year according to I. Hela (Finland, 1922–51) and F. Bergsten (Sweden, 1825–1927); (2) the rate of land uplift in mm per year according to I. Hela (1922–51); (3) the rate of secular variation in sea level in mm per year according to E. Lisitzin (1924–60).

SOURCES: Hela, *Fennia* (1953), 31; Lisitzin, E. 'Land uplift as sea level problem', *Fennia*, 89:1 (1963), 8; *Fennia* (1964), 13

Table 1   SECULAR VARIATION IN SEA LEVEL (OBSERVED LAND UPLIFT) AT FINNISH PORTS IN MM PER YEAR, ACCORDING TO DIFFERENT AUTHORS

	Witting 1898–1912	Witting 1898–1927*	Model 1904–37	Hela 1922–51	Rossiter 1940–58	Lisitzin 1924–60	Rossiter (1962)	Kääriäinen precise levellings
Kemi		(11·7)	7·2	6·4±1·2	8·5±1·4	7·3±0·9	6·74±0·50 (1920–62)	7·82
Oulu (Uleåborg)	10·3	10·7	6·3	6·3±1·2	7·0±1·3	7·1±1·0	6·09±0·28 (1889–1962)	7·56
Raahe (Brahestad)		(11·7)	7·5	7·4±0·9	8·0±1·4	7·8±0·7	7·12±0·42 (1923–62)	8·27
Jakobstad (Pietarsaari)			8·7	7·6±0·4	9·2±1·4	8·2±0·7	7·83±0·37 (1914–62)	8·13
Vaasa (Vasa)	9·2	8·7	8·0	7·2±0·7	7·6±1·3	8·0±1·1	7·54±0·17 (1884–1962)	7·65
Kaskinen (Kaskö)			6·8	7·6±0·7	6·7±1·4	7·4±0·7	7·54±0·78 (1927–62)	7·00
Mäntyluoto	7·4	6·6	6·8	6·5±0·4	5·3±1·4	6·4±0·6	6·30±0·32 (1911–62)	6·35
Turku (Åbo)		(5·4)	3·3	4·8±0·6	2·5±1·5	4·4±1·2	3·69±0·48 (1922–62)	4·67
Hangö (Hanko)	4·5	4·0	3·6	3·5±0·6	1·1±1·5	3·1±0·5	3·05±0·14 (1871–1962)	2·86
Helsinki (Helsingfors)	0·8	2·8	2·8	3·1±0·4	−0·4±1·5	2·5±0·5	3·15±0·18 (1879–1962)	2·16

*Brackets indicate data from another station in the vicinity.

SOURCES: Lisitzin, *Fennia* (1964), 14; Rossiter, J. R. 'An analysis of annual sea variations in European waters', *Geophysical Journal of the Royal Astronomical Society*, 12 (1967), 282.

of different methods for eliminating disturbing effects and from the different time periods of the calculations. Elimination of the disturbing factors on the basis of the sea-level data themselves has considerable advantages over the other methods because the Baltic is a shallow and virtually enclosed sea basin, with semi-enclosed gulfs and extensive archipelagos, where considerable changes in water quantity and marked local effects of piling-up of water by the wind occur.[14]

Figures calculated from sea-level data apply only to coastal areas. A. Sirén obtained a fuller picture of the pattern of uplift in the inland areas of Finland from a study of water-level variations of lakes over a period of time,[15] but it was not until Kääriäinen made his calculations from the two precise levellings of Finland that anything like a complete picture of present land uplift was obtained. A provisional map of land uplift in central and southern Finland was produced in 1953 and a more accurate map based on improved calculations and more complete material ten years later (Fig 3).[16] Comparison of Kääriäinen's map with isobases (lines through points of equal uplift) drawn by geologists from the present heights of raised shorelines, which have been dated geologically (Fig 4),[17] shows good agreement, supporting the view that, in the long term, land uplift in Fennoscandia is remarkably uniform.[18]

The first levelling of Finland, carried out between 1892 and 1910, extended to approximately 65°N. The second levelling, beginning in 1935, was completed for the area covered by the first in 1955, and by 1963 had been extended to the north of Finland. The second levelling was necessary for several reasons: many of the bench marks of the first levelling had been moved or destroyed over time and needed replacement; it was desired to extend the network to northern Finland; and, not least, 'on the basis of sea-level recordings and geological research, it was known that elevations of bench marks had changed by several decimetres because of the land uplift'.[19] In northern Finland, land-uplift values are conjectured on the basis of mareograph records from the Arctic coast and geological data (Fig 3); accurate values will be obtained by relevelling after about fifteen years. The precise levellings allow relative uplift between bench marks, or the pattern of tilt, to be calculated. They are converted to absolute uplift values by being tied to the average of the mean uplift values of twelve mareographs along the Finnish coast. The pattern of tilt is not thereby changed, but the position of the tilt in relation to sea level is ascertained.[20]

The calculations based on mareograph records give initially the

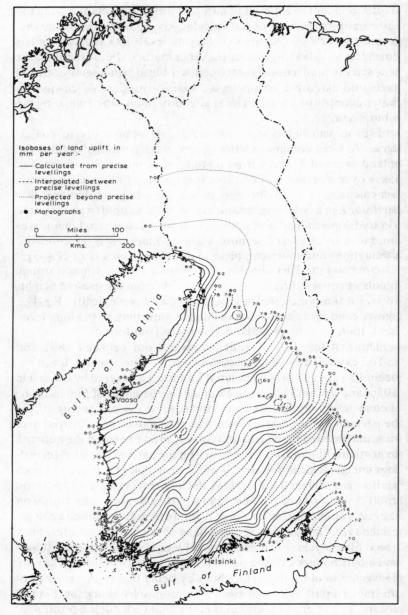

Fig 3 Land uplift in Finland according to the results of repeated levellings.
SOURCE: Kääriäinen, *Fennia* (1963)

secular change in sea level, which is the difference between long-term changes in the level of the sea and absolute land uplift. To obtain figures for absolute uplift in relation to the centre of the Earth, as opposed to uplift in relation to mean sea level, it is necessary to take into consideration the eustatic changes in sea level during the period of observation. The question is complicated by the lack of accurate records. It appears that, during the present century at least, a eustatic rise of sea level has occurred. There are a number of possible causes: changes in the Earth's crust, affecting the sea bottom and coast, thus enlarging or diminishing the volume of the water basin; sedimentation and volcanic activity; and glacial activity.[21] Since the end of the nineteenth century, a widespread recession and melting of glaciers has corresponded to the contemporary rise of sea level, which is variously estimated to be between $0 \cdot 5$ and $3 \cdot 5$ mm per annum.[22] Meteorologists have noted a simultaneous warming of the atmosphere during most of this period, although there is evidence of a reversal of this trend since about 1940.[23] The values for observed uplift, or secular change of sea level calculated from mareograph readings, are thus the difference between crustal and eustatic movements. The contemporary rise of sea level appears as a gradual subsidence of stable coasts. In land-uplift areas, the slow eustatic rise of the sea surface results in an apparent reduction of the absolute land-upheaval rate.

To convert the values of secular sea-level change into absolute rates of land uplift, I. Hela added an average value of 8 ± 3 cm per 100 years, which approximately covers the values for the mean rate of eustatic change given by a number of authorities.[24] Fig 2 shows the isobases of the present rate of uplift calculated from Hela's data with and without the correction for eustatic change, as well as the secular variation of sea level calculated by Lisitzin. Hela's values of absolute uplift along the coast were used by Kääriäinen in converting his relative uplift values, obtained from precise levellings, to absolute uplift values.[25] In Table 1, no correction has been made for eustatic sea-level change, and Kääriäinen's figures have been reduced accordingly. A map showing absolute land-uplift values for a wide area of Fennoscandia has been prepared using Kääriäinen's land-uplift map of Finland and similar maps recently compiled on the basis of data from repeated levellings in Sweden, Denmark and the Baltic states. A correction of $0 \cdot 8$ mm a year for the assumed eustatic rise of the sea level has been added to the values of the relative changes of sea level and land to give the absolute values shown on the map (Fig 5).[26]

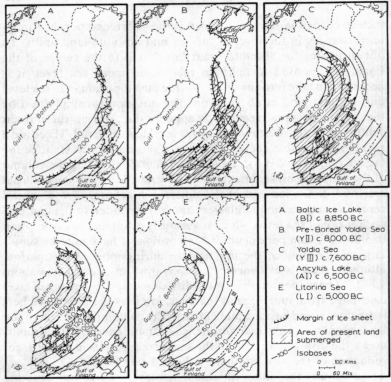

Fig 4　Paleogeography of Finland and isobases.
SOURCE:　Hyyppä, *Annls Acad Sci Fenn* (1966), 153–68

Relatively little is known about eustatic variations. Longer- or shorter-term irregularities are probable, and the average values given by different authors show marked variations. The various calculations for recent eustatic sea-level changes are based either on a world average calculated from world-wide tide-gauge data since about 1900, or on cryological data (data on ice-melting) which may be less accurate since they vary considerably in time and place. Kääriäinen pointed out that a more accurate understanding of eustatic movements will be obtained by an extensive network of bench marks which are periodically relevelled.[27] Recent research indicating that the Earth's crust in many parts of the world is less stable than has previously been assumed must lead to reassessment of data provided by tide-gauge readings. So far, the extent to which local crustal movements are real and the extent to which in many areas they are only apparent, owing to systematic errors in levelling, has not been satisfactorily determined.

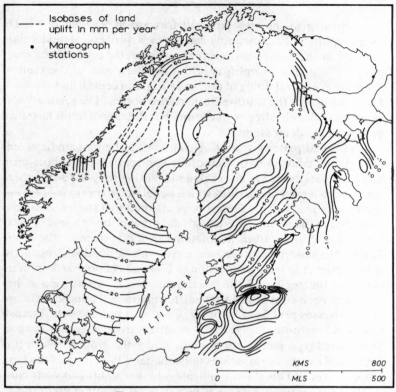

Fig 5   Land uplift in Fennoscandia.
SOURCE: Kukkamäki, *Problems of recent crustal movements* (1969), 50, with additions to 1971

The nature of land uplift

The theory that land upheaval is due to isostatic readjustment of the Earth's crust after being depressed by the weight of the Quaternary ice sheets was first suggested, with reference to Scotland, by T. F. Jamieson in 1865.[28] The retreat of the Fennoscandian ice sheet and the consequent changing relationships of land and sea levels were investigated in Finland by M. Sauramo.[29] Isostatic readjustment began during the period of deglaciation, but simultaneously the release of water from the melted ice produced changes in the level of the sea so that, at the end of the ice age, the central part of the glaciated area, including much of Finland, was below sea level. The amount of isostatic readjustment was greatest where the ice was thickest, and the rebound correspondingly faster.

According to the view first put forward in Sweden by G. De Geer, uplift in Fennoscandia has been a process of updoming, greatest in the centre and decreasing regularly towards the margins.[30] The centre of uplift is in the northern part of the Gulf of Bothnia. A general tilting of the land surface in central and southern Finland towards the south-east therefore occurs. The recovery was rapid immediately after deglaciation, but the rate of uplift has since progressively decreased.

The broad pattern of post-glacial uplift in Fennoscandia seems remarkably uniform both temporally and spatially, but short-term and local variations are not excluded. Witting suggested that there were short-term irregularities which he related to periods of exceptional seismic activity.[31] Others have claimed that the irregularities were due to the nature of Witting's data (based on sea-level observations) and arose from fluctuations in the surface of the sea.[32] Some relationship between seismicity and uplift does appear to exist, however: a large proportion of Finland's minor earth tremors occur in the region of the maximum rate of uplift, and it has generally been considered that earth tremors in Fennoscandia are due to stresses produced by uplift. Current research at the Finnish Geodetic Institute in Helsinki involves experimenting with a liquid-filled pipe placed horizontally under the ground, which it is hoped will enable observations to be made of the tilting of the land week by week. This should indicate whether uplift proceeds constantly or in a series of jerks, and help to clarify whether uplift shows longer-term periodicies or not. The general opinion has been that the uplift is fairly smooth and regular, and that complications are due to variations in sea level. E. Lisitzin observed that although the question of whether uplift occurs continuously or spasmodically has not been solved, it is adequate to assume a constant and regular uplift, as expressed in the mean rate of upheaval.[33] With regard to spatial variations in the pattern of uplift, it has been suggested that the upheaval of land takes place not as a plastic warping but as a complexity of movements by a mosaic of blocks in the faulted Pre-Cambrian basement.[34] It is possible that the various blocks move at different times and by different amounts.

Increasing evidence of local movements of the crust in other areas of the world has led to consideration of other possible causes of uplift in Fennoscandia. Soviet scientists tend to emphasize the role of 'neotectonic' processes: irregular crustal movements inherited from the tectonic structure of earlier periods. They regard post-glacial uplift as a complex interaction of glacio-isostatic and neotectonic movements; glacio-isostatic uplift is recognized as having been intensive during the period immediately after deglaciation, but is thought to exist only in attenuated form at present.[35] Long-term tectonic trends appear to be evident in the tendency shown by Pre-Cambrian shields to rise — both the Canadian and Fennoscandian shields were rising prior to glaciation. North American and Soviet researchers have concluded that recent uplift is the combined result of short-term glacio-isostatic effects of large amplitude superimposed upon slower tectonic movements having a much longer time scale.[36] Studies of the secular variation of the gravity field in Fennoscandia may help to clarify the problem of whether land uplift is caused by the viscous inflow of sub-crustal magma to reach isostatic equilibrium, or by horizontal compression of the crust causing changes in its volume, or by the operation of both.[37] Glacial isostasy continues to arouse discussion.[38] The causes of land uplift may well prove to be a combination of isostatic and other tectonic factors. The latter may be responsible for irregularities in the smooth curve through time of the former and for regional anomalies. Until more data have been collected, it is adequate to maintain as a working assumption that, whatever its causes, the Fennoscandian land uplift is a regular and uniform phenomenon.

However, a distinction must be drawn between absolute and observed uplift. When land emergence is considered, the absolute rate of uplift is less significant than the actual vertical displacement of the shore due to secular change of sea level, in which the effects of eustatic change are included. W. Ramsay was the first to explain the changes of level in Fennoscandia as an interplay of isostatic and eustatic components. He studied the relationship between land uplift and the changing sea level during Late-Quaternary time in northern Europe, and explained the apparent post-glacial subsidence of land in parts of Fennoscandia as a rise in sea level at a more rapid rate than continuing land upheaval.[39] A number of sea-level rises occurred during the Litorina stage of the Baltic, which began in the sixth millennium BC and corresponded to the post-glacial climatic optimum (Atlantic period). As a consequence, there were periodic transgressions in southern Finland, but the more rapid uplift further north meant that transgression did not occur, only a slowing-down in the sea's continuous regression.[40]

The interrelationship of eustatic changes and crustal movements through time has been studied by M. Okko, who examined the relationship between the level of the sea in the past, indicated by raised shorelines, and present-day land-uplift values. She produced

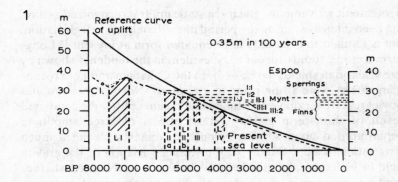

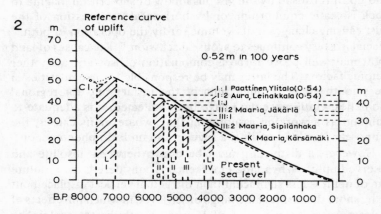

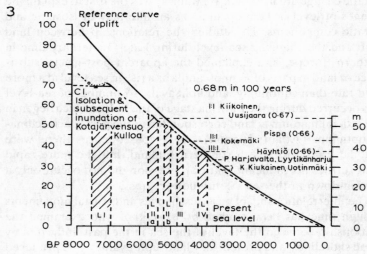

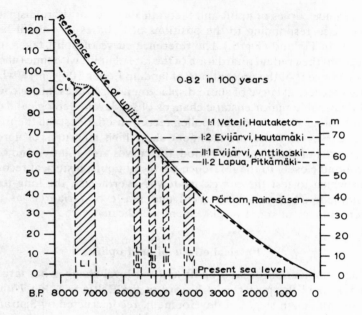

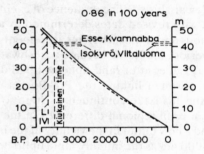

Fig 6 Shore displacement in the regions of Helsinki, Turku, Pori and Vaasa. Reference curves of uplift and curves of shoreline displacement at the present isobases of 0·35m in 100 years (Helsinki region, diagram 1), 0·52m in 100 years (Turku region, diagram 2), 0·68m in 100 years (Pori region, diagram 3), 0·82m and 0·86m in 100 years (Vaasa region, diagram 4). Cl = *Clypeus* limit, marking beginning of Litorina. L I – L IV = Litorina sea-level stages Altitudes of finds of prehistoric waterside dwelling places from the comb-ceramic cultures (I:1 – III:2) and Kiukainen culture (K) indicated with placenames.
SOURCE: Okko, *Annls Acad Sci Fenn* (1967), 22, 25, 29, 31

reference curves of uplift and theoretical curves of shore displacement, corresponding to the positions of isobases of present land
uplift in Finland (Fig 6.) The reference curve of uplift takes into
account the gradual retardation of the rate of uplift with time (about
one per cent of the present rate of land uplift per 100 years), while
the theoretical curve of shore displacement also takes into account
the probable major eustatic changes of sea level. Geological data,
archeological evidence and pollen records used to test the theoretical curves of shore displacement show high measures of agreement.[41] For the historical period, the curves are tentative and correspond closely to the reference curves of uplift; historical records
on which to test the curves are few. Nevertheless, the long-term
interaction between land uplift and sea-level variations as the
determinant of shore displacement is indicated.

Physical effects of land uplift

The combination of land uplift and sea-level changes has largely
determined the post-glacial history of the Baltic Sea. Fig 7 illustrates the main stages of development, reconstructed by Sauramo
on the basis of raised shorelines dated by the chronology of varved
clays and pollen analysis.[42] The sequence of events is summarized in
Table 3, p44, with revised dates determined by a variety of stratigraphical methods and radiocarbon measurements. In the immediate
post-glacial period, the Baltic became a freshwater lake referred to
as the Ancylus Lake, after land upheaval had dammed the sound
across central Sweden linking the Pre-Boreal Yoldia Sea to the
ocean. The Ancylus Lake continued to drain to the sea by way of
central Sweden until regional differences in the rate of land uplift
forced it to find a new outlet in the vicinity of the later Danish straits.
After about 6000 BC, as the initially rapid uplift began to slow down,
the rising level of the ocean flooded the Danish straits and transformed the Ancylus Lake into the Litorina Sea, which progressed
through various substages to become the Baltic of today.

The regression of the Baltic has left its legacy in the form of
raised beaches and marine deposits. A well-preserved sequence of
raised beaches, dating from 3,500 years ago to the present, occurs in
the Siikajoki area of Ostrobothnia.[43] Marine clays, deposited in the
areas submerged by the sea after the retreat of the ice, have become
exposed and are extensive along Finland's southern and western
coasts, providing fertile soils. A 'depositional, pedological and veg-
etational distinction'[44] can be observed between former sub-aquatic

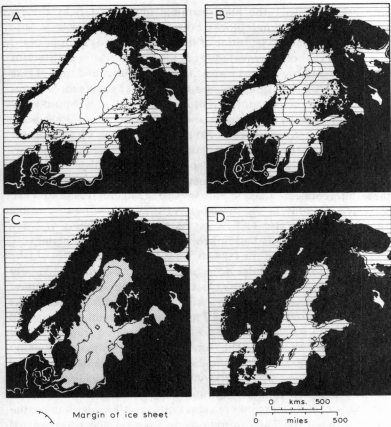

Fig 7 Main stages in the development of the Baltic Sea: (A) Initial stage of
Pre-Boreal Yoldia Sea, c 8200 BC (B) Final stage of Yoldia Sea, c 7000 BC (C)
Ancylus Lake, c 6500 BC (D) Litorina Sea, c 5000 BC.
SOURCE: Sauramo, *Fennia* (1939), 4, 5, 6, and *Annls Acad Sci Fenn* (1958), 50,
        410, 454, 484

and supra-aquatic areas, separated by the metachronous highest
shoreline or marine limit. Washing by wave action below the limit
has left bare rocks and stonefields, and deposited fine-grained water
sediments, which are generally absent above it.[45]

Land uplift has influenced the development of not only the Baltic
but also the Finnish lakes. Most of the lake basins of central Finland
originated through the isolation of arms of the Baltic before the
beginning of the Litorina. Subsequent changes in the form, size and
outlets of the lakes have resulted from land uplift. At first, their
outlets were to the north-west or west, into the Gulf of Bothnia; the

Salpausselkä ridges, the huge terminal moraines left by the ice across southern Finland, blocked the flow of water southwards to the Gulf of Finland. The tilting of the land surface as a result of the more rapid rate of upheaval towards the Gulf of Bothnia tilted the lake basins and caused successive changes of outlet and thus of lake level, as well as transgressions on the south-eastern shores of the lakes. Breaches to the south eventually occurred at two points, the first about 4100 BC at Heinola and the second about 3000 BC at Vuoksenniska, forming respectively the present outlets of the Päijänne and Saimaa (Saimen) lake systems.[46]

Changes of lake outlet have also been recorded historically. The sudden breaching in 1604 of a new outlet at Kostianvirta for the three interconnected lakes, Pälkänevesi, Längelmävesi and Vesijärvi, led not only to the drying-up of their original outlet at the Sarsa rapids, but also to new rapids coming into being at Ihari, where formerly straits had linked Pälkänevesi and Längelmävesi, and to the lowering of the lake surfaces to expose 99 sq km of lake bottom (Fig 8).[47] A similar occurrence in Karelia (in the area later lost to the Soviet Union) took place in 1818, when the transgressive lake Suvanto breached a narrow sand ridge separating it from Lake Ladoga. Suvanto's level fell by 7 m, its former outlet westwards to the Vuoksi (Vuoksen) river dried up, and about 5,000 ha of lake bottom were exposed. The emerged area provided valuable meadows, which could in places be harvested twice in a year, and bog ore, which was used in the Värtsilä ironworks. Disputes over the new land led to one death and protracted lawsuits, and the parcelling of the emergent area was only completed with the assistance of the army. The lowering of the lake surface also revealed tree stumps which had been drowned by the lake's earlier transgression.[48]

Differential land uplift influences the direction of river flow, causes changes in watersheds, and affects lake shorelines, lacustrine deposition, and the nature and direction of flooding. These influences were little understood in the nineteenth century, when the lowering of lake levels by cutting artificial outlet channels became a popular means of obtaining new land for cultivation. In 1830, a canal was completed at Kaivanto through the Kangasala ridge, a narrow neck of land separating the lakes Längelmävesi and Roine. Water burst through the dam protecting the excavations as it was being opened, and swept away the completed construction works. A channel 18 m wide, double the width of the canal, was created, and the level of Längelmävesi sank 1·8 m to that of Roine.

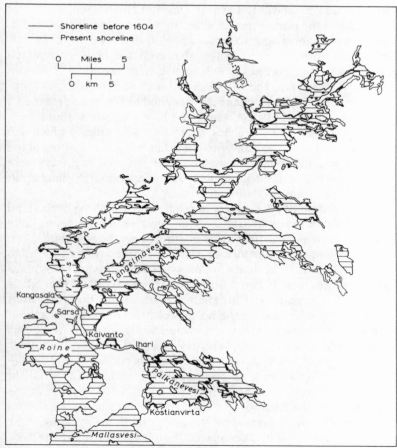

Fig 8 Lakes affected by land uplift in Tavastia: Pälkänevesi, Längelmävesi and Vesijärvi. The level of the lakes has been lowered twice in historical time. In 1604, the sudden formation of a new outlet at Kostianvirta led to the drying up of the original outlet at the Sarsa rapids and created new rapids at Ihari, where the flow through the former straits was reversed. The second fall happened in 1830, when water pressure swept away a newly completed canal at Kaivanto, causing the Ihari rapids to dry up.

SOURCE: Blomqvist, *Svenska Tekniska Vetenskapsakademien i Finland, Acta* (1926), plate 1

The outlet at the Ihari rapids dried up, and over 2,000 ha of meadow and cultivable land were gained from the former lake bottom (Fig 8). A similar occurrence in 1859 was more spectacular, when a canal was constructed across the Jaamankangas terminal moraine to link lake Höytiäinen southwards via another lake, Pyhäselkä, to

Saimaa. The canal was to lower the level of Höytiäinen, which had its outlet to the north-west, in order to prevent flooding around its lower-lying shores and to obtain new arable land from its flat-bottomed northern part. Water shattered the newly completed canal locks, the lake level fell by 9½ m in less than a month, exposing 130 sq km, and the torrent threatened the town of Joensuu. The new discharge channel broadened to 500 m and reached a depth in places of 30 m.[49] Along the lake's southern shore were exposed former sandy beaches, shore bogs and forests, which had been inundated by the transgression resulting from the tilting of the lake basin to the south-east by land uplift.[50] Canal engineers were blamed for both disasters, but water pressures caused by land uplift played a part outside their calculations.[51]

The position of lake outlets in relation to the tilting of the land determines patterns of transgression and regression along lake shores, which in turn affect the formation of peatbogs around lakes. Regression of the water surface occurs on shores rising faster than the rate of uplift at the lake's outlet, while transgression takes place where shores are being uplifted more slowly than the lake's threshold. The pattern of differential uplift means that regression typifies shores located on the north-western side of the threshold isobase, and transgresssion characterizes shores on its south-eastern side. Consequently, lacustrine deposits become exposed to the north-west while flooding and bog formation occur to the south-east. The water level on the northern shores of Höytiäinen fell by c 2 m between about 3000 BC and AD 1859, while at the southern end the level rose by c $2 \cdot 5$ m.[52] In lake basins where the overflow channel is located on the most rapidly rising shore, continuous transgression takes place. Peat lands surround the lake basins in the Kokemäenjoki (Kumo älv) river system as well as the lake Oulujärvi (Ule träsk), the outflows of which have remained towards the centre of uplift, and thus against the direction of tilt, since their isolation from the Baltic. Not only does transgression induce peat formation along the lake shores, but also the raising of the water-table causes bogs to develop in adjoining areas.[53]

Impeded drainage as a result of land-tilting is a significant factor in the development of peat lands. Where watercourses flow towards a region of higher uplift rate, the decreasing velocity of flow tends to cause bog formation. Conversely, uplift continuously steepens the profile of rivers flowing towards a region of lower uplift rate, so that the flow is speeded up and the water-table lowered. There is a large measure of correspondence between the regions of Finland where

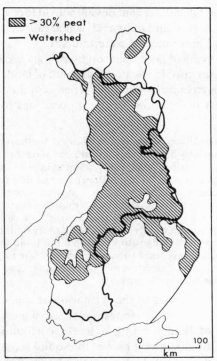

Fig 9   Areas in Finland where peat land covers more than 30 per cent of the land surface, and watershed of regions drained towards the centre of land uplift. The average peat cover for Finland as a whole is 31·9 per cent of the land surface. SOURCE: *Atlas of Finland 1960*, maps 8 and 11:15

peat land covers more than 30 per cent of the land surface and the regions where drainage is towards the centre of uplift, primarily towards the Bothnian shore (Fig 9).

A. L. Backman recognized that peat lands in central Ostrobothnia developed chiefly through the formation of bogs on dry land, and only to a minor degree through the overgrowing of lakes by vegetation. He estimated that 95 per cent of bogs there were formed in this way.[54] Later work has shown that this figure included bogs which formed in coastal areas immediately after emergence, before the newly exposed land could be colonized by forest. In Ostrobothnia, the majority of peatbogs date from the emergence of the land from the sea (95 per cent on land which emerged in the last 500 years, 60 per cent on land which emerged 1,000 to 2,000 years ago). In the interior of Finland, 40 per cent of bogs formed on newly emerged land, while 50 per cent developed on forest land. The main factor in both cases is land upheaval, which causes land emergence, land-tilting and hindrance of watercourses.[55]

While the effects of land uplift on hydrology are significant, and occasionally catastrophic, the physical result of land upheaval that is consistently spectacular is the emergence of land along the coast. One of the best descriptions of the process was by Topelius in a lecture of 1855:

> First a sandbank forms, sometimes linked to the shore, sometimes separated from it by deeper water. When the shoal rises to less than 1½ feet below the mean sea level, reeds begin to appear. After a few years, the shallows are exposed at low water, bare and desolate, covered with sand, small stones and driftwood. A few years more, and the shoal is permanently above the water level, although occasionally flooded at high water. Now can be seen rushes and one or two blades of grass growing in the summer, only to be washed away by the autumn waves. Finally, the waves no longer top the shoal but build regular shorelines along its slopes. Grass takes root, and in ten or fifteen years the former sea bottom becomes a meadow worthwhile harvesting. Another twenty years and deciduous trees grow.

Topelius also referred to the formation of small, grass-covered islets known as *vattuungar* alongside larger islands; and to *halsar*, narrow necks of land forming a treeless isthmus between two islands, where the shallowest part of the sound separating them has emerged. Another typical feature, which he did not mention, is the small bays in inlets cut off partly or completely from the sea by land emergence, and called in Ostrobothnia *fladar, bottnar* or *brunnar*. They may be linked to the sea only at high water, and in time become completely cut off and overgrown to form lakes and marshes.[56]

Finland's total increase in area as a result of land emergence is substantial. Noting that the increase of land due to uplift depends on the topography of the sea bottom, H. Renqvist used sea charts and Witting's calculations of the rate of uplift to calculate Finland's areal addition. On the basis of uplift alone, he came to a figure of 664 sq km a century, to which he added 169 sq km for the estimated effects of silting and vegetation growth; this was rounded to the figure of 1,000 sq km a century or 1,000 ha per annum for Finland's total areal increase.[57] T. J. Kukkamäki estimated Finland's increase in area on the basis of uplift alone (using Kääriäinen's provisional figures for the rate of uplift[58] as 710 sq km a century (Fig 10).[59] Smeds estimated that Swedish-speaking Ostrobothnia grows by about 200 sq km a century, equivalent to the area of 'a medium-large parish'.[60] Table 2 shows the increase for certain individual communes according to earlier studies based on land-survey maps. It has been estimated that Finland will be joined to Sweden across the middle of the Bothnian Gulf after about 3,000 years, and that in about 5,000 years Finland will have gained from the sea in the west an area equivalent to the land in the east lost to Russia by World War II. Offshore from Oulu, the emergence of some 70 islands during the next 130 years will create a new archipelago, while by the year 3000 the island of Hailuoto (Karlö) will have become joined to the mainland.[61]

Table 2 THE AREAL INCREASE OF SOME OSTROBOTHNIAN COMMUNES THROUGH LAND EMERGENCE, CALCULATED FROM LAND-SURVEY MAPS

    (A)   Mainland communes with an offshore skerry guard
    (B)   Skerry-guard communes

Commune	Total area in sq km (and date)	Areal increase in sq km (and period)	Total percentage increase	Average annual increase in sq km	Average percentage increase
A Kronoby (Kruunupyy)	329·0 (1934)	12·72 (1762–1934)	4·02	0·07	0·02
Malax (Maalahti)	220·6 (1890)	8·43 (1760–1890)	3·97	0·06	0·03
B Bergö	38·9 (1890)	9·58 (1760–1890)	32·67	0·74	0·25
Björköby	87·2 (1942)	23·40 (1760–1942)	36·67	0·13	0·20
Replot (Raippaluoto)	151·3 (1942)	38·70 (1760–1942)	34·36	0·21	0·19

SOURCES: Brander, G. 'Om tillandningen och landhöjningen i Kronoby', *Terra*, 46 (1934), 140; Smeds, *Malaxbygden* (1935), 30, *Geogrl Rev* (1950), 106, and *Svensk Geogr Årsb* (1950), 126; *Statistisk Årsbok för Finland*, 11 (1889–90), 11; *Suomen Tilastollinen Vuosikirja*, Uusi sarja, 32 (1934), 34.

In an examination of land emergence, other factors besides land uplift — delta formation, wind and wave action, currents, water-level variations, ice, plant growth and human activity — have to be taken into consideration. If land uplift alone were the operative factor, the increase in land area would depend directly on sea-floor topography and coastal slope. These are, of course, critical factors, but delta formation is also significant. The shape of the major river deltas is determined by the positions and relief of the islands through which the sediment is carried, the form of the sea floor across which it is deposited, and the regularity of the coast at the river mouth. All these factors, as well as the amount of sediment

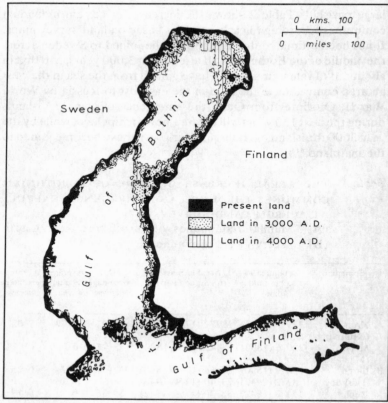

Fig 10   Displacement of the Finnish coastline during the next 2,000 years.
SOURCE: Kukkamäki, *Terra* (1956), 122

brought down by the river, also affect the speed of delta growth, which is slowest on open, steeply sloping coasts. The existence of a skerry guard hinders the removal of sediment by sea currents, wind and waves, and sediment accumulates in inlets and sounds where currents are weak. Islands channel the deposition into particular areas, thus facilitating rapid growth; the Kyrönjoki (Kyro älv) delta, channelled by the Vaasa archipelago, is advancing by nearly 2 km a century. The speed of delta growth also depends partly on the number and depth of hollows to be filled on the sea floor. Where the coast is flat, even if it is open, delta formation can be rapid; the horizontal growth of the Siikajoki delta, for example, is more than 1 km a century.[62] The most rapidly advancing delta along the Finnish coast is that of the Kokemäenjoki, where large amounts of sediment are channelled into a long, narrow, restricted estuary; the advance is 3 to 4 km a century, representing an average annual addition of 10 to 20 ha of land, if short-term fluctuations in water level are ignored.[63] The vertical growth of deltas is less easily measured, as it is difficult to distinguish from land uplift. J. E. Rosberg estimated that the vertical growth of the Kyrönjoki delta due to sedimentation was about 30 cm a century.[64] While delta formation speeds up the process of land emergence, it is in turn accelerated by land uplift, which continuously raises new areas over which alluvial sedimentation can take place. Uplift allows alluvium to be spread over a wider area in a shorter time than would otherwise be the case. It also allows alluvium to be recarried further downstream and, as a result, river entrenchment occurs continuously.

When uplift and sedimentation bring the sea floor to a certain critical depth, plant growth can take place. Colonization by vegetation may begin at 1½ to 2 m depth if not hindered by strong currents or an exposed situation. In a sheltered, flat-bottomed location, this limit may be a considerable distance offshore. Once it gains a hold, vegetation is a rapid creator of new land, since it is an important agent for binding loose material. However, uplift remains important in raising the sea bottom to a level shallow enough for plant growth to begin.

The shore-forming actions of winds, waves, currents, water-level changes and ice have been discussed by U. Varjo.[65] Winds and waves are of relatively minor importance in creating new land, especially on coasts protected by a skerry guard. The direction of wave activity is itself continually changing over time through the emergence of land, though on more exposed coasts, winds and waves with a long fetch may be responsible for the building of shores and dune formation. Against the shore-building action of wind and waves must be set their abrasive activity, especially on shores consisting of loose material. Currents play a similar dual role: abrasion combats land formation, while the material removed is redeposited elsewhere in sheltered bays and inlets. The work of drift and pack ice in winter is another minor factor, transporting material which is redeposited when the ice melts. The area over which abrasion takes place also continuously changes as a result of uplift. As shoals and reefs emerge, loose sediments — sand, gravel and small pebbles — are washed off the higher rocks and settle in underwater depressions, to re-emerge later. Abrasion combined with emergence leads to a resorting of loose material, with finer deposits accumulating in depressions and later providing more fertile soils.

Short-term fluctuations in water level are significant in a different way. Although tides are negligible (with a range of 2 to 4 cm in the Gulf of Bothnia), seasonal changes of water level range between 20 and 30 cm on average. The tendency is for high water in winter and late summer, and for low water in April, May and late autumn. Fluctuations are caused by winds, air-pressure changes, rain and meltwater, and may deviate greatly from the average. Extreme deviations of short duration occur particularly in the shallow, restricted Gulf of Bothnia, with values of $\pm 1\frac{1}{2}$ m from normal water level recorded at Kemi and ± 1 m at Vaasa.[66] In the Vaasa archipelago, the water level has been known to change by $\frac{1}{2}$ m in a night. The flat shore means that a vertical change of this magnitude produces a great horizontal variation in the position of the shoreline, with a wide coastal belt subject to alternate flooding and exposure. The area of temporarily but periodically emergent land can cover many hectares, having an important influence on geomorphology, biology and cultural geography. There is a wide area over which the sea's erosive power can operate, and over which littoral vegetation dominates. The influences on human activity of this periodically emergent land reflect in the short term the longer-term effects of land emergence due to uplift.[67]

In practice, it is difficult to separate the effects of land uplift from those of other physical processes in the creation of new land. To the role of natural factors must be added that of human activity, which is of increasing importance in the creation of new land.[68] The inter-relationship of the various factors is illustrated in Fig 11. It is clear that land uplift is the major factor, influencing in addition many of the others. Uplift causes continuous emergence along the whole coast; the other factors operate over relatively short periods and unequally in different places.

The emergence of land in turn affects other aspects of physical geography, a significant effect being constant renewal of the vegetation succession which colonizes the emerging land as the sea recedes. Generalization about the succession is difficult, although salt-water plants are virtually absent in the brackish water of the Baltic. The general sequence from open bays and inlets to reeds and rushes (the pioneer species, which begin to colonize before the land has emerged), then to sedges, other grasses and herbaceous plants, and finally to forest, varies in detail from place to place and from year to year. The plant communities at any given place depend on latitude, situation, exposure, salinity, shore slope and the nature of the underlying shore material. There is no well-defined order of succession, and it is difficult to isolate the effects of land uplift from other factors. It is clear, however, that land uplift has the effect of constantly shifting seawards the vertical zonation of coastal vegetation. Where uplift is rapid, as in Ostrobothnia, the plant communities in each zone are unable to reach full development before species from a higher zone begin to invade.[69] The pioneer tree species on emergent land is generally alder, which can colonize ground too wet for other trees. Once established, growth is at first rapid because of abundant ground water, but as the water-table falls, owing to continued uplift, other species such as spruce are able to invade. Two major influences of land uplift on forest development in the Ostrobothnian skerry guard are identifiable. The first is the outward movement of the alder belt, followed by the spruce, as the land emerges. The second is the deterioration of the forest at higher levels as the land rises, owing to the sinking of the water-table and the drying-out of the ground surface.[70]

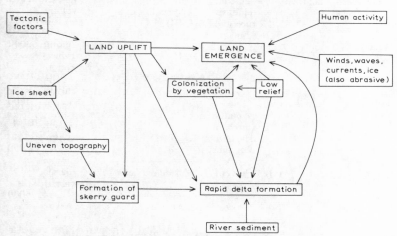

Fig 11   Interrelationship of factors causing land emergence

Land uplift has widespread consequences in physical geography, many of which are equally significant in human geography. Physical facts such as the development of lakes, the emergence of land and the influence on vegetation are intimately bound up with human geography. Human activity, such as the lowering of lake levels and the artificial reclamation of coastal areas, affects the natural course of events. In turn, the natural course of events consequent upon land uplift has profound influence on human activity and the cultural landscape.

Table 3 COMPARISON OF PLEISTOCENE GLACIAL STAGES, POLLEN STRATIGRAPHY IN SOUTHERN FINLAND, STAGES IN THE DEVELOPMENT OF THE BALTIC SEA AND PREHISTORIC CULTURES IN FINLAND

Years AD/BC	Pleistocene stages	Pollen stratigraphy (southern Finland)	Stages of the Baltic Sea	Prehistoric cultures	Years AD/BC
			Mya Sea		
1000		(ix) Sub-Atlantic (pine, alder)	Iron		1000
0					0
				Bronze Age	
1000		(viii) Sub-Boreal (Birch, alder, hazel, elm, pine, spruce, oak, linden)	(L IV) Litorina Proper (L III)	Kiukainen culture Boat-axe culture	1000
2000	Post-Flandrian glacial				2000
3000			(L II) Litorina Sea	Late comb-ceramic culture Typical comb-ceramic culture	3000
4000		(vii) Atlantic (birch, alder, hazel, elm, pine, oak, linden)	LI Stone Age	Early comb-ceramic culture	4000
5000		(vi)	Mastogloia Sea	Suomusjärvi culture	5000
6000	Bipartition of ice	(v) Boreal (pine)	A Ancylus Lake	(Askola sites)	6000
7000	Late glacial	(iv) Pre-Boreal (birch)	(YV) Yoldia Sea YI		7000
8000			B III		8000
9000	Ss II Ss I	Late Weichselian (iii)	Younger Dryas (tundra)	Baltic Ice Lake B I	9000

Ss I & II = Salpausselkä I & II

Sources: Based on Donner, J. J. *The geologic systems* (1965), 264; 'Towards a stratigraphical division of the Finnish Quaternary', *Commentat Physico-Math*, 41 (1971), 302; Alhonen, P. 'The stages of the Baltic Sea as indicated by the diatom stratigraphy', *Acta Botanica Fennica*, 92 (1971), 14; Siiriäinen, A. *Suomen Museo* (1969), 68–9, (1972), 10, *Finskt Museum* (1973), 6–9, 11, 14, and personal communication.

3

The Human Problem

Land Uplift and Early Settlement

THE EMERGENCE OF land is the physical result of land upheaval which has the most marked and direct impact on human activity. Along the Bothnian coast, in particular, 'the contribution made by the sea to the land is a reality for those who farm or fish along the shore'.[1] Land emergence is an important fact in understanding the evolution of settlement in Finland (as in Scandinavia generally), and settlements of the Stone Age, Bronze Age and Iron Age are closely related to former coastlines. The earliest settlers in Finland were predominantly hunters and fishermen, and sought waterside dwelling-places. As the land rose and the sea receded, coastal inhabitants were forced to move their settlements on to newly emergent areas to maintain contact with the sea. Most archeological finds lie in sequence, with the older dwelling-places situated further inland and at a higher level than the younger ones, the actual altitudes depending on the rate of land uplift (Table 4). The archeological evidence has been correlated with geologically dated raised shorelines, and this has enabled an absolute chronology to be established (Table 3).[2]

The oldest signs of human habitation, found at Askola in southern Finland, probably date from about 6500 BC and are related to the shore of the Ancylus Lake. The Askola sites appear to belong to the Suomusjärvi culture, lasting from the seventh to the fifth millennium BC, the dwelling-places of which were mainly situated on the shores of the Ancylus Lake and the early stage of the Litorina Sea. The Suomusjärvi culture developed through the introduction of the craft of pottery into the series of comb-ceramic cultures (c 4100–1900 BC), which correlate with various sea-level stages of the

45

Table 4 HEIGHTS ABOVE PRESENT SEA LEVEL OF FINDS FROM SUCCESSIVE STONE AGE CULTURES ALONG THE FINNISH COAST

Culture	Height above present sea level in metres		
	Helsinki area	Turku area	Ostrobothnia
Suomusjärvi	30–40	50–70	90–100
Comb-ceramic			
Early	27–30	40	70–80
Middle or typical	25–26	35–38	57–67
Late or degenerated	23–24	31–34	53–56
Boat-axe	19–20	28–30	46–50
Kiukainen	16	21	37–40

SOURCE: Äyräpää, *Fennia* (1952), 288–94.

Litorina (Fig 6, pp 30–1). In the interior of Finland, Suomusjärvi and comb-ceramic dwelling-places were related to the successively transgressional and regressional shorelines of the Finnish lakes.[3] The comb-ceramic finds can be divided into three main phases: early; middle or typical; and late or degenerated. Within each phase, earlier and later forms can be distinguished, while local variations occur. A recently discovered form, later than the three main phases, is the Pyheensilta type in south-western Finland. The successive phases describe changes in ornamentation; the sites are closely equated with land uplift, with one below the other in chronological order.

The economic basis of the pre-ceramic and comb-ceramic cultures was hunting, fishing and sealing. From about 2200 BC, new immigrants to western Finland brought the boat-axe culture and introduced animal husbandry. Their settlement was more widespread, related to pastures on the fertile emergent clay soils of southern and western Finland rather than primarily to the coast. In Ostrobothnia, however, the boat-axe culture did have a coastal location, which may have been partly related to emerging pastures along the shore.[4] Boat-axe people were absorbed by the pre-existing population from about 1900 BC to produce the Kiukainen (Kiukais) culture, in which fishing and hence coastal dwelling-sites resumed their former importance. The geographical distribution of finds from the main Stone Age cultures is shown in Fig 12. The end of the Stone Age in Finland is dated between 1300 and 1200 BC.

The chronological distribution of archeological remains into belts at successive heights can also be observed subsequent to the Stone Age. The sequence is particularly clear in southern

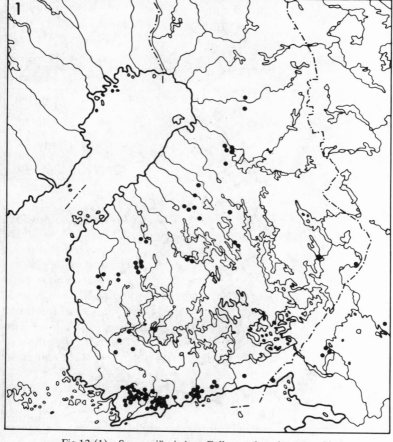

Fig 12 (1)   Suomusjärvi sites. Fuller explanation on p 50.

Ostrobothnia, where shore displacement was rapid because of the high rate of uplift and the flat coast (Fig 13). In the islands of Åland (Ahvenanmaa), too, is a well-preserved sequence, continuing unbroken from the early comb-ceramic phase to the end of the Bronze Age. The possibilities of sealing probably attracted population from the Finnish mainland coast to the islands as they emerged from the sea. All the comb-ceramic phases are found in an area of 2 or 3 sq km, the earliest settlement being situated on an old shore 55 m above the present sea level and later dwellings on successively lower shores down to a height of 39 m. At the end of the comb-ceramic period, immigrants from the west brought the Scandinavian

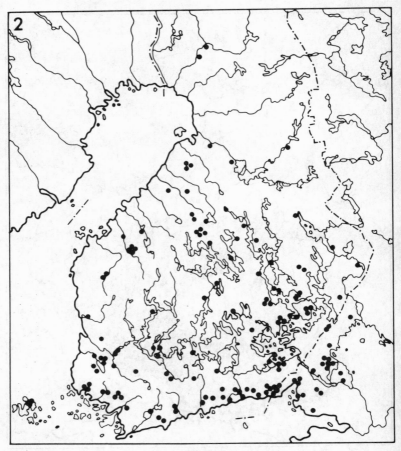

Fig 12 (2)   Early and typical comb-ceramic sites. Fuller explanation on p 50.

pitted-ware culture. Land emergence allowed them to make use of an expanding area, and their dwellings are found at successive heights from 38 m to 31·5 m above the present sea level. Evidence of the Kiukainen culture is found at a height of about 28 m and Bronze Age finds are concentrated around 21 m.[5]

Grave cairns from the Bronze Age lie scattered in a belt along the length of the contemporary Finnish coastline. The coastal inhabitants traded furs from the interior of Finland for their imported bronze implements, and probably carried on both fishing and primitive agriculture. A marked decrease in Bronze Age finds after 500 BC suggests a cultural decline, caused possibly by a clima-

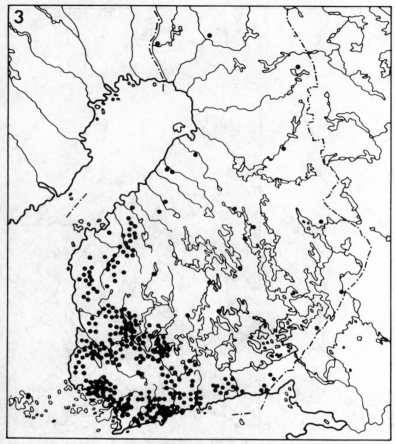

Fig 12 (3)   Boat-axe finds. Fuller explanation on p 50.

tic deterioration or an interruption in trade, or perhaps by the introduction of a new burial custom without grave goods. How far the coastal Bronze Age population was compelled to emigrate or how far it survived by changing from a trading and agricultural economy to a hunting economy, which was typical of the Finnish interior throughout the Bronze Age, remain unsolved questions.[6] Archeological evidence from the succeeding Pre-Roman Iron Age in Finland is rare, although not non-existent; signs of a coastal agricultural population have been found at places in southern and western Finland, while inland lived hunting groups.[7]

The Iron Age proper in Finland began with the arrival of the

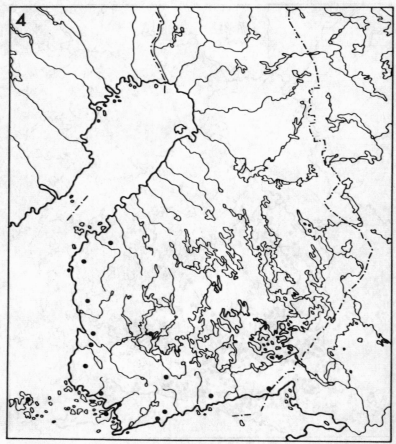

Fig 12   Distribution of finds from Stone Age cultures in Finland: (1) Sites of the
Suomusjärvi culture (c 6500-4100 BC); (2) Sites with early and typical comb-ceramic
pottery (c 4100-2800 BC); (3) Distribution of boat axes (c 2200–1900 BC); (4) Sites
of the Kiukainen culture (c 1900–1200 BC).
SOURCE: Kivikoski, E. *Suomen historia*, I (Porvoo, 1961), 23, 32, 34, 62, 69;
Finland (1967), 23, 33, 35, 49

ancestors of the present Finns from south of the Gulf of Finland
during the first centuries AD. The first comers were probably hunters and fur-traders, who initially came seasonally and then settled
as agriculturalists in south-west Finland. Later settlers followed the
Kokemäenjoki valley and reached Tavastia during the third and
fourth centuries. The Finns settled river valleys inland, leaving the
coast uninhabited. A separate centre of Iron Age settlement, probably a continuation from the Bronze Age, developed in southern

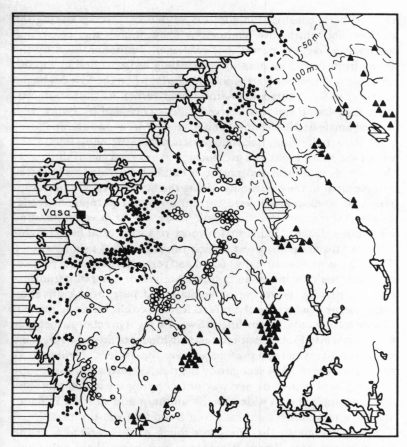

▲   Suomusjärvi culture (c. 6500 - 4100 B.C.)

○   Boat-axe culture (c.2200 - 1900 B.C.)

●   Bronze and Iron Age cairns (c.1000 B.C - 800 A.D.)

Fig 13   Archeological finds and shore displacement in southern Ostrobothnia.
SOURCE: Meinander, *Nordenskiöld-Samf Tidskr* (1946), 71, 82, 85

Ostrobothnia until the ninth century, when evidence of Iron Age settlement disappears. Åland, on the other hand, was occupied by Swedes during the sixth century.[8] Swedish settlement gradually spread to south-west Finland after about AD 1000 in association with the expanding sphere of activity of the Christian Church, and the southern coast of Finland was settled by Swedes during the twelfth and thirteenth centuries. They found the coast and archipelago lacking permanent settlement, although used by the Finns from inland as hunting and fishing areas, called in Finnish *erämaa* and in Swedish *erämark*. Similarly, when the Swedes began to arrive in Satakunta and Ostrobothnia during the thirteenth century, they found the fertile river valleys occupied by Finns, who hunted and fished in the uninhabited coastal areas and archipelago.[9]

Although the Finns had their agricultural settlements inland, the use of the shore areas and archipelago as *erämark*, as of the unsettled forests in central and northern Finland, provided an essential complement to their economy during the Middle Ages; while cropping and stock-rearing were carried on in the permanent settlements, fishing and hunting took place up to several hundred kilometres distant. Individual owners of farms established rights over certain areas of forest, which often included fishing-waters. These areas were seasonally visited and regarded as private property, which could be inherited, sold, exchanged or otherwise transferred. Eventually, pasturing of animals and burn-beat cultivation might occur,[10] which, in the inland forests, could form the nucleus of new settlements. According to Swedish legal practice, which was introduced into Finland with the establishment of Swedish rule, new settlers were given legal preference over the owners of *erämark*. A royal directive of 1334 recognized the right of newcomers to occupy outlying land whose owner was not carrying on agriculture: the directive applied to a wide area of southern and western Finland, and gave new settlers a measure of freedom from taxation.[11]

Along the coast, the Finns lost much of their *erämark* to the Swedish incomers. There is evidence that some Finns sold their rights to the Swedish settlers, but often they lost their property through Swedish legal principles overriding Finnish customary rights. In 1303, King Birger Magnusson issued a directive to the governor of Finland supporting Swedish colonizers of *erämark* belonging to inhabitants of Tavastia and apparently situated on the Satakunta coast.[12] Swedish settlers along the coast followed the Swedish practice that the owners of the shore owned offshore fishing rights; this led to conflicts with the inland Finns who had traditionally used the coast and archipelago for fishing. A number of judgements in the fourteenth and fifteenth centuries recognized the coastal settlers as legal owners of 'enclosed waters'. The meaning of this term (in Swedish *inbundna vatten* and translated into Finnish as *umpeutuneet rannikkovedet*) has been subject to varying interpretations. The Finnish expression has been misinterpreted in some quarters as meaning emergent land, but it seems probable that the term referred to coastal waters with legally ratified boundaries, and came to mean that the coastal villages owned the offshore waters. The term 'enclosed waters' is a specifically Finnish medieval legal term and appears to be related to the assertion of Swedish legal rights over Finnish customary ownership.[13]

Despite subsequent changes of the language boundary in some places, the distribution of settlement established by the two language groups in the thirteenth and fourteenth centuries is significant for the understanding of later responses to land emergence. The Swedes settled along the coast as fishermen and stock-rearers. The gradual disappearance of fishing-waters and the coalescence of land areas as a result of land emergence complicated the disputes over fishing and land-ownership rights that continually arose. As time went on, the continual emergence of land, especially in Ostrobothnia, provided important possibilities for the extension of cultivated land in the Swedish coastal parishes.

Effects of coastal land emergence on fishing

The earliest references to fishing-waters going out of use because of land emergence can be found in tax returns from the end of the sixteenth century; sporadic references occur in court records during the following hundred years. From the end of the seventeenth century, documentary evidence of the effects of land uplift is complemented by cartographic sources, which increase in number and accuracy in the eighteenth century. Fuller documentation accompanied the expansion of land-survey activity — descriptions of the livelihood of individual villages were appended to many of the land-survey maps and provide particularly valuable information. The disappearance of fishing-waters and the appearance of meadows in their place, primarily along the shores of the Gulf of Bothnia, attracted special attention during this period. One of the questions which Hiärne asked in his enquiry of 1694 concerning natural phenomena was 'on the emergence of land in the north of the Bothnian Sea.' Elias Brenner, a judge and antiquarian, replied:[14]

It has been observed from olden times how more and more land has gradually appeared along the shores of coastal bays and lakes in Ostrobothnia. Even in living memory, at numerous places where seventy or eighty years ago fishing-sloops and barques freely sailed, many hundred cartloads of hay are now harvested annually. This does not occur only in a few places but is found to be true over the whole land.

Gabriel Tavonius, rural dean of Närpes (Närpiö) in Ostrobothnia, mentioned in another reply a specific case:[15]

The quarter-mile [2·5 km[16]] wide area between the sea and the parsonage at Närpes has become land within a hundred years, as old people can testify from what their parents told them. They themselves remember, too, that where the best bream fisheries were forty or fifty years ago is now found good hay land which is tolerably dry; while what was sea 100 years ago is now well-drained meadow.

The transformation of fishing-grounds into meadows and fields provided evidence to support the water-diminution theories of Celsius, who collected observations from around the Gulf of Bothnia. The sequence of changes was particularly noticeable in the skerry guard; channels in the outer skerries, which could be passed by large ships half a century earlier, were by 1743 only navigable by small ships and boats. The outermost skerries in Ostrobothnia, apparent forty or fifty years before as only a stone or two, were now visible as long reefs projecting from the water. Fishermen along the low-lying Ostrobothnian shores had been forced in the space of thirty years to find new fishing-banks for their sweep-nets, and within sixty years to move their houses three times towards the sea shore. In Björköby, near Vaasa, was a meadow where forty years earlier seine fishing had been carried on. Places under water sixty years ago were now ploughed and harvested, and old people could go dryshod where water came up to the knee in their youth. Celsius paid special attention to seal stones, favoured places for shooting seals. At Vaasa and Turku, among other places, 'the stones on which seals formerly rested, and which are noted and valued in old divisions of inheritance and contracts of sale, stand now either so high out of the water that the seals can no longer climb up, or are on dry land, and are excluded as no longer usable from later tax records'. Seal stones provided the basis for the calculations made by Celsius of the rate of water diminution.[17]

Runeberg, too, recorded observations made in the course of his land-survey operations in the Vaasa archipelago:[18]

In the summer of 1762, I journeyed to Björkö, 4 miles [40 km] out to sea from Vasa, for the tax assessment in progress there. All the old men there present affirmed that the water was receding, and that meadows along the shores were thereby expanding, shoals emerging and firmly fixed rocks in the sea becoming exposed.

A reference by the inhabitants of Björköby to the disappearance of fishing-waters occurs in a land-survey description of 1722, relating that places 'where they could formerly fish had become dry land and meadow, while on the other hand the meadows had become overgrown by forest'.[19] A description of the neighbouring village of Vallgrund by the land-surveyor Jonas Cajanus in 1754 included a list of fishing-places, several of which had become dry land.

Further north, land emergence at the mouth of the river Kemijoki (Kemi älv) affected salmon fisheries, with the result that farmers had difficulties in meeting the tariffs payable to the Crown for the privilege of salmon fishing. Evidence was brought to court in 1723 that certain of the fishing-grounds formerly used by farmers from the whole of Kemi parish, whose fishing-huts and harbours were still visible, had become meadow land; elsewhere, fishing-places had become so shallow that in dry years they dried out almost entirely, while other places could be reached with difficulty by fishing-boats of only one-tenth the capacity of boats that fished there earlier. The problems of emerging fishing-waters were not new to the area. The farmers had requested the provincial governor in 1679 for a reduction of the tariff because of poor catches consequent upon land emergence.[20] Even at the end of the sixteenth century, land emergence had been disturbing salmon fisheries and led to disputes over the position of offshore boundaries; their settlement in 1596 incidentally determined the northern coastal boundary of Ostrobothnia.[21]

The loss of old fishing-grounds through land emergence was partly compensated by new ones in the outer skerries. In the southern Vaasa archipelago, the inhabitants of Bergö were forced to develop the fishing-waters of the outer skerry guard as the waters close to the main island became too shallow, and emerged; because of the distance from the village, seasonal dwellings with harbours, boathuts and small cultivated plots had begun to grow up in the vicinity of the fishing-places in the outer archipelago by the beginning of the eighteenth century. In Malax, on the adjoining mainland, it became noticeable that the fishing-grounds close to the shore had become poor in fish as a result of land emergence. In a description of Malax in 1725, the land-surveyor Eric Höijer commented that 'the fishing-water has formerly given much fish, but has now much emerged so that now no more is caught than for household needs . . . The fishing of Baltic herring in the summer scarcely repays the work.'[22] Land emergence was also blamed for the decline of fishing in Vörå (Vöyri). A description of Vörå parish in 1753 by

M. Jacob Haartman, the original of which is now lost, was summarized by H. G. Porthan in the newspaper *Åbo Tidningar* in 1792 and included the remark that 'fishing in later times has been scarcely profitable, since the best fishing-places have disappeared as a result of land emergence.'[23] This assertion is supported by the land-survey descriptions of the coastal villages of Vörå in the 1750s. A common observation was that fishing was formerly one of the main livelihoods but had declined as land emergence converted the fishing-waters to meadow land. In several villages, fishing no longer provided sufficient for household needs, and the inhabitants were forced to concentrate their efforts on farming. In Tuckur village, fishing in the Vörå å had ceased altogether because of emergence. Quantitative evidence of the difficulties caused for fishermen by land emergence is found in C. F. Stierwald's land-survey description of 1766-7 for Hailuoto, although the possibility of exaggeration by the inhabitants cannot be discounted in a survey undertaken to assess taxes:

> It is generally asserted that fishing along the shores here is uniformly declining, which is properly supposed to be due to the fact that the land is emerging or the water diminishing; inasmuch as it is declared that within living memory more than fifty seine-sweeps have been converted to dry land along these shores.

The declining returns from fishing were discussed by Eric Cajanus in his description of the Ostrobothnian parish of Kronoby (Kruunupyy), published in 1755:

> A general complaint against the annual decline of fishing is heard here as elsewhere, which seems without doubt partly to be due to the annual emergence of land: for the places through which fish formerly used to pass from larger water bodies to smaller, that is to say through sounds and streams, have in part completely emerged and in part become so shallow that fish such as pike and whitefish, which are rather timorous and do not like to venture into shallow water, now no longer come into the archipelago, as their usual routes are denied to them. It would be desirable to start excavating the channels which are here becoming land and are so shallow, so that the fish could come in more easily and consequently more could be caught.

Cajanus noted further evidence of the emergence of land in finds of boat keels and rusted iron anchors at distances of up to 10 km from the contemporary shore. Places at the mouth of the Kronoby å, which twenty or thirty years before could be navigated by a fully loaded fishing-boat, had by 1755 become so shallow that it was almost impossible to sail there with a small portable boat, while 'the places which seventy or eighty years back were the best whitefish

seine-sweeps are now changed partly into meadow and partly into
rough pasture.'[24]

The decline of fishing was not the result solely of the disappearance of fishing-grounds. It should also be seen in the context of the
depletion of fish stocks through over-fishing (fishing during spawn-
ing was not prohibited until 1766 and in practice continued after
this) and of the increasing possibilities of agriculture. Jonas Cajanus
noted in his land-survey description of 1752 for Vikby, in Mustasaari parish near Vaasa, a state of affairs that was symptomatic for
the whole area:

> The villagers gain no profit from fishing, as toil and skills yield nothing
> from this activity, particularly when year by year the fishing-water is
> becoming dry land. Baltic herring can be fished in the open sea, but this
> is not often undertaken by the inhabitants because of the long distance.

Similar statements appeared in the contemporary descriptions of
other villages situated, like Vikby, at the river mouth of the Laihianjoki (Laihela å or Toby å). In the sixteenth century, there had been a
wide bay here which was intensively fished by the inhabitants of the
surrounding villages. As the bay emerged, the fishing-places moved
outwards. The description of Hälsingby in the mid-eighteenth century stated that the village's old fishing-waters provided pasture in
dry summers, while the inhabitants of Vaasa, who also fished in the
vicinity, complained of bad catches because the best inlets for
fishing had emerged. Disputes arose over the disappearing waters,
which belonged to the surrounding villages in common. Not only
were there disagreements over the use of the remaining fishing-
places, but also arguments arose over the emergent land as it
became possible to use it for cattle pasture and hay land.[25]

The decline in fishing continued in the nineteenth century. Many
of the mainland farmers ceased fishing altogether except during
years when grain harvests were bad. The parish priest of Malax
noted in an account at the end of the eighteenth century that,
although fishing had been the main livelihood earlier, the increase
in population and the decline of fishing because of land emergence
had taught people to be better farmers. At the same time, land-
tenure reform provided a stimulus for new cultivation. By the end of
the nineteenth century, fishing had completely lost importance for
the inland inhabitants of the coastal parishes, although it continued
to be carried on by those living along the shore and in the
archipelago, where new grounds became shallow enough for
seine-fishing as the old ones dried up.[26]

The Influence of Land Uplift on Towns and Harbours

In the nineteenth century, evidence of the human consequences of land emergence, such as former anchorages and the remains of shipwrecks far from the water's edge, the increasing difficulties of navigation and the continuous transition from fishing to agriculture, gave inspiration to Topelius in his lectures, popular presentations, school readers, poems and tales.[27] For the farmer, the consequences of land uplift are positive in that his land area is increased; they are negative for the fisherman, who is forced to find new moorings and fishing-places, and for the merchant, who must look for new harbours and fairways.[28] The appearance of new rocks and shoals above water level every generation means that sea charts rapidly become out of date. On occasion, this has been advantageous: Topelius related how the shallowing sea bottom confused British men-of-war assailing Ekenäs (Tammisaari) and may have contributed to the capture of a British boat which attacked Kokkola (Gamlakarleby) during the Crimean War in 1854. In normal times, however, the dredging of harbours and channels and the periodic changing of the courses of fairways are expensive economic facts. 'In the lives of city ports, adjustment must be paid for in persistent dredging of channels or in the construction and maintenance of new outports.'[29]

Topelius was particularly fascinated by the effects of uplift on the Finnish coastal towns, which he described in one of his lectures in the following words:

> Many of them were originally founded on deep harbours and convenient navigation channels, and two or three hundred years afterwards found themselves quite unexpectedly a good distance from the coast, as though a mocking nature wanted to amuse itself by making them, against their will, inland towns.

Helsinki was moved ninety years after its foundation to a more suitable location because the combination of uplift and sedimentation at its original location, on the Vantaanjoki (Vanda å) river mouth, prevented ships reaching it. Turku remains at its historic location around the cathedral, although already by Topelius's time larger ships were forced to anchor in the roads 3 km from the town. Two kilometres upstream from Turku in the Aurajoki (Aura å) valley is Koroinen (Korois), which was Turku's predecessor as the bishop's seat during the thirteenth century. Larger vessels were eventually unable to reach Koroinen, and there are indications that merchants had already erected business houses in the early thir-

teenth century on the later site of Turku.[30] Turku Castle was built at
the end of the century on an island at the mouth of the Aurajoki to
protect the harbour adjacent to the cathedral. Land uplift has
joined the island to the mainland and caused the river estuary to
become shallower. The harbour has gradually moved downstream
and in the last hundred years has become established at the river
mouth, adjacent to the castle.

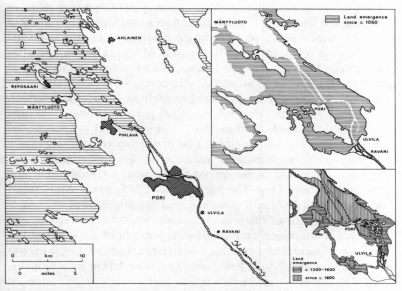

Fig 14   Shore displacement and harbour removal at the mouth of the Kokemäenjoki. The main map shows the present coastline and the location of Pori, with its
outports at Mäntyluoto and Reposaari. Earlier coastlines and harbour towns are
shown in the insets.
SOURCE: Säntti, *Fennia* (1951), 70, 76

The most classic case is at the mouth of the Kokemäenjoki, the
rapid silting of which has been accelerated by uplift: the harbour
here has moved six times in six centuries.[31] The harbour removals
have influenced the historical development of settlement (Fig 14).
Pori (Björneborg), founded on the coast in 1558, replaced earlier
ports at Ulvila (Ulfsby), founded in 1332, and Ragwalda (the
present Ravani); the last grew up in the twelfth century and
replaced an even earlier trading-place at Teljä, which was reached
by river-going boats in the eleventh century. Pori has not moved
(despite being burnt down in 1852), but having lost its coastal

location it is now dependent on outports which must be continually moved. The present harbours are at Mäntyluoto and Reposaari (Räfsö), respectively 21 and 30 km from the town. The development of settlements such as Pihlava, between Pori and Mäntyluoto, is a continuation of the process of outward movement of coastal settlement in response to the recession of the sea.

Vaasa is another well-known example, vividly depicted by Topelius: 'Vasa in vain attempted to dredge a channel to the Old Harbour, as it was called, which formerly held as many ships as desired, but was none the less forced to load ships a mile away at Brändö, until the fire of 1852 finally allowed Vasa to pursue the receding sea to Klemetsö.' The location of Vaasa before and after the fire can be seen in Fig 15. Vaasa had been founded in 1606 at Mustasaari, still then an island, adjacent to Mussor harbour (a medieval trading-place mentioned as early as 1348). Stadssundet, as the harbour became called, was already shallow and could only be reached by small craft; in 1640, a new harbour came into use 1 km to the west at Hästholmen. This in turn became shallower as a result of uplift, and ships were forced to anchor further and further from the shore and to be served by lighters, a troublesome and expensive undertaking. The period after 1765, when staple rights were conferred on Vaasa, saw the rapid development of shipbuilding and expansion of the port. The shallowness of the harbour was an obvious hindrance and discussions were held on whether the whole town should be moved to a better site. Instead, a new output was founded in 1789 at Palosaari (Brändö), 10 km to the northwest. The distance from the town, however, in view of the bad roads of the time, was a disadvantage; to offset this, a canal was excavated along the old sound, leading to Stadssundet. It was completed in 1845, and allowed smaller vessels once more to reach the town itself, while the loads of larger ships anchored in the roads could be transported more easily in lighters. The destruction of almost the whole town of Vaasa by fire in 1852 led to renewed public debate over whether it should be moved to a new site nearer the coast. The town was refounded as Nikolaistad in 1854 (receiving Old Vaasa's municipal privileges in 1862), 6 km away on an adjoining island, Klemettilä (Klemetsö). This has since become joined to the mainland by uplift. As ships became larger, a new outport was eventually required, and in 1893 a new harbour was completed 3½ km further west on Vaskiluoto (Vasklot). The process is one of historical repetition. The 1,000 m-long causeway across the inner harbour, linking Vaskiluoto to the present town of Vaasa, can be compared

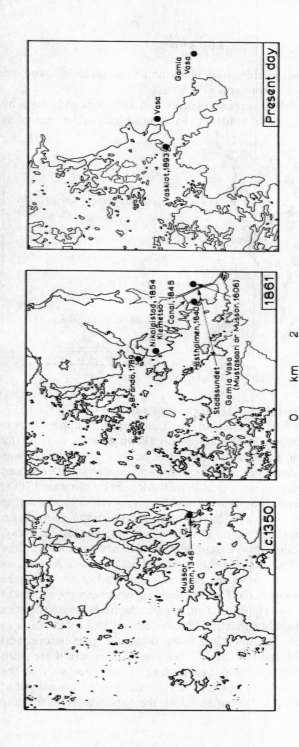

Fig 15　Vaasa — movements of the town and its harbours. The dates of the foundation of towns and harbours and the opening of the canal are indicated. Finnish equivalents of Swedish names on the map are: Vasa = Vaasa, Gamla Vasa = Vanha-Vaasa (Old Vaasa), Brändö = Palosaari, Klemetsö = Klemettilä, Vasklot = Vaskiluoto. The 1350 map is based on Renqvist, H. 'Vasatraktens topografi, landhöjning och geografiska namn', *Fennia*, 44:3 (1924), and the 1861 map on a sea chart of that date

with the 300 m long bridge over Stadssundet, which once linked the
harbour at Hästholmen with Old Vaasa.[32]

The fortunes of Vaasa can be contrasted with those of Nykarleby
(Uusikaarlepyy). Land uplift played a major part in the decline of

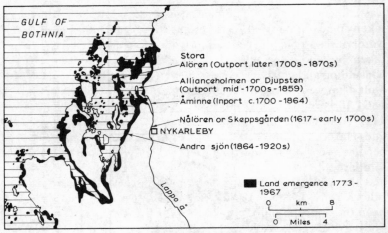

Fig 16   Nykarleby and its harbours

the latter as a port (Fig 16). For the first hundred years after 1617,
when the town was founded at the Lapuanjoki (Lappo å) river
mouth, its harbour was at Nålören on Skeppsgården, next to the
town's northern end, but as the river became shallower it was
moved 2½ km northwards to Åminne, where pitch distilleries and
shipbuilding wharves were established. Already by the later 1700s,
however, the harbour at Åminne was becoming troublesome owing
to shallowness, and ships increasingly called at the outport on
Allianceholmen (later called Djupsten), some 5 km farther away,
where shipbuilding wharves had been established since the middle
of the century. The largest ships could only reach Stora Alören, an
island 10 km from the town, and the approaches to this were
through shallow channels. The shipbuilding wharves were moved to
Stora Alören in the 1840s, and meanwhile the harbour at Djupsten
became so unsuitable that it officially ceased to be Nykarleby's
outport in 1859. The town had burnt down the year before, and
proposals were made to rebuild it on a new site where there were
better harbour possibilities. The leading Vaasa shipowner of the
day offered to move his business to Nykarleby if it were rebuilt at
Karvat in Oravais (Oravainen), but the inhabitants eventually

rebuilt their town on its old site in the 1860s. There was a sharp decline in its importance as a port and shipbuilding centre after the fire, with sea captains and shipping interests moving to other ports. The last ship to be built at Stora Alören, named appropriately in the circumstances *Zachris Topelius* (whose home town was Nykarleby), was launched in 1873. The final move of the town's harbour had taken place nine years earlier. Until 1864, there had been warehouses and loading-places at Åminne, from where goods were taken by sloop-rigged cargo boats to Stora Alören — a time-consuming and costly process. A new loading-place was therefore built 4 km west of the town at Munkgrundet in Benäsviken, and in 1864 all harbour traffic moved to 'Andra sjön', as it became called.[33] Åminne became remembered only as 'Gamla hamnen' (the Old Harbour). The harbour at Andra sjön has since, in turn, become too shallow, and is no longer used by ships. It was already seldom visited in the 1920s. Now only small pleasure boats use it, and the 150 m-long stone jetty and an old warehouse remain as relict features in the landscape. The recent history of Nykarleby has been the opposite of that of Vaasa, which did move after its fire of 1852. Although suitable port facilities are more important than the site of the town (as indicated by Pori), the shallowness of the harbour was a decisive factor in the failure of shipping interests to return when Nykarleby was rebuilt on its original site. There was a decline of trade at the end of the nineteenth century in competition with Vaasa and Jakobstad (Pietarsaari), and Nykarleby gradually died as a port. It had practically no industry and grew little in population until the last few years; for long it remained Finland's smallest town.

Variations of the same theme are repeated along the whole coast of Ostrobothnia. Almost every town has its 'Gamla hamnen'. Jakobstad's harbour is now 5 km to the north at Alholmen (Leppäluoto), having been moved at least once since the town's foundation in 1652. The sea formerly extended to the centre of Jakobstad, located 1 km north of Pedersöre (Pietarsaaren maalaiskunta) which, thought to have been founded in the mid-thirteenth century on an island and mentioned as a harbour in fourteenth-century documents, had lost its coastal location by the 1600s. Maps of Jakobstad in the seventeenth and eighteenth centuries show the harbour located on a sound north-west of the town. A shipbuilding wharf was established in the vicinity in 1798, but by 1827 it was in difficulties because larger ships could no longer reach the shipyard on account of the annual reduction in water level. After 1885, the harbour at Alholmen was developed in place of the old town harbour, and in 1890 the town purchased emergent land in the vicinity to extend the harbour area.[34] Gamla hamnen is now only used by pleasure boats, although traces of the former tar trade are still visible on nearby rocks. Harbour extensions at Alholmen in 1955 and 1972–3 depend on dredging to maintain the required depth. Modern dredging techniques can considerably delay the effects of uplift, and proposals to construct a new outport further away at Ådön await the attraction of industry requiring a deep-water harbour to justify it economically. Jakobstad's competitor is Kokkola, with its outport 5 km westwards at Ykspihlaja (Yxpila). The port lies on what at present is one of the best natural harbours in the Gulf of Bothnia and has become a focus for new settlement. It is the successor of two earlier harbours: Vanhasatama (Gamla hamnen), which is now used only by pleasure boats; and Salmi (Stadssundet), now 3 km inland in the centre of the town. Salmi was a wide inlet in 1620, when Kokkola was founded; the site was chosen 2 km north of Kaarlela (Karleby) church which, although in the Middle Ages situated on an inlet, had by the seventeenth century become too far from the coast to serve as a port. Kaarlela and other old churches in the vicinity are now, as a result of land uplift, situated on hills.[35]

On a smaller scale, villages and individual farms are similarly forced to move their harbours and boatplaces. Their removal has a direct expression in the landscape in the form of new harbours and the relict features of old ones, and an indirect expression in the new roads needed to reach more distant locations, with accompanying changes in patterns of settlement. As villages become cut off from the sea, small, private jetties alongside individual farmsteads are replaced by larger, common boatplaces, which are situated farther away at suitable locations with steep shores. Common harbours are frequently found at river mouths. In Malax, the harbour at Åminne is common for both villages of the parish, which has only a short coastline; the harbour, situated at the mouth of the Malax å, has replaced earlier boatplaces now inland. A deed from 1686 referred to fishing-huts at Åminne belonging to the inhabitants of Övermalax in the upper valley, which could no longer be used because of land emergence. Similarly, farmers from the inland parish of Laihia (Laihela) carried on fishing and in the sixteenth century had fishing-huts at Hälsingby, which was then situated at the mouth of the Laihianjoki but is now an inland village. Likewise, fishing-huts belonging to several villages existed formerly at the mouth of the Vörå å.

The flat shores of Hailuoto (Fig 17) afford numerous examples of the effects of land emergence on harbours. The island's settlements originally grew up on Kirkonsalmi, a former sound providing a protected harbour; later, the harbours were moved to the northern and southern entrances of the sound. The common harbour at

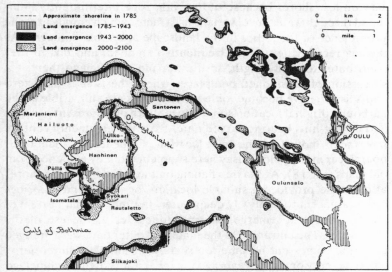

Fig 17   Land emergence in the vicinity of Hailuoto and Oulu, 1785–2100
SOURCES: Ylinen and Matala, *Maankohoamisen merkitys Suur-Oulun Kaavoitukselle* (1968), and a sea chart of 1785

the northern end, marked on eighteenth-century maps, is now more than 1 km from the shore, and present-day Kirkonsalmi is a virtual lake, a remnant of the old sound. Until 1930, the island's regular boat connection to Oulu used a jetty at the head of Ojakylänlahti, on the east side of the island. When the bay became too shallow, a new jetty had to be built at Ulkokarvo, more than 2 km away. Characteristic of the shores of Hailuoto are groups of seasonal fishermen's dwellings and fishing-huts. Two of the best-preserved groups are at Marjaniemi in the west and at Rautaletto in the south-east of the island. At the latter, older cottages built on the shore sixty or seventy years ago are now several hundred metres inland with younger cottages closer to the present shore.

Boatplaces in varying stages of use and abandonment are found along the length of the Ostrobothnian coast. In Maxmo (Maksamaa), north-east of Vaasa, former boat-mooring rings can be seen many metres from the water's edge, and stone jetties inaccessible to boats occur in meadows or are found overgrown by woodland. They may vary in length from a few metres to 80 m or more, depending on the importance of the boatplace and the steepness of the shore. Long jetties stretching across emergent land are necessary on low shores because of the wide zone intermittently inundated through water-level variations, a factor which emphasizes the prominence of the jetties in the landscape after abandonment. As the sea recedes, jetties are frequently extended, and this further contributes to their length. In the Maxmo archipelago there is a succession of abandoned boatplaces where the islands of Österö and Västerö have become joined. Boatplaces are still visible at the harbour's original location some 600 m south of its present position and fishing-huts bearing carved dates from the eighteenth century have been moved to the new location. Evidence of abandoned boatplaces in the field is elsewhere supplemented by evidence from old maps (Fig 18). At Maxmo fladan, on the mainland, steep shores at one time provided a suitable location for jetties and mooring-places adjacent to relatively deep water. In time, the flat bottom of the bay began to emerge, causing difficulties in the use of the boatplaces. The entrances to the inner and outer bays were dredged at various times but became too shallow again. The church jetty, where seventy or eighty years ago the inhabitants of the archipelago moored their boats when they came to church, no longer reaches the shore. In living memory fishermen in sailing-boats used the inner bay, and boathouses lined the shores until the mid-1930s. Boathouses remained at the outer bay until ten or twenty years ago. Now only the stone foundations and jetties remain, and the villagers are forced to use the harbour at Grånässkatan, 2 km away.

The ultimately futile attempts to keep the harbour entrances open by dredging repeats what fishermen have done in the Vaasa archipelago for centuries. Modern excavating machinery allows the work to be more substantial and the results less temporary. A large-scale undertaking in the mid-1960s involved the dredging and excavating of a number of boat channels, locally important to the inhabitants, in the Maxmo archipelago; the costs were borne almost entirely by the State. The work required the widening and deepening of narrow, shallow sounds; the reopening of one sound that had become completely dry; the removal of stones and the dredging of deep channels across shallow basins. Seinälotsund, which had ceased to be navigable about fifty years previously, has been

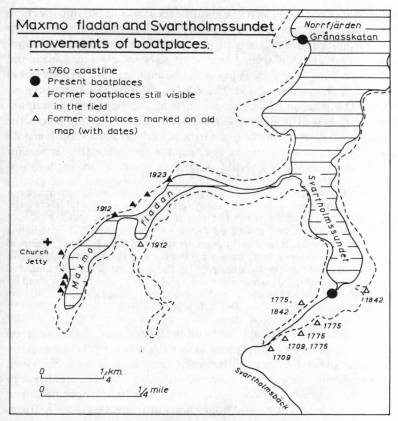

Fig 18   Maxmo fladen and Svartholmssundet — movements of boatplaces.

reopened. The excavations saved local fishermen an hour's boat journey to their main fishing-waters, and they were no longer threatened with having to move their harbours to new locations distant from their farmsteads.

At Petalax (Petolahti), south of Vaasa, a two-stage movement of boatplaces and boathouses is evident. The typical pattern at the existing harbours of Bockören and Vägviken is for the boathouses to be lined along a comparatively steep shore, with a few remaining older boathouses and old stone foundations marking the line of a former row some metres behind. As the sea has receded, old boathouses have been physically moved downshore or replaced altogether by new ones. Movement of boathouses within the harbour area in the short term is complemented in the long term by the removal of harbours to more suitable locations as old ones become unusable. The remains of slipways and boathut foundations are visible at locations with slightly steeper slopes, such as Resgrynnan, Storgrund and Gålören, situated at varying distances from the present shore. A causeway of boulders that once linked Resgrynnan to the mainland remains visible as a line of stones on the emergent land. These harbours were in use until the 1930s, and the remains in the field, as well as old maps, indicate a similar pattern of successive rows of boathouses moving downshore as the sea receded. The area as it was twenty-five years ago, some years after the last major harbour removal, was vividly described by W. R. Mead:[36]

> By 1948, former islands like Storgrunden had been swallowed in a sea of grain and grass. Colloquially, they retained their old island names, the scattered depressions their old inlet terminology. The two fishing harbours had migrated to deeper waters on the wings of the broadening delta. Clean white fishery sheds contrasted with their grey and neglected predecessors now inaccessible by boat. Landwards, the evidence of former water levels was engraved on the boulders which encumbered the wooded islands while alongside, and drawn out of the clayland by winter frost and summer heat, wooden stumps recalled the poles on which fishers dried their nets half a century ago.

In Björköby, the old harbour at Bodvattnet, 1 km from the village centre, has been replaced since the 1940s by Svedjehamn, a further kilometre away.[37] Between the old and new harbours, intermediate boatplaces on former islets linked to the mainland by boulder causeways have been abandoned more recently. The remaining fishing-huts and boathouses at Bodvattnet, dating from the mid-nineteenth century, are preserved by the village museum. Former jetties are visible as lines of stones extending upshore. Also preserved are the stone foundations of a boathouse formerly used as a base for taking passengers and mail across the Bothnian gulf, for which the villagers gained freedom from taxation and military service between 1617 and 1809, along with the inhabitants of Holmön, on the Swedish side. The last entrance to Bodvattnet is an excavated channel through a morainic ridge across the entrance of the harbour. An earlier attempt to keep a channel open by an artificial cut is still visible in the landscape further inland and corresponds to the highest part of an old sound (thus the part emerging first), which from the evidence of eighteenth-century maps once separated Björkö from former islands to the north-west. The remains of abandoned harbours are found elsewhere on the island both near the present coast and in the forest, for example at Vikarskat and

Skaghamn. Land-survey documents of 1856 include a list of fishing-hut places, many of which are now at inland locations, leaving stone foundations. With Björköby in mind, Mead summed up the visual results of the movement of harbours in the following words:[38]

> In some places it is possible to detect as many as three sites — one deserted, one in the process of decay and one in the process of development — on a sequence of three ridges. A handful of fisherfolk are repeating here a response which must be thousands of years old in the coastal economy of the Baltic.

Human Consequences of Hydrological Changes Resulting from Land Uplift

In addition to the direct influence of the changing distribution of land and water on settlement and economic activity there is the indirect effect of changing hydrological conditions. This is not limited to coastal regions. Inland, differential rates of uplift affect the development of lakes: changes in lake outlets result in land emergence of another type. Uplift also has practical implications of a more indirect nature: the drainage of swamps, the maintenance of navigable depths in lakes and the damming of water for hydro-electric power must all take land uplift into account. River development is affected by the continuous lowering of the base level through shore displacement. The profiles of rivers and streams are consequently disturbed: rapids appear in their beds and river navigation is impeded. River flow is hindered by differential uplift, causing problems of agricultural drainage. As the land rises, the water-table falls in relation to the ground surface, in time causing wells to become unusable. Town drainage systems are affected both by the falling water-table and by the emergence of land at sewage outlets along the coast.

Occurrences such as sudden changes of lake outlet have an immediate human impact, although once the human adjustment is made there is little more to relate. The drying-up of the Sarsa rapids, for example, ended salmon-fishing and put a finish to the operation of the watermills there; mills were built to take their place on the new rapids at Ihari. A large area of bottom land was exposed for cultivation and pasture. However, the change soon receded into the past and remains only a memory; 'the wicked Ihari rapids brought Sarsa to pauperdom', according to a local saying.[39]

The effect of land uplift on rivers is more continuous. The

displacement of their base level assists the erosion of loose material from the river beds, exposing boulders and rocks and causing rapids to develop. This has resulted in many coastal rivers, which in the absence of roads were formerly important communication routes, eventually becoming unnavigable. The human consequences of drainage disturbance are especially marked in Ostrobothnia, where rivers, streams and drainage channels flow towards a coast at which uplift approaches its maximum.

The rivers in Ostrobothnia assumed particular significance with the development of tar-distilling during the seventeenth and eighteenth centuries. The export of tar from the Ostrobothnian interior required the location of the distilleries on navigable rivers, but the increasing difficulties of navigation became a constant cause of complaint during this period. In common with the other rivers of Ostrobothnia, the Kyrönjoki, formerly an important route from Isokyrö (Storkyro) to the sea, has become unnavigable since the seventeenth century, despite many attempts to dredge it and remove the offending rapids. The problem steadily worsened as uplift continued to raise the level of the rapids above the water level at the river's mouth. Disputes over clearance operations frequently led to lawsuits; removal of rapids was already a bone of contention in the mid-fifteenth century. During the sixteenth and seventeenth centuries, there were frequent disputes between local farmers, who were responsible for keeping the channel clear, and farmers from further upstream who used the river for navigation. Similar disputes arose during the seventeenth and eighteenth centuries at the mouth of the Laihianjoki, as land emergence interfered with boat traffic from the inland parish of Laihia. The inhabitants of the villages at the river mouth were unwilling to be responsible for maintaining the channel unless upstream villagers also participated in the work. Navigation was not the only concern; channels needed to be kept open to allow fish to swim upstream, and the Vörå å had to be cleared in the seventeenth and eighteenth centuries to prevent fields flooding and to keep the water flow sufficient for mills on the lower course of the river.[40]

The emergence of land at the mouths of smaller streams may obstruct the flow and cause flooding upstream; maintenance of streams was thus frequently a matter of common concern to all the farmers in a village. Failure to keep to agreed arrangements could lead to court, and a case which came before the Vörå district court in 1816 is typical. Two farmers from the village of Kärklax, who owned meadows near the upstream course of the small river flowing through the village, summoned the downstream farmers for failure to keep cleared the outlets of the stream. Each owner was responsible for the upkeep of the section of the channel crossing his land, and the negligence of the defendants was causing the plaintiffs difficulty in keeping their meadows adequately drained. The defendants admitted liability and agreed to clear the stream channel. Arrangements for deepening and widening streams and clearing rapids recur in the village records of Kärklax in the later 1800s and 1900s.

One of the foremost means of agricultural improvement during the nineteenth and twentieth centuries has been drainage. Besides the draining of swamps and bogs and the artificial reclamation of lakes and bays, this has involved constant clearing of streams and drainage channels to overcome floods. The Kyrönjoki provides a well-documented example. Although the river had become virtually unnavigable, dredging of the rapids continued during the later eighteenth century to improve the flow of water in an attempt to counteract spring flooding. In 1814, farmers of the upstream parish of Ilmajoki (Ilmola) took the initiative to clear the Hanhikoski rapids in Isokyrö, further downstream. Work began under State direction in 1817. The improvement of the flow in the upper river, allowing the quicker run-off of flood water, necessitated in turn the clearing of rapids downstream and the dredging of the river's distributaries in order to avoid severe flooding in the lower stretches of the river. The work required the participation of farmers in parishes from Ilmajoki to the river's mouth. Each farm was required to supply a stipulated number of days' work, the amount depending on the size of the farm and the benefit expected from the measures. Work continued until 1824, when two new distributaries were excavated and the four existing ones were dredged. Flood water accumulated, however, in Norrfjärden, a former bay which had become a lake near the mouth of one of the distributaries. Cultivated land in the vicinity was consequently suffering damage. The water level in Norrfjärden was almost a metre higher than the sea, and to solve the problem a canal was dug between 1845 and 1851, providing a more direct outlet seawards. The extensive dredging of the early nineteenth century gave only temporary relief, however. New dredgings of the distributaries were necessary in 1890 and 1899 (Fig 19). None the less, by shortening the flood period, the schemes were instrumental in enabling farmers to bring the low-lying delta land of the Kyrönjoki under the plough, and it was possible at the land reallocations which took place in the twentieth

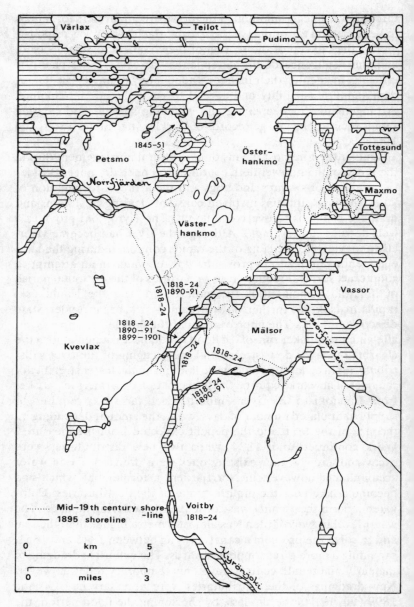

Fig 19   Stream clearance at the mouth of the Kyrönjoki in the nineteenth century.
SOURCES: Rosberg, *Bottenvikens Finska deltan* (1895), plate XII; dates from
Åkerblom, K. V. *Korsholms historia* (1956), 42–7

century to move farmsteads on to the reclaimed land.[41] However, continuing land uplift, allied with river sedimentation and vegetation growth, has brought recurring difficulties with the Kyrönjoki's drainage. Between 1929 and 1933, the main distributary of the river was dredged with a modern scoop dredger; renewed dredging has taken place since 1945, and on a still larger scale from 1969. Claims have been made that recently intensified drainage of swamps for forest improvement has worsened spring flooding by allowing more rapid run-off from peat lands, but agricultural necessity has continued to be the decisive factor in justifying the dredging. A less important beneficiary has been small-boat traffic in the lower course of the river. New problems have arisen, however, through the annual fish losses reported in recent years in Maxmo, at the mouth of river. By exposing certain clay minerals to the air, large-scale dredging has increased the acidity of the water. Similar problems have occurred at the mouths of other rivers in the vicinity which have been dredged under the auspices of Vaasa water district. While farmers obtain assistance in the form of State loans and grants to finance the dredging, local fishermen complain at the lack of compensation for lost catches.

Difficulties for agriculture of a different nature may result through changes in the level of the water-table as the land rises. In sandy areas, the drying-out of the ground owing to the falling water-table can be a problem. The effects of the changing water level on the arable and meadow land of the sandy island of Hailuoto were described in the mid-eighteenth century by Stierwald. He found the arable land poor and infertile, consisting of 'loose and sterile' sandy soils, and what little fertility the land had was lost as the sea receded from the shore and the land stood higher out of the water. Even in the best years, it was necessary to purchase grain from the mainland. Meadow land was also affected by the falling water level. The older meadows, situated some distance from the shore, were annually declining in fertility and growth, eventually resulting in abandonment unless alder could grow and improve the fertility with leaf-humus. Other inland meadows included dried-out bogs and drained swamps, which varied in fertility. The most fertile meadows were along the sea shore, in places that were sheltered from the waves of the open sea and where sedimentation provided nourishment for the grass. Even here, grass growth began to decline a few years after emergence as the land rose higher above the water level.

Effects of land uplift on the water-table and on drainage channels are also felt in other ways. Wells which have dried up because of the falling water-table, especially near the sea, have to be deepened or abandoned. Drainage ditches need constant upkeep: frequent excavation of their outlets is necessary to maintain outflow and prevent arable land becoming flooded. The problems are not restricted to rural areas. In towns, too, the planning of drainage systems has to take land uplift into consideration. In 1895, F. E. Hellström, in a medical thesis, examined from the viewpoint of hygiene the effects of land emergence on the town drainage of Kokkola. He concluded that at the time of the town's foundation in 1620 its site was unsuitable hygienically because of its low-lying situation. The town was partly surrounded by boggy ground and the water-table was high, with the result that the ground was damp and parts of the town were subject periodically to floods. However, from the seventeenth to the late nineteenth century, the town rose by more than 2 m; this helped to improve town drainage, since it was easier to remove waste water. The ground had become drier and less subject to flooding, and the construction of drains was easier. At the same time, new problems arose. In places, the flow of water from old drains, which had become cut off from their former outlets, was impeded. In particular, Salmi, the inlet on which the town had grown up, had become dry land. As early as 1651, a map recorded that Salmi suffered from 'shallow water and is emerging annually'. By 1895, all that remained of the inlet was a canalized stream, the flow of which was insufficient to carry away the water from the town drains which had their outlets here. Periodic dredging was undertaken in an attempt to maintain the depth and outflow of the canal, but in dry weather the flow could cease altogether.[42] The situation remains problematical at the present time. In 1972, plans were in hand to dredge the stream channel, while proposals were under discussion to build a reservoir upstream to regulate water level and improve flow in order to eliminate the stagnant water in Salmi.

Coastal land emergence was one of the factors that had to be taken into consideration by the town authorities of Vaasa in locating a new purification plant for the town's sewage system in 1971. The two alternative sites lay respectively on the northern and southern sides of the town. The latter site was rejected because the purified waste would have flowed into Kaupunginselkä (Stadsfjärden), a bay which is already shallow and becoming rapidly shallower as a result of uplift, sedimentation and vegetation growth. The site at Palosaari, on the northern side of the town, was close to relatively deep water, with fewer dangers of pollution. The new plant, serving the whole town, is fed by a series of pumps, which are necessary because the town's main sewers, following the lines of former sounds, are low-lying and flow is impeded by continuing land uplift. Sewage outlets flowing towards the direction of increasing uplift rate are in danger of stagnating if care is not taken. The lower section of the canal to Vanha-Vaasa (Gamla Vasa), the old town, was dredged in the early 1960s to assist the flow of water from the former Stadssundet and other drainage channels. The dredging also permitted small boats once more to reach Vanhasatama (Gamla hamnen), the old harbour at Hästholmen. On the north side of Vaasa, dredging is keeping the rapidly disappearing bay of On-kilahti (Metviken) in existence. It was formerly the inner harbour at Palosaari, but it has become extremely shallow as a result of uplift. The policy of the town is to keep the area as open water for recreational purposes and as a small-boat harbour.

Responses to hydrological changes resulting from uplift — as to disappearing fishing-waters, fairways and harbours — are characterized by short-term counteraction and long-term adjustment. The hydrological changes are negative for the landsman, just as the emerging sea bottom is negative for the seaman. However the seaman's loss represents a gain for the landsman, who can offset hydrological difficulties against the opportunities offered by the emergence of new land.

Emergent land as a resource

It is as a resource that emergent land has its main significance. The natural grassland that is the first stage of vegetation succession on emergent land traditionally provided valuable meadow land and pasture. Cultivation followed at a later stage. Nowadays, the traditional uses are rapidly being displaced by new forms of land use, in particular recreational ones, which have given shore areas an enhanced value.

The first use made of emergent land, while it is still low-lying and wet, has tended to be for pasture. Its value depends on the shore gradient: on steep slopes, the pasture fringe is narrow and of limited economic use; where the gradient is minimal, a pasture belt several tens of metres wide may occur. The width of grazing is also affected by the diurnal and seasonal variation in water level. The grazing of strips of emergent land alongside cultivated land, and alongside forested areas if they are easily accessible, remains common practice, although a decline is noticeable. Formerly, the harvesting of reeds for fodder was common and constituted the initial stage in the utilization of emerging areas. Young reeds were harvested with a scythe by wading or from a boat. They provided valuable supplementary winter fodder for cattle and horses. In the mid-eighteenth century, reeds accounted for one-sixth of the fodder collected in certain parts of the Vaasa archipelago. Not infrequent disputes over harvesting testify to their value. Court cases concerning Vallgrund village in the Replot archipelago give two examples: in 1758, two farmers from Vallgrund laid a complaint against a farmer from Replot village who had cut reeds from Vallgrund's emergent meadow land; in 1821 a dispute arose between two farms in Vallgrund over the harvest of rushes and arrow grass from a shore meadow.[43] Reeds are no longer generally harvested for fodder; the woody stems are not preferred by cattle, and better-quality feeding-stuff is available. Reed-harvesting was still common in the inter-war period, however, and enjoyed a temporary renaissance during World War II as a source of supplementary fodder. The former widespread incidence of reed-harvesting is still remembered locally and is recorded in placenames such as Hässjeholmen and Hässjefladan, both occurring in Maxmo; a *hässje* (Fi *haasia*) was the frame on which reeds and other 'sea fodder' were dried after harvesting. Its use on Hailuoto was described by Stierwald in the eighteenth century. He noted that the hay was dried on frames instead of in stacks or barns; although use of the frame was more troublesome, its advantage was that the hay remained fresher and better for the cattle. The harvest consisted primarily of shore grass which, because of its greater saltiness and pithiness compared to 'land' hay, was more likely to become stale and deteriorate in barns. Harvesting of reeds and shore grass continued to be common on Hailuoto until the 1950s. Abandoned grey hay-barns still characterize the shores of Hanhinen and Syökari, two former islands which are now attached to Hailuoto on the south-east, and of Kirkonsalmi, the remnants of the sound that formerly separated them from the main island. One of the last places where harvesting of shore grass occurs is on Isomatala, an island which has emerged off the south-east shore largely in the last thirty or forty years. The decline of reed-harvesting has disturbed the autumn shooting of grey geese, which are less attracted to the reeds now that there is no renewed growth of young shoots after cutting, and the geese tend to migrate south earlier than previously. Fowling, particularly for geese and ducks, is a traditional activity in the reed-covered emerging sounds and marshes of Hailuoto, and autumn shooting rights are leased out by the islanders.

The use of emergent land for natural meadow and pasture formerly played a central role in the economy of Hailuoto. Sheep,
cattle and horses grazed freely along the shores and in the forest.
Sheep were the main livestock during the nineteenth century, their
numbers reaching some 4,000 at their maximum; they were put out
to graze the emergent shore pastures at midsummer and rounded up
at Michaelmas. Cattle-rearing expanded with the development of
the dairy movement at the end of the nineteenth century. Cattle
grazed the forest and shore pastures during the summer, returning
each evening to the farmsteads for milking. The harvest from the
shore meadows provided winter fodder. Most meadows on
Hailuoto were natural, consisting primarily of emergent land, and
bog meadows in the inner part of the island. The low-lying situation
of the hay land meant that it easily became waterlogged at high
water or with heavy rain. The most valuable meadows were along
the shores of Hanhinen. After hay harvest there, the cattle were
taken from the rest of the island to graze the meadows, and along
the shores of Hanhinen there were autumn cowsheds, so that the
cattle did not need to be taken back to the village at night. The
women crossed Kirkonsalmi each morning and evening to milk the
cows. There were also a number of cottages on Hanhinen which
were inhabited during the harvest period and again in autumn when
the cattle were rounded up to be taken back to the village for the
winter.[44] When Stierwald wrote in 1767, he recorded that after the
meadows on Hanhinen were harvested, they provided autumn pasture for horses and other animals, although this had the drawback
that the horses tended to intrude on the hay-frames. The greater
part of Hailuoto's meadows were situated on the shores of Hanhinen and Syökari, which in 1767 were still separate islands. Later,
as the smaller islands became joined to the main island through land
emergence, the animals were kept on the north-western side of the
island (Hailuoto proper) by a fence, which was opened after harvest. Free grazing of animals gradually ceased in the mid-1950s.
The number of sheep on the island had already greatly declined;
even by 1929, there were only half as many as at the nineteenth-
century peak, and by 1969 the number had fallen to 400. The shore
pasture has become overgrown by scrub, although natural meadows
continue to be harvested in places, for example in the emerged
sound between Hanhinen and Syökari. Hay-barns, an abandoned
cowshed and the disused meadow cottage remain as a reminder of
the old system. The barns are still used, but only one farm in the
immediate vicinity grazes cattle there in the autumn.

Similar systems of pasturing cattle on emergent land were found further south in the Jakobstad and Vaasa archipelagos. At the mouth of the Kyrönjoki, where the existence of the archipelago meant that emergent pastures and meadows were frequently cut off from the main village by water, an extensive system of *fäbodar* arose. *Fäbodar* were temporary summer settlements where cattle were grazed: a fully developed system of summer pasturing and grazing, comparable to that in the Swedish and Norwegian mountains and in the Alps, occurred in Finland only in parts of Ostrobothnia and some places in eastern Finland. At the mouth of the Kyrönjoki, they were primarily meadow *fäbodar* on emergent land, cattle being taken to graze for the autumn after hay harvest. They were sometimes used in conjunction with forest *fäbodar,* where cattle grazed during spring and early summer. At its simplest, the system was similar to that on Hailuoto, with twice-daily trips being made to milk the cattle, and a cottage which was lived in for the duration of the harvest. This often developed into a semi-*fäbod* system, in which the women stayed overnight and transported the milk back to the farm only once a day. A further development was to process the milk at the *fäbod* into sour-milk products, which were taken back every few days or once a week. The full system was found where the women stayed for the whole duration of the grazing period, processing the milk into butter and often cultivating small potato patches. There is evidence of *fäbodar* along the Ostrobothnian coast as early as the sixteenth century, and the system reached its culmination in the later nineteenth. *Fäbodar* were often found in groups, and the meadows belonging to different owners were grazed in common. The autumn grazing period generally lasted one or two months, although further out in the archipelago it continued longer. In Bergö, where a full *fäbod* system developed on the emerging shores of a group of skerries north-east of the main island, the animals grazed after hay harvest at the beginning of August until the end of October. The older women of the village lived there for the whole period. Besides cattle, a large proportion of the village's horses and sheep grazed there. *Fäbodar* tended to disappear where land emergence caused the water barrier to vanish, as occurred, for example, in Iskmo and Petsmo, north of Vaasa. The system was formerly widespread in the Vaasa area, and often represented the first stage before permanent settlement, following the retreating sea, developed.[45]

In former times, the narrow belts of natural meadow along the shore were widened to create *lövängar* (deciduous meadows) by human interference with the natural vegetation succession on emergent land. The most typical *lövängar* in Finland occurred in Åland, where both shore meadows and meadows cleared in the forest were utilized. Natural succession from deciduous to coniferous forest was interrupted by continual clearing, hay-harvesting and grazing, and the variety of deciduous species in Åland gave the *löväng* landscape a park-like appearance. Ostrobothnian *lövängar* were characterized by alder, the first tree species to invade the flat emergent shores. The meadows were maintained by clearing away the trees, except for individuals left at intervals of 3 to 4 m to provide leaf-humus and to prevent the ground drying out, so that coniferous species did not invade. The trees were periodically pruned and deciduous seedlings were cut away, leaving only sufficient to replace the older trees at the end of their life span. In Ostrobothnia, the creation of *lövängar* often represented the first phase in taking emergent land into occupation. On Bergö, for example, all the land emerging in the course of 200 years was used as *löväng*, leading to a dramatic expansion of the 'settled' (i.e. non-forest) area between the sixteenth and eighteenth centuries. In the eighteenth century, *lövängar* provided the most important hay land in the archipelago. The meadows were not fenced off from the adjoining forest, and generally the forest-meadow boundary was not constant. Although the practice of clearing *lövängar* delayed the invasion of coniferous species, continuing land uplift resulted in the innermost meadows eventually drying out as the water-table sank in relation to ground level. The meadows gave way to scrub, and birch, followed by spruce, invaded. The decayed remains of abandoned hay-barns in the forest were the last reminders of the former existence of *lövängar*. On the other hand, as reed-covered water emerged along the shore, *lövängar* took the place of the reed harvest. The growing practice of creating *lövängar* led to a decline in the importance of reeds as a source of fodder.[46]

At the end of the eighteenth century, natural meadow frequently accounted for 90 per cent of the agricultural land in the coastal villages of Ostrobothnia. A large proportion was situated on newly emergent areas. C. E. Böcker wrote in 1815 that 'in living memory several thousand *tunnland* [1 *tunnland* = 0·49 ha] in Mustasaari parish have risen above the water surface and become fertile meadows.'[47] Towards the end of the nineteenth century, however, the importance of natural meadow began to decline in response to the development of commercial dairy farming and the accompanying change to cultivated grassland, which gave higher-quality fodder. The cultivated area has been expanded in the twentieth century primarily by ploughing natural meadow land and to a lesser extent by draining bogs and clearing new areas from the forest. Arable land along the coast is situated for the most part on emergent shores and inlets and on clays deposited by streams in former bays.

The relationship between present agricultural land and land emergence in the coastal villages is evident in a number of ways. Old shorelines are frequently preserved as field boundaries. The position of former coastlines is also reflected in placenames with endings such as *ö, holme, vik, sund* and *näs* (island, islet, inlet, sound, foreland) in Swedish-speaking areas, and elsewhere by their Finnish equivalents *saari, luoto, lahti, salmi* and *niemi*. Names of bays and inlets often remain as fieldnames, while the positions of old islands are reflected not only by placenames but also by the distribution of cultivated and uncultivated land, the former islands remaining as higher, forested land surrounded by newer, arable land. In Maxmo commune, the proportion of the land area under cultivation becomes gradually smaller outwards from the mainland to the outer archipelago. Although factors such as population density and degree of isolation are involved, the broad pattern of decreasing arable area outwards is what would be expected as a result of land emergence. The topography of much of the archipelago corresponds to the higher, forested, former skerry-guard parts of the mainland; whereas on the mainland and to a smaller degree in the inner archipelago, agricultural land lies on the later emergent clays and silts deposited in depressions on the sea bottom. In the middle and outer archipelago, rocky and stony areas have emerged, while the depressions into which the finer material has been washed from them are still partly under water. Corresponding inversely to the decreasing percentage of arable land outwards is a broad pattern of increasing diversity of occupational structure; in the archipelago, the traditional economy of fishing combined with small agricultural holdings and forestry has been replaced by multi-occupational livelihoods, in which smallholdings with one or two milk cows, special crops such as strawberries, mink-farming, subsidiary fishing for mink fodder, forestry and winter construction work are all important.

Although, particularly since World War II, a greater variety of subsidiary occupations have made their appearance, the development history of fishing–meadow–arable as land emergence has progressed is typical for the Ostrobothnian archipelago and the mainland coast. Sounds with fishing-weirs at the beginning of the

twentieth century in Replot, for example, had become drainage
channels for the reclamation of adjacent bog meadows for arable
land by the 1930s.[48] Smeds examined the influence of land
emergence on the historical extension of settlement in Malax,
where the sequence of changes from fishing to agriculture constituted a fundamental theme.[49] In Petalax, farming has been
extended without empoldering at the mouth of the river, where
marine regression leaves a steadily broadening estuarine plain.[50] A
land-partition map and documents from the later eighteenth century record that the smaller delta of that time, known as Slätan, was
set aside as common grazing for livestock and horses. The growing
delta became the horse pasture for the whole parish, grazing rights
being sold by periodic auction. Slätan was brought under the plough
in the 1930s. Offshore, the shallow reed-filled waters provide a
natural preserve for ducks and other waterfowl. Antecedent to the
extension of the agricultural margin are changes in duck-shooting
areas, as reed beds along the shore dry out and new reeds appear
elsewhere. Close to Vaasa, the reed-filled water of Kaupunginselkä
is another haunt of waterfowl. Among the decayed boathouses and
jetties of Munsmo harbour, on the southern side, can be found
discarded punts, used for negotiating the shallow water in pursuits
such as duck-shooting, as well as abandoned fishing equipment,
including a small variety of conoid fish-trap (Sw *ryssjä*, Fi *rysä*) used
for catching shallow-water fish. The transition from water to land is
epitomized by the proximity of the virtually abandoned harbour to
extensive areas of recent reclamation.

The detailed succession of uses as land emerges can be illustrated
by case examples from Maxmo. The main arable area lies on a
former bay named Ölingsfjärden, where the sequence can be traced
from maps and other records. Ölingsfjärden and an inlet called
Finnholms gyttjan formerly separated the villages of Maxmo and
Kärklax. An agreement in 1667 recognized Maxmo's right to fish in
Finnholms gyttjan, while 'Allings Fiählen' was reserved for the use
of Kärklax.[51] The bay appears on two maps of 1709. Local tradition
relates that bream, which are found in shallow, vegetation-filled
waters at river mouths, were fished here in the eighteenth century.
On a map of 1763, Ölingsfjärden had largely emerged and provided
natural meadow. The name Hopäng, which the area still bears,
suggests that communal harvesting, known in Swedish as *hopslåtter*,
was carried on. The occurrence of this can be dated fairly accurately, since the area was still water in 1709 and was partitioned among
individual landowners in 1772. Communal harvesting of emergent

meadow land was sometimes resorted to if the yield was unreliable or uneven. Today, the landscape of Ölingsfjärden shows the characteristic features of an extensive emergent area where meadow land has been converted to arable. It consists predominantly of cultivated grassland, grazed by cattle after hay harvest, and fields dotted with the characteristic grey hay-barns of Ostrobothnia. Short-term leys (3 to 4 years) alternate with grain (1 to 2 years), the normal arable rotation. A more recent sequence of uses, occurring almost within living memory, is provided by Svältmar, a former bay on the west coast of the Maxmo peninsula. This was partitioned among the individual farmers of Maxmo village in 1845, when the area consisted largely of sedges and arrow grass. Reeds were still harvested from the wettest part in the 1880s, and crucian carp, related to bream, could be caught. Later, the area provided natural pasture. In the 1930s, it was drained, limed and brought into cultivation with the aid of a State grant. Grass, especially timothy, is the main crop. State premiums to promote new cultivation on small farms have been an important stimulus to expanding the cultivated area in Maxmo, as elsewhere in Finland. It is frequently the more recently emerged land which is most easily brought under the plough; an example is provided by Sund farm in the village of Tottesund. A premium was received in 1953 to bring into cultivation 1 ha of rough pasture, partly covered by alder, which had been described in 1870 as newly emergent land, damp, treeless and used as natural meadow. The work of clearing, draining and liming was undertaken during the summer of 1953, and an autumn crop of oats was sown. The following year grass was sown. This was harvested as hay for three or four years, after which grain was again sown and the rotation continued. Oats was the first crop for practical reasons: grass had to be sown in early summer, whereas oats could be sown immediately after autumn ploughing. Elsewhere, cultivation may be gradually extended on to emergent land as it rises. On the northern shore of Maxmo fladan, there was formerly a small inlet, where reeds were harvested forty-five years ago by sickle from a boat. By the 1930s, the inlet had dried out sufficiently for sedge growth and was used as natural pasture. At about this time, it was brought into cultivation after a drainage ditch had been dug and the area had been limed. The first crop was timothy, which was later rotated with grain and clover (the last doing best). Since then, the whole northern shore of Maxmo fladan has been brought into cultivation, and ploughing extends a little further down the shore each year. A newly ploughed strip is usually not sown until the following year. At first, crops fare less well than on the older cultivated land, and growth in spring tends to begin later. No particular crop sequence needs to be followed when cropping is extended on to emergent land, since the newly ploughed area is heavily limed. As the shore is here relatively steep, no drainage ditches are necessary. After the initial transition period, no appreciable difference in growth between the newer and older cultivation is noticed, except with grass, which tends to begin growth earlier on the lower, damper ground.

Emergent land is favoured for cultivation because of the relative ease of clearing. Shore land becomes suitable for ploughing once it rises sufficiently for it to be seldom flooded and harmful salts are drained out as it becomes drier. A. A. Säntti noted that in certain areas recently brought under the plough on the coast of southern Satakunta, clover and oats were successfully grown despite periodic flooding; growth began three or four weeks later than in higher-situated fields, but the harvest was ready at about the same time.[52] The low salinity of the Baltic greatly facilitates bringing new coastal areas into cultivation.

Agricultural reclamation on naturally emergent land is a continuous occurrence along the Bothnian coast.[53] In recent times, the process of bringing emergent land into use has been speeded up by damming coastal flats normally flooded at high water, as for example in the Kokemäenjoki delta.[54] One of the largest areas to be brought into cultivation in this way was Söderfjärden, south of Vaasa. This was formerly a large bay, in which good catches of fish were obtained according to sixteenth-century tax returns. By the eighteenth century, it had begun to emerge and to be colonized by reeds. It was described by Runeberg in 1765:[55]

> Söderfjärden is a shallow body of water in Solfveå chapelry of Malax parish, 8,000 ells [1 ell = 0·59 m] in length and 4,500 in width: this bay is linked to another large bay of the sea through a winding sound 20 to 100 ells wide . . . When the emergent land was measured, in connection with a dispute over ownership, I occasioned to learn that the meadow land, which had emerged around Söderfjärden, had increased in area by one and a half *tunnland* [0·74 ha] annually.

By the beginning of the next century, the bay had as a result of land uplift become too shallow for fishing, and reeds and sedges were harvested for fodder. Proposals were made to drain the bay in the nineteenth century, but it was not until the 1920s that the work was undertaken. The total area of Söderfjärden is 2,300 ha, and in 1911 some 1,430 ha were still half a metre under water. When drainage began, about two-fifths of the old bay were already good-quality meadow, while the rest provided a harvest of reeds, rushes and arrow grass. Now, no less than fifty-two farmsteads are situated there, and the 350 holdings which own land there have an average of 6½ ha each. Clover and timothy are important crops, and before World War II 60 per cent of Finland's export of timothy seed was grown there.[56] A reconstruction of the Söderfjärden project was undertaken in the early 1960s, involving renewal of 45 km of ditches and construction of a new pump station. Proposals have also been made to underdrain it, which would add an estimated 300 ha to the arable area.

In addition to Söderfjärden, several other schemes have been undertaken in the Vaasa area since 1945 (Fig 20). Details are presented in Table 5. Most of the schemes entail improvement of low-lying, recently emerged and emerging land rather than reclamation of extensive areas from the sea directly. Drainage is assisted by State grants and loans, and individual schemes are undertaken as common enterprises by landowners under plans drawn up by the local water-district office. Similar schemes have been undertaken at various points along the coast of Satakunta and south-west Finland. During the 1950s, when enthusiasm for coastal land reclamation was at its peak, proposals were put forward for a series of larger projects, which would have involved the damming and drainage of more than 1,000 sq km of shallow coastal waters, and transformed large parts of the archipelago into mainland areas.[57] New schemes are unlikely to be instituted, however, in view of recent changes in Finnish agricultural policy, which no longer favours an increase in arable area. Part of the land reclaimed by existing schemes has been left for timber production instead of being ploughed. The drained land grows high-quality birch, which is of increasing value for the wood-processing industry, including nowadays pulp mills.

Farmers have traditionally been in favour of schemes to accelerate land formation to gain more agricultural land. The progressive change from an agricultural to an industrial economy has meant, however, that the traditional response of the farmer is being displaced by the needs of industry. Water areas proposed for draining in the 1950s are now seen as potential freshwater reservoirs. At Jakobstad and Uusikaupunki (Nystad), islands of the skerry guard have been linked with one another and with the mainland by dams to create lakes, the brackish water of which soon turned to fresh water from the rivers and streams flowing into them. In the former scheme, a lake covering 75 sq km between Larsmo (Luoto) and the

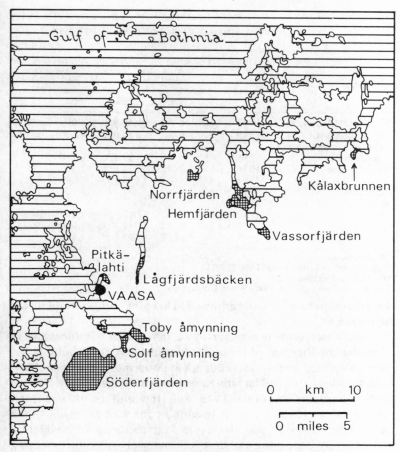

Fig 20   Coastal land-reclamation projects in the Vaasa area.
SOURCE: Information from Vaasa Water-District Office

mainland was dammed in 1962 and 1963 to provide fresh water for
a pulp and paper mill. At Uusikaupunki, a freshwater reservoir
covering 37 sq km has been created for industrial purposes, and a
similar scheme has been proposed in the vicinity of Vaasa.[58] The
Larsmo scheme was extended to nearly 90 sq km in 1969 by damming part of the Öja skerry guard to the north. The possibility of
regulating the water level of such lakes can alter the pattern of
subsequent land emergence. A recent proposal has been made to
maintain the freshwater lakes at Larsmo and Öja by allowing their
water level to rise with land uplift. Existing regulations requiring the

Table 5 COASTAL LAND-RECLAMATION PROJECTS IN THE
VAASA AREA DURING THE POST-WAR PERIOD

Name of project	Date of drainage	Area ha	Length of embank- ment km	Construction costs (embank- ment and pump station Fmk†	Annual operat- ing costs‡ Fmk†	No of land holdings involved
Pitkälahti (Långviken)	1947	127	0·30	455,832	6,000	90
Lågfjärdsbäcken	1949	220	0·60	225,612	4,500	120
Toby åmynning (Tuovilan- joensuu)	1953–4	450	14·31	889,420	6,100	30
Vassorfjärden	1956	179	2·60	272,868	2,300	30
Hemfjärden	1957	553	6·05	593,098	7,000	430
Norrfjärden	1958–60	443	4·80	331,170	4,800	190
Solf åmynning (Sulvan- joensuu)	1960	600	8·70	815,584	4,200	240
Söderfjärden	1962–4	1,767	0·15	349,471	5,000	560
Kålaxbrunnen	1965	50	0·14	95,400	1,800	20

*Reconstruction
†100,000 Fmk = £10,000 = $24,000 (1972).
‡Pumping and maintenance.
SOURCE: Information from Vaasa Water-District Office.

water level to be constantly adjusted in keeping with sea level would
first have to be altered.

Land emergence is a factor to be taken into consideration in
planning the location of industry along the coast. In Oulu, it has
been calculated on the basis of depth measurements from sea charts
that an additional 160 ha will have emerged in the vicinity of the
town's harbours between 1943 and the end of the century.
Emergence can be accelerated in conjunction with extension of the
deep-water harbour and the associated dredging of navigation
channels. By depositing the dredged material on to the emerging
land behind artificial embankments, additional land for industrial
purposes would be created close to the harbour.[59] Shallowing inlets
and emerging shores have facilitated the reclamation of land for
harbour extension, industrial expansion and other construction
purposes in many of Finland's coastal towns. Dredged material has
been used to fill out about 12 ha of additional land for Kokkola's
harbour at Ykspihlaja, and in Vaasa the oil harbour is built on
filled-out emergent land at Vaskiluoto. In towns such as Pori,
Rauma (Raumo) and Helsinki, reclaimed shore land has been used
for industrial purposes and for housing. While such activities as
dredging and shore reclamation are by no means unique to Finland,
both are closely related there to the necessity of adjusting to land
uplift.

As Finland has become increasingly industrialized and urbanized, and the agricultural significance of emergent land has declined, its significance for other uses has increased. One of the most important developments in recent years has been the growing attraction of shore areas for private recreational dwellings and other recreational purposes. In this, the post-war rise in the standard of living has been decisive. The number of dwellings not serving as permanent residences, such as summer and week-end cabins and cottages, and country houses, has rapidly grown since 1950. The second, temporary, home has become part of the modern Finnish way of life. Increasing pressures on shore areas are leading to more careful assessments of emergent land. H. F. Pölönen, writing of the lake shores of eastern Finland, observed that 'with the rise in land values, more and more attention has begun to be paid to emergent land.'[60] He was concerned with the results of artificially lowered lake levels, but his words are even more applicable to the constantly emerging sea coast. Access to water is one of the prime requisites for a summer cottage, with the result that a host of new problems concerning the ownership of emergent land have made their appearance in recent years.

The potential value of emergent land is evident. Disputes over its ownership are not a new phenomenon. Celsius mentioned in 1743 that 'disputes have been brought to court over to whom the emergent land should belong, for example in the Ostrobothnian skerry guard.'[61] Land emergence entailed extra work for land-surveyors; it seemed to Runeberg that 'ownership disputes arise over the additional land annually.'[62] Local parish histories contain numerous references to disputes between farmers over emergent land. They were not confined to the rural population. The inhabitants of Jakobstad, for example, were arguing over the ownership and use of emergent land with neighbouring villages in the eighteenth and nineteenth centuries.[63] Disputes over emergent land commonly led to its partition among disputants in accordance with ancient legal rights. As Mead noted, 'the process of reclamation involves both legal and agricultural operations.'[64] The partition of emergent land among landowners became an established procedure, which, codified in legislation in the nineteenth and twentieth centuries, has been variously modified in response to the increasing complexity of land ownership.

The emergence of land poses various problems of use — whether regarding settlement, fishing, navigation, agriculture or, more recently, leisure activities — which are partly solved by the individual in the context of the natural, cultural and economic setting. The use of emergent land is further affected by the solutions found to the more complex problems arising over its ownership and partition. Together with local customs, which often represent survivals of ancient traditions, legislation is an important factor influencing the response of individuals to emergent land, particularly in relation to its tenure and use. Two variables operate to give character to a particular area: the resource variable and the human variable.[65] Legislation and customs are components of the human variable and interact with the resource variable represented by emergent land.

4

The Institutional Framework: Finnish Land-tenure Principles and Legislation

The Land Reforms of the Eighteenth Century

MAN'S RESPONSE TO change in his physical environment depends not only on the nature of the physical influences but also on factors such as the principles and ideas of society; his response is often expressed through or influenced by social institutions. The customs and laws regulating emergent land are conditioned by the general principles of land tenure and land legislation applying in Finland. A principal aim of land legislation during the last two hundred years can be broadly stated as the creation of a rational system of land use based on private use and ownership of land. The modern pattern of land tenure in Finland derives from the Great Partition (Sw *storskifte*, Fi *isojako*), which began in Ostrobothnia in the second half of the eighteenth century. The Great Partition aimed at ending the open-field system and consolidating arable holdings to improve agricultural efficiency, and at dividing among individual owners the forest and other land owned in common by the village.

At that time, the pattern of land holding was extremely complex. Arable land was privately owned but distributed in numerous strips or plots in open fields. Meadows were in part privately owned and in part commonly owned. Forest and other outlying land was held in common. The unit of ownership for commonly owned land was in general the village; however, smaller groups of landowners often owned meadow or other land in common as a result of joint inheritance. The intermixed ownership of arable land, the logical outcome of earlier primitive measuring techniques and communal

89

methods of farming,[1] had become an obstacle to agricultural
improvement by the eighteenth century. The partition into strips
(Sw *tegskifte*, Fi *sarkajako*) prevented individuals from experimenting with new methods or new seed, and from draining their
land. The scattered, interspersed parcels could not be fenced and
worked individually, since one farmer would have to cross another's
crop in order to cultivate his own. All agricultural operations had to
be performed at the same time. Private enterprise was not possible,
and this imposed restrictions on agricultural development. Common pasture and forest rights led to disputes and wasted opportunities, discouraging private land settlement.

The idea of repartition as a means of consolidating highly parcel-
led property was introduced in a decree of 1749 containing instructions for land-surveyors. Land could be redistributed with the consent of all the landowners in the village. However, the reluctance of
the peasantry to accept such a radical reform resulted in the decree
remaining ineffective beyond certain limited areas of Sweden.[2] The
real foundation for reform of the land-tenure system was a new
decree of 1757, which stated that the best means of improving
agriculture was for every farmer to receive his arable land, meadow
and forest combined in one parcel. To overcome the peasants' fear
that land redistribution would result in their getting less or worse
land than before, the principle was established that the allocation of
poorer quality land would be compensated by allowing a larger
area. The partition could be carried out at the request of one
landowner in a village against the wishes of the rest, all having to
share the cost.

The 1757 decree stipulated that the Great Partition was to be
initiated immediately and unconditionally where geographical
measurement and tax assessment of the land had already been
carried out. This applied principally to Ostrobothnia, and the first
stage of the Great Partition in Finland began in the Vaasa area the
same year. A general survey and tax assessment of land in
Ostrobothnia had been decreed in 1749. E. O. Runeberg was
appointed head of Finnish land-survey operations and established
his office in Vaasa in 1750. A geographical mapping and description
of the livelihood of each village was initiated, and the work undertaken in the following years constitutes the main source of information on land use and land tenure in the area during the eighteenth
century.

The early *storskifte* decrees were relatively short and simple,
stating the principles to be introduced but containing little detail on

practical procedure. Later, as the Great Partition was initiated in different parts of the country, the practical difficulties and short-comings of the regulations became evident, and they were supplemented during the latter half of the eighteenth century by a series of decrees of increasing complexity. Different regions of Sweden had particular requirements which were dealt with by special legislation; the Great Partition in Finland was regulated by its own decrees from 1762, and there were supplementary regulations for the various provinces. Two decrees for Ostrobothnia came into force in 1766, when special land-partition courts (Sw *ägodelnings-rätter*, Fi *maanjako-oikeudet*) were set up in each parish to supervise the Great Partition and deal with disputes arising from its implementation. The most important decree concerning Finland as a whole was issued in 1775, and led to the Great Partition being applied more energetically.

Whereas the earlier fragmentation and widespread distribution of parcels had ensured that in practice all holdings received an even mixture of good and poor land, the Great Partition[3] introduced the principle of grading the land according to value, taking into account its character, fertility and situation. The 1775 decree stated that holdings were as far as possible to be comparable with each other in land characteristics; where a larger area had to compensate for poorer quality, the extra costs and work necessary on poorer land were to be considered as well as the potential yield. Lakes, rocky areas, marshes and wasteland were regarded as unusable and excluded from the grading, being allotted to the holding in whose boundaries they fell. Coastal fishing-waters were left in the common ownership of the village, and roads, main drainage ditches and areas for common use were also excluded from the partition. The land allocated to each owner was placed as near as possible to his farmstead, following the order of the farmsteads in the village, or was positioned by agreement among the villagers; lots were drawn in cases of disagreement. In exceptional cases, farmsteads were moved voluntarily out of the village to a new location. Since it was not possible for everyone to receive the exact value of land due to him, compensation was to be paid to individual farmers for any loss incurred. However, before the partition could proceed, the agreement of the landowners to the grading was necessary; cases of disagreement were to be settled by the land-partition court.

Problems of grading meant that the ideal of one parcel per holding was not in practice achieved; a single farmer often received ten or fifteen parcels. This was an improvement on the earlier multiplicity of small strips, which could number several score to each farmer, but unwillingness by farmers to accept that a greater share of poorer land was equal to a smaller share of better land resulted frequently in each soil type being subdivided among all the farmers. The usual practice in Finland of a three-part partition, taking arable land, meadow and forest separately, and the common allocation to a farm of both home-meadow and out-meadow, also increased the number of parcels per holding. The 1775 decree fixed a maximum per farm of four parcels of arable land, four of meadow and two of forest, representing a compromise between the ideal and the realities of the situation.

A continued form of intermixed land ownership, incompatible with the principles of the Great Partition, was caused by areas of land owned by a holding in one village within the boundaries of another. Such areas are known in Swedish as *urfjäll* (Fi *ulkokyläpalstat*). Early confusion over whether they should be included in the partition of a village's land was clarified by the decree of 1775, which stated that *urfjäll* standing in the way of the Great Partition could be exchanged, without the consent of the owner, against full compensation in land at a more suitable place. As a result, many outlying possessions, the cause of numerous earlier disputes and legal actions, were exchanged. Such a rationalization was not, however, possible in every case, and *urfjäll* have continued to be a cause of land disputes.

The share of each holding in the commonly owned meadow, forest and other outlying land of the village was determined from the relative tax values of the holdings. Tax liability was formerly based on periodic assessments of the value of holdings, but in time it came to be a fixed value, and a royal proclamation of 1789 guaranteed that once a tax assessment had been made it would remain unchanged. In Ostrobothnia, the general tax assessment carried out after 1749 was the basis of partition. Associated with the Great Partition was the final fixing of the basis of land taxation where this had not already been done.

In earlier times, when settlement was sparse and the value of holdings fairly equal, each holding seems to have corresponded to one tax unit. Subsequent subdivision and amalgamation of holdings led to a proportional subdivision and amalgamation of such units. With the resultant variation in the liability of different holdings, the tax unit became a measure of the value of different holdings in relation to one another, and the tax assessment of a holding in proportion to the total assessment of the village became the basis of division in the use of common land. Under the system of communal agriculture, the relative amounts of labour to be provided by each farm and the share of the harvest to be received by each, as well as grazing and forest rights, had been similarly determined. The most common tax unit became one known in Swedish as *mantal* (Fi *manttaali*). This originated as a personal tax, but during the sixteenth century became a tax on the land's productivity and was divided at the subdivision of holdings similarly to other tax units.[4] In 1924 land ceased to be taxed in Finland on the basis of *mantal*, but the concept retains its importance as a cadastral unit determining a holding's share in a village and its commonly held land, and is fundamental to an understanding of land partition. At the Great Partition, commonly owned land was divided according to the *mantal* of each landowner: the share of each owner in the total assessed value of the land was determined by the value of his *mantal* calculated as a fraction of the combined *mantal* of all the landowners in the village. Thus two holdings with the same *mantal* could be allocated different areas if the land valuations differed. The value of arable land and meadow received by each landowner at the Great Partition was equivalent to what he previously owned, and the remaining share of the total value due to him on the basis of his *mantal* was allocated in forest and outlying land. This procedure of division firmly established the principle of private ownership of all categories of land, and, together with the consolidation of arable holdings, promoted individual initiative, which was considered the most effective method of ensuring efficient land use.

Whereas in Sweden the Great Partition was replaced by new land reforms in the early nineteenth century, its influence in Finland was more fundamental, continuing after Finland's separation from Sweden in 1809 to become a Grand Duchy under the Russian Crown. The policies and legislation of the last years of Swedish rule continued almost unchanged in Finland during the first half of the nineteenth century. From Ostrobothnia, the Great Partition was gradually extended to most parts of Finland during the late 1700s and the 1800s, and in parts of northern Finland it has only been undertaken in the twentieth century. However, the first phase of the Great Partition did not altogether fulfil the hopes of its originators as far as the development of a rational system of land tenure was concerned. The reduction in the number of parcels on each farm, although not insignificant, was not so great as had been hoped. Compromises were dictated by, among other things, the conservatism of the peasantry. Discussing the area of present-day Sweden,

S. Helmfrid has suggested that the *storskifte* legislation can be viewed as presenting a model plan for land distribution which, when put into practice, had to be modified through a series of compromises with the reality presented by natural and cultural geography.[5]

The first important result of the Great Partition was the fortification of private ownership rights. Other land reforms of the period also contributed to this. Earlier restrictions were eased against the sub-division of holdings and removed against the establishment by farmers of tenant holdings or crofts (Sw *torp*, Fi *torpat*) on their land. From 1747, subdivision of farms was permitted, provided that the parts were self-supporting. Restrictions on the establishment of crofts, previously the privilege of the nobility, were gradually eased during the first half of the 1700s and largely removed in 1757. In 1762, landowners were permitted to settle cottagers on their land; in return for their small cottage holdings (Sw *backstuguområden*, Fi *mäkitupa-alueet*) the cottagers worked for the landowner. Crofters, too, usually paid rent in the form of a fixed number of days' work for the landowner. The establishment of crofts and cottages guaranteed the main farm a permanent and cheap labour force, which could be used to bring new areas into cultivation on the individual land holdings created by the Great Partition. After 1789, restrictions on land, except for certain restrictions on the use of forest land, were limited for the most part to the obligatory land-parcelling regulations of the Great Partition and the remaining restrictions on the subdivision on holdings. The principle of individual ownership and use of land was established within a system which had as its aim a more flexible and efficient agrarian structure.

Fragmentation of Land in the Nineteenth Century and Counter-Measures

During the course of the nineteenth century, certain inherent contradictions in the principles of land use which had gained dominance during the eighteenth century became increasingly manifest. The limited success of the Great Partition in creating a rational land-tenure pattern based on consolidated holdings was counteracted by increasing fragmentation. This arose from the rapid increase of population in the nineteenth century. Significant factors were better agricultural techniques, improvements in living standards and reduced mortality rates. The total rural population of Finland increased from 1,044,000 in 1815 to 2,373,000 in 1900. In Ostrobothnia, the rural population grew even more rapidly, trebling from 227,000 to 689,000.[6] Not only did this result in the continuing subdivision of holdings, which was facilitated by further easing of restrictions in the second half of the nineteenth century; it also led to a substantial increase in the number of crofters and cottagers. Land fragmentation and the eventual attempts to counter the process were in turn reflected in the treatment of emergent land.

The tradition of private ownership in a predominantly farming economy inevitably resulted in the regular subdivision of farms among heirs. The expansion of the cultivated area promoted by the Great Partition permitted subdivision to continue without loss of self-sufficiency. Restrictions on subdivision were eased in 1864, when the required level of self-sufficiency was lowered and, in addition to subdivision among heirs, the creation of new holdings for a specific purpose, usually for sale, was permitted. Minimum size levels were further reduced in 1883 and 1895, and all restrictions on subdivision were abolished in 1916. The main period of fragmentation in Finland began after 1895. Ostrobothnia, however, had followed its own course: the exceptionally rapid increase of rural population here meant that by the beginning of the twentieth century there were twice as many landowners as in 1815.[7]

The increasing number of holdings was accompanied by internal fragmentation. Rigid adherence to the principle of equal rights for all heirs (with daughters receiving half as much as sons before 1879) was an important factor. E. Jutikkala has explained the process as follows: 'When the farm was subdivided, it was the custom to give every part-owner a share in every arable parcel belonging to it. Thus scarcely a hundred years had passed since the Great Partition before the pattern of land tenure was as chequered . . . as before it.'[8] The maximum of ten parcels per holding stipulated in 1775 soon became the minimum, owing to the compromises made at the Great Partition and to the subsequent partitioning at various times of commonly owned land (including emergent land). The most common form of subdivision in the nineteenth century was through informal agreement among part-owners (Sw *sämjodelning*, Fi *sovintojako*), without legal ratification in court. This was sometimes undertaken with the assistance of a land-surveyor, but often instead by the farmers' own arbiters. In parts of Ostrobothnia, a new partition into strips arose, resembling that existing before the Great Partition, with all the drawbacks this entailed.[9]

In an attempt to counteract excessive internal fragmentation of holdings in areas where the Great Partition had already taken place, a second major land reallocation, known since 1916 as the New Partition (Sw *nyskifte*, Fi *uusjako*),[10] was introduced in the Land Survey Ordinance of 1848. This can be requested either where there is a multiplicity of parcels or where the form and distribution of parcels is unsatisfactory. At the same time, common land, such as the beds of drained lakes, reclaimed swamps or emergent coastal land, can be incorporated in the redistributed holdings. The reallocation depends on previous ownership: every part-owner receives, after grading, land equal in value to that of his previous holding. Where commonly owned land is included, the share due to each landowner depends on his *mantal*. The maximum number of parcels per holding is six. Further provisions to ensure a rational land-tenure pattern state that parcels should not be irregular, pointed, or long and narrow, but as rectangular as possible, and the boundaries should be delineated with straight lines or along 'natural' divisions such as roads or watercourses. By the 1848 ordinance, the whole village territory was to be reallocated, but this was amended in 1916 to allow only a part of a village to be dealt with if desired.

Before 1916, the Great Partition Adjustment (Sw *storskiftesreglering*, Fi *isojaonjärjestely*), as the New Partition was then called, was difficult to set in motion because it required the consent of all the landowners of the village, or a special decree of the Finnish Imperial Senate. Until 1881, it could not be put into operation, even if unanimous agreement was forthcoming, until a Great Partition Complement (Sw *storskifteskomplettering*, Fi *isojaon täydentäminen*) had been undertaken where it was necessary. This had been introduced in 1848 to overcome difficulties arising where the original partition was incomplete (for example, where the boundaries were not fully marked or the maps and documents had been lost or destroyed) and involved re-marking the boundaries between holdings; at the same time, a division of smaller commonly owned areas and land exchanges could be effected to ensure a more rational layout. The absurdity of such an operation if the land was to be redistributed anyway, together with the difficulties of obtaining unanimous agreement, meant that repartition was rare before 1881, when it became possible for landowners to choose between the two operations. By the last two decades of the nineteenth century, a reorganization of land tenure in many Ostrobothnian villages, in particular, had become unavoidable, and a number of reallocations took place. By the general reform of land-partition legislation in 1916, which amplified and amended previous legislation, a New Partition, if found to be necessary, could be put into operation at the request of any individual landowner in a village, and the procedure was simplified. The main provisions of the New Partition remained unchanged in the new Land Partition Act of 1951.

The New Partition has been undertaken far less extensively than the Great Partition and remains a live issue in many areas. It is a more radical and complex operation. The purpose is to consolidate and rearrange the farm structure so that holdings are conveniently situated with respect to farm buildings and lines of communication, and are easier to manage. This reorganization has involved the removal of farm buildings to new sites and includes the planning of new roads and drainage schemes. In areas where it has been completed, a new pattern of rural settlement has been created. Nucleated villages, left untouched by the Great Partition, have been replaced by dispersed settlement. The Vaasa area stands out as an area where a comparatively high proportion of the land has been redistributed. However, the New Partition is by no means a total solution to the problem of fragmentation, and the law is 'forced to compromise between general and private interests'.[11] By reorganizing land tenure to create a more rational pattern, the New Partition provides a means of dealing with the internal fragmentation of holdings, but it cannot reduce the number of landowners nor increase the size of holdings, since redistribution depends on what each landowner previously owned.

The post-independence land reforms

Subdivision of holdings, such as occurred particularly in Ostrobothnia, was not the only cause of fragmentation of land tenure. There, but to a greater extent in other parts of Finland, the leasing of crofts and cottages provided an alternative to extensive subdivision of holdings during the nineteenth century. While the number of independent holdings in Finland increased between 1749 and 1901 from 31,155 to 118,619, the number of leaseholds increased in the same period from 5,193 to 160,525.[12] The number of crofts at first increased most rapidly in Ostrobothnia, where between 1767 and 1805 the increase was the greatest in Finland. Younger sons often became crofters on the home farm, paying only nominal rent or day work; such situations were often of temporary duration, changing with each generation. In the nineteenth century, as the subdivision of holdings gained momentum, the increase in the number of crofts slackened in Ostrobothnia. In central and southern Finland, however, new holdings consisted largely of crofts and cottages. In coastal villages, the tenure of emergent land was affected by the establishment of crofts and cottages in two contrasting respects: crofters and cottagers were regarded as landless and therefore not automatically entitled to rights in a village's commonly held property, such as emergent land; they received these rights, however, as a result of Finland's post-independence land reforms, which enabled the landless to purchase holdings for themselves.

The land question contributed to the social instability prevailing at the time of Finland's declaration of independence from Russia in 1917. Discontent caused essentially by rural over-population was focused on the land-tenure structure and led to a series of measures which, with the aim of promoting social stability, recognized the importance attached to the ownership of land at all levels of rural society. The first of the reforms, the Leasehold Redemption Act or 'Crofters' Law', was passed in 1918. Supplemented by a series of laws between 1919 and 1926, the measures enabled tenants to purchase their leaseholds and a fixed area of forest land, if necessary with the help of State loans; purchase did not require the landowner's agreement. Related to the redemption of leaseholds was Lex Kallio, passed in 1922 (named after Kyösti Kallio, then Minister of Agriculture and later President of Finland). This, and other measures in 1922 and 1926, provided for the creation of land-settlement holdings for purchase by landless farm workers with the help of State loans. Additional land could be granted on similar terms to owners of holdings too small to be viable, and independent residential holdings could be created. The reforms produced an increase in the total number of farms and a major reduction in the number of leaseholds. By the time of the agricultural census of 1941, 95 per cent of the 285,822 holdings with at least $0 \cdot 25$ ha of cultivated land were held by independent owners.

Further fragmentation of land ownership resulted from the Land Acquisition Act of 1945. This was necessary to resettle the population displaced from the areas ceded by Finland to the Soviet Union in 1944. The opportunity was taken also to settle the war-disabled, widows, orphans and veterans. Land was obtained through voluntary sales, from State land, and by compulsory purchase. In order to maintain the ethnic balance, Swedish-speaking areas were largely excluded from the resettlement scheme, although applicants other than the displaced population were entitled to receive land in their own communities. Nearly 110,000 new holdings were created under the Act, of which 45,000 were farms and smallholdings; the Act also made provision for acquiring additional land to enlarge small farms.[13]

State intervention during the period of independence, justified on the grounds of social necessity, has helped to produce a land-tenure structure in which the average Finnish holding is too small for efficient farming. As Smeds pointed out, 'the inevitable result of the continued subdivision of farms, of the emancipation of the tenants and of post-war settlement activity is an aggravation of the smallholder problem, which has long been a crucial point in Finnish farming.'[14] These same factors have also aggravated the problems of tenure arising on emergent land.

The number of farms showed a continuous increase until 1959, due both to State-supported settlement activity and to the virtual absence after 1916 of legislation preventing the subdivision of farms. Recent years have shown a reversal of this trend. The Land Acquisition Act was repealed in 1958 by the Land Disposition Act, by which the formation of new holdings became secondary, mainly limited to the completion of settlement work in northern Finland. The principal aim of the new Act is to improve the viability of existing holdings through external and internal rationalization, to be brought about respectively by enlarging holdings and by land-improvement measures. The 1960s saw for the first time a reduction in the number of farms. A significant factor is rural depopulation, resulting from the increasing urbanization of Finland and emigration to Sweden. Accompanying changes in agricultural policy have led to a revision of the system of financial incentives so that it no longer promotes a continued increase in farm numbers. The creation of new land-settlement holdings was virtually ended by an amendment to the Land Disposition Act in 1967. Loans to obviate the subdivision of holdings on inheritance, first introduced in 1936, have been expanded, as have loans for the purchase of additional land, while further disincentives to the partitioning of farms have been introduced.

Although highly significant for promoting more rational agriculture, the new trends are less marked in the land-ownership structure as a whole. A reduction in the number of farms does not necessarily mean that the total number of land holdings will fall to a corresponding extent. The number of forest holdings has continued to increase. As Finland becomes an increasingly urban society, the demand for privately owned summer-cottage plots is rapidly growing (Table 6). By 1968, one household in ten had a place in the countryside for recreational use, and the number of recreational dwellings is growing by more than 8,000 a year.[15] Provisional figures from the Central Statistical Office of Finland indicate that at the end of 1970 nearly 179,000 households owned summer cottages. The new value which shore areas in particular have gained for recreation is of major significance in assessments of emergent land.

Table 6 SUMMER COTTAGES IN FINLAND, 1939–68, AND SWEDISH-SPEAKING OSTROBOTHNIA, 1939–71

Date	Finland	Swedish-speaking Ostrobothnia
1939	21,000	2,600
1950	40,000	3,600
1960	87,900	5,800
1962	100,800	6,200
1968	152,793	10,391
1971	—	13,689

SOURCES: Vuori, O. 'Kesähuvilanomistus Suomessa', *Turun Yliopiston Julkaisuja*, C3 (1966), 185; Kemppinen and Linkojoki, *Valtakunnansuunnittelutoimiston Julkaisusarja* (1972), 9, 36–41; Regionplaneförbund för Vasa län, 'Stomplan för Vasa' (Vasa, 1972), table P2.

Of significance for land-survey purposes are the number of properties entered in the land register. Registered properties are the basic units both for land-survey operations and for determining shares in commonly owned property, including emergent land. The number of registered properties in Finland rose from 128,500 in 1895 to 333,579 in 1924.[16] The dramatic rise since 1924, passing the million mark by 1959, is shown in Fig 21. Many more properties are registered, however, than are accounted for by the number of landowners. The separation of lots for sale to another landowner as summer-cottage plots, particularly since World War II, results in the creation of new properties. The regulations are unclear about registering such areas under the earlier property register number of the new owner, and they are consequently formed into separate registered units. Additional land for farm enlargement is most commonly provided in the form of complete holdings which have come up for sale; an effective amalgamation into a single operational unit takes place, but the holdings usually remain in the land register as separate units. While it is possible for registered properties with the same owner to be re-registered as a single holding, this is not in practice often done except at a New Partition. Rationalization of

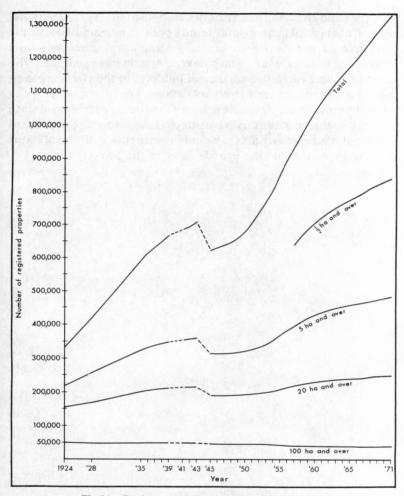

Fig 21   Registered properties in Finland, 1924–71.
SOURCE: Data from *Official Statistics of Finland*, XIV A, 69 (1973), 46

the land-tenure structure, therefore, has only a minor influence on the number of registered properties, although a slackening of the increase can be expected as subdivision on inheritance becomes less common and the number of farms ceases to grow.

Changing circumstances are reflected in changes in land-tenure policies, principles and legislation. These provide an essential background against which human responses to emergent land must be viewed; the latter cannot be understood without the former. The complex and changing nature of this response mirrors the complexity and changes of general land-tenure policy: the dominance of the principle of private ownership is an important cause of many anomalies of land tenure which have arisen on emergent land; the dramatic increase in the number of holdings in the twentieth century has introduced further complications. Detailed examples can show how the principles and themes of land-tenure legislation since the mid-eighteenth century have affected the response to emergent land, but it is necessary first to examine more closely the legal status of emergent land and the specific laws relating to it.

5

The Legal Status of Emergent Land

Principles of Water Ownership

THE EMERGENCE OF land poses a unique problem in land tenure.
Until other arrangements have been made, emergent land is legally
regarded in the same way as sea bottom for ownership purposes.
This basic principle was laid down in the Law Code of 1734, the
codification of Swedish legislation that still remains the basis of law
in Finland. A provision, still in force, of the Code of Land Laws (Sw
Jorda Balk, Fi *Maakaari*) states: 'If a lake or part thereof grows into
meadow, then the meadow or land is owned by him who ruled over
the lake.' This applied to land which emerged through natural
agencies; land emerging as a result of deliberate human activity,
such as the lowering of lake levels, is subject to special provisions.
The principle is the same for land emerging along the Finnish coast:
'natural accretion of land accrues to the property which was before
ruling over the water from which the emergent land appeared.'[1] The
owner of a water area owns the area with the underlying and
overlying space. Emergent land is legally owned by the owner of the
sea bottom from which it has emerged, and hence by the owner of
the water area.

When the pattern of tenure on land was reorganized by the Great
Partition, water areas were not included. The Law Code of 1734
dealt separately with the partition of land and water. The *storskifte*
decrees referred only to the partition of land, while the codification
of Swedish land-survey legislation in 1783 stated that 'fishing was to
remain in common usage'. This was clarified in 1807 as meaning
that water areas were to be treated independently from the Great
Partition on land. Although the 1783 legislation specifically excluded Finland from its operation, the Finnish *storskifte* decrees

103

contained no special provision, and the same principle was therefore held to apply (this was confirmed in 1798).

The principles on which ownership of water areas is based go back to the earliest written laws in Sweden, the *landskapslagar* or provincial laws of the thirteenth and fourteenth centuries, which codified legal regulations existing earlier as verbal traditions. Although each province had its own laws, these were largely in agreement, and often if a provision in one province's laws was missing it could be supplemented with a decree from the laws of another province. According to the Uppland Law Code (*Upplandslagen*), which dates from about 1296, the water area lying within a stone's throw from the shore belonged to the adjoining village. The underlying principle was that a man's power extended as far as he could make it effective. This is particularly evident in the Östergötland Law Code (*Östgötalagen*), dating from the end of the thirteenth century or the beginning of the fourteenth. On land, the village territory extended as far as a shout could be heard on a quiet day when sounds were muted. The water belonging to the village was that within reach of a boathook thrown over the shoulder from the stern of a 9-ell-long boat moored at right angles to the shore. The extent of effective power was determined by controlling the conditions in which it was demonstrated: in the one case the day had to be quiet, in the other the boathook had to be thrown backwards over the shoulder instead of forwards.[2] The general principle on which water ownership has since been grounded in Swedish and Finnish law was formulated in the Hälsingland Law Code (*Helsingelagen*), dating from the 1320s or 1330s, in the simple statement: 'He owns the water who owns the land.' Against open sea and in large bays, the water immediately adjacent to the shore belonged to the village. According to the Uppland Law Code, two villages on opposite sides of a channel or water body were each entitled to half of the water area, while the Östergötland Law Code affirmed that the middle line was the boundary between two villages in rivers and sounds.

Swedish rule in Finland introduced Swedish laws. Judgements from the first half of the fourteenth century demonstrate the extension to Finland of the principle that fishing-waters belonged to the owners of the adjoining land.[3] The provincial laws were combined in the mid-fourteenth century in King Magnus Eriksson's Land Law, which was essentially a codification of the older law texts rather than a new law and was mainly based on the Östergötland and Uppland Law Codes. This confirmed that a village adjacent to a water body owned as much of it as it had 'influence over', that water bodies and sounds between two villages were to be divided in half, and that the middle-line principle applied in rivers and streams. King Christopher of Bavaria's Land Law of 1442 was a variant of Magnus Eriksson's and did not differ substantially. The land codes of the fourteenth and fifteenth centuries remained in force until the recodification and revision of legislation in the Law Code of 1734, in which the provisions concerning water ownership remained largely unchanged. The Code of Land Laws stated:

> If a river, water body or sound lies between villages, then each owns half. The law is the same if an island is situated in the middle of a lake or stream. If it is situated nearer to one side, then the island belongs to the owner of the water, according to the boundary demarcation and village division . . . If a village lies at the end of or alongside a larger water body, then it owns the water area and islands according to its boundaries and position. If anyone has *urminnes hävd* [time-honoured customary occupancy] of out-islands, fishing or fishing-skerries, then he has the right to retain it undisputed.

These provisions were clarified in the Fishing Statute of 1766, which, referring to landowners' rights with regard to sea fishing, stated:

> Sea fishing within an archipelago is privately owned by the owners of the surrounding shores and islands; but adjacent to the open sea, or where there is no skerry guard, as well as outside an archipelago, the private rights of the land- and shore-owners to fishing and water stretch no further than the coastal shallows lying along the shore and stretching out from it; but where there are royal or ancient common fisheries within an archipelago, or someone by *urminnes hävd*, tax assessment, legal authority or other indisputable reason can prove private rights to fishing around rocks, islands or shallows outside an archipelago and in the open sea, then these rights remain undisturbed.

The same principles were reaffirmed in the Fishing Statute of 1865. An additional provision defined more precisely the extent of a village's private ownership: coastal shallows (Sw *landgrund*, Fi *rantamatala*) were regarded as extending for a distance of 200 Swedish fathoms (556 m) outwards from where a steady depth of at least one fathom (1·78 m) began. Open water beyond the village waters was common to the whole realm and could be used by anyone.

The general principle was that every village owned the water situated nearer its shores than any other village's. In cases of dispute, the middle-line rule was accepted as the basis of division. The main exception was where ownership of a particular area of water fell to someone else by a legally recognized title. *Urminnes hävd* (Fi *ylimuistoinen nautinta*) was a common legally accepted title, defined in the Code of Land Laws as 'where a person has possessed and used real estate or rights undisputed and unhindered for so long that no one remembers or can say with certainty how his ancestors or relatives first obtained them'. *Urminnes hävd* also provided a legal title on land to *urfjäll*, the small areas of land owned by a holding in one village within another's boundaries. *Urfjäll* adjoining the shore or comprising small islands in another village's fishing-waters formed a second exception to the rule that fishing-waters belonged to the adjacent owner. Where there were no definite natural boundaries such as a shore, *urminnes hävd* was valid only if the area was marked by a fence or other recognized boundary; mere occupancy was not sufficient. The importance of definite boundaries around *urfjäll*, expressed in the Uppland Law Code, was reaffirmed by a provision, still in force, of the Law Code of 1734. Since *urfjäll* was a strictly delimited area, it followed that water adjacent to *urfjäll* belonged to the village within whose boundaries it lay. The owner of *urfjäll* possessed no rights to offshore waters unless by special legal title such as a court judgement or *urminnes hävd* of the adjoining water area. Essentially, the ownership of water areas depended on the position of villages and their boundaries.[4]

Provisions for marking village boundaries on land existed in the ancient laws and in the Law Code of 1734. In practice, however, boundaries were commonly based on custom, without any written agreement, or on local agreements which had not been officially ratified.[5] They remained as such often for centuries, without any official demarcation, unless a dispute arose and was settled in court.[6] Customary boundaries (Sw *hävderår*, Fi *nautintarajat*) and informally agreed boundaries (Sw *sämjorår*, Fi *sovintorajat*) were not recognized as valid in law. Until the Great Partition, therefore, there were frequently no legal boundaries between villages, which were separated by commonly owned forest and water. Since the land and hence the adjoining water were not in such cases divided by a legally binding agreement, water areas could consequently belong in common to all the landowners in several villages or even in several parishes. Both the Law Code of 1734 and the Fishing Statute of 1766 specifically stated that fishing-waters could be used by any landowner in a group of villages owning them in common, and that the inhabitants living nearest the shore were not allowed to prevent those living further away from fishing. The Great Partition, while not dividing water areas among individual owners, indirectly led to the division of fishing-waters between villages.[7] By demarcating village boundaries on land, the Great Partition automatically determined ownership of offshore waters according to the principle that 'he owns the water who owns the land'.

The principle that shore-owners own the adjacent water was not to be interpreted after the Great Partition as meaning that individual landowners in a village owned the water adjacent to their land. Just as the forest and outlying land of a village before the Great Partition belonged in common to the landowners within it, so was the water owned in common by the landowners of the village, whose shares were in ratio to the value of the land they owned in the village, according to their *mantal*. Although it was possible for landowners to partition their water areas, this remained an independent operation unconnected with the Great Partition, as was the actual demarcation of water boundaries between villages.

In fact before 1902 there was no special procedure laid down by law for the marking of water boundaries. At the Great Partition, according to J. N. Lang, 'separate water boundaries were not geodetically determined and demarcated, clearly because the law had always laid down that disputes concerning ownership rights to water should not be involved in land-partition operations'.[8] Although boundaries were often drawn across water on land-partition maps, Lang explained that they merely indicated which islands and other land areas belonged to which village, and did not have any significance in themselves. Generally, village water boundaries were only properly demarcated to delimit the area to be divided at a partition of the water area between individual owners. Such partitions were rare, and village water boundaries remained for the most part unmarked.[9] K. Haataja summed up the position: 'Still at the beginning of the twentieth century, the water boundaries between villages were in general not marked, despite the fact that the Code of Land Laws . . . contained a statute stating where the water boundary ought to be.'[10] This state of affairs helped to produce a large degree of uncertainty regarding water-ownership conditions in Finland.[11]

Thus, although the basic principles concerning the legal ownership of water areas were firmly established, in practice uncertainty led to many disputes. A general reform of water legislation in 1902 included provisions designed to rectify the situation. Many points concerning water rights and ownership which were ambiguous in the earlier laws were clarified, although the essential basis of water rights remained unchanged. One law decreed that all water boundaries between villages should be immediately demarcated, in order to remove the uncertainty regarding water ownership. This decree was repeated in the Land Partition Act of 1951.

The 1902 legislation clearly stated that every village owned the water area which was nearer its shores than another village's. Large islands and archipelago groups carried the same rights as the mainland shore, but smaller islands did not. Unowned small islands fell to the owner of the water in which they were situated; if owned by a holding in another village, they carried no rights to the surrounding water unless by recognized legal title. The law remained unclear, however, as to when an island was considered big enough to carry water-ownership rights.[12] The distance of water ownership from the shore was redefined: in bays at least 8 km across (small islands were not considered to break this distance), on open shores and beyond the skerry guard, the village water extended 500 m from where at normal water level the depth was 2 m. The water was owned up to a similar distance around islands belonging to the village farther out than this. As before, the general rule did not apply in the case of a legally valid title to a particular water area.

Water boundaries were to be demarcated except against the open sea. The generally stated reason for this exception is land uplift, which causes the 2 m depth contour to move outwards and hence produces a continuous outward movement of the seaward boundary.[13] Beyond the village waters, Finland's territorial waters are, as a law of 1966 puts it, 'State-owned common water areas'. The effect of land uplift, therefore, is theoretically to cause a continuous transfer of water from State to village ownership as the boundary moves outwards. In practice, a boundary between village waters and State-owned common waters may be demarcated provisionally to distinguish between the areas where only the village landowners have fishing-rights and those where anyone may fish. Such a provisional demarcation between the State and Björköby was completed in 1972. A line drawn 500 m from the 2 m depth contour on sea charts was found to have so many crooks and bends that a compromise boundary consisting of a minimum number of straight lines was agreed on, leaving certain areas belonging to the State on the Björköby side of the boundary and *vice versa*. A revision of the boundary can be requested at any time by the villagers, to take into account future land uplift. On the shoreward side, the boundary of water areas is defined in the Water Law of 1961 as the shore at mean water level (also continuously moving outwards). Within this, the area of emergent land begins.

The Village Concept

The village concept is fundamental to an understanding of water-ownership rights. However, the question of what constitutes a 'village' for water-ownership purposes is a complex one in Finnish law.[14] The difficulty arises from the partial coincidence of a number of related but distinct concepts: these may be termed the historical village (Sw *by*, Fi *kylä*), the fiscal village (Sw *kameral by*, Fi *kameraalinen kylä*), the area of common ownership known in Swedish as a *samfällighet* and in Finnish as a *lohkokunta*, and the area divided at a land partition (Sw *skifteslag*, Fi *jakokunta*). These four concepts generally, but not necessarily, concern the same territorial area.

The historical village is the village which came into being as a result of the original settlement of the land, and was a group of farms (in some cases a single farm) which held their land together in the same group of plots or set of strips (*tegskifte*) before the Great Partition. This is the unit which is the subject of water-ownership rights. According to K. A. Moring, 'the village as far as water rights are concerned is the unit created by settlement and not the collection of holdings entered in the land rolls and other records'.[15]

The group of holdings entered under the same village name in the land rolls, which were compiled from the sixteenth century as a record of land taxes and later replaced by the land register, formed the fiscal village. This is solely an administrative unit, and the transfer of holdings from one village to another in the land rolls did not effect a change in water-ownership rights.[16]

A *samfällighet* or *lohkokunta* is an area situated within a common boundary and owned partly or completely in common by a number of owners. The whole area need not be in common ownership; the term often continues to be used for an area which has been in common ownership and subsequently partitioned. The individual owners' shares in the commonly owned land are based on *mantal*. A village normally constitutes such an area of common ownership, since the farms in one village formerly owned pasture and forest in common. However, before the Great Partition, often more than one village, each with its own separate group of plots, owned the surrounding forest in common within a single peripheral boundary, forming an area of common ownership which comprised several villages, all the landowners of which had shares on the basis of *mantal* (or its predecessors).[17] In this case, each village constituted a separate area of common ownership in respect of the area owned individually by the village, while the group of villages formed a single area of common ownership with regard to the land common to them all. Conversely, a smaller group of landowners within a village may own an area in common within marked boundaries, as for example when the arable land of a farm is shared among several heirs but outlying land is left undivided.

A *skifteslag* or *jakokunta* is technically the area undergoing partition at a particular land-survey operation such as the Great Partition or New Partition, although the term often continues in local usage for the area after the partition. Normally, a village constituted a single unit for the purpose of the Great Partition. However, in some cases a village was divided into several units, within each of which the partition was undertaken separately; these do not count as separate villages for water-ownership purposes. Similarly, if the outlying land owned by several villages was partitioned as a single operation, then all the villages formed a single *skifteslag* for that operation, although they may have been separate *skifteslag* for the reallocation of their arable land. Several villages may form a single unit of partition for all of their land where they own a substantial area in common or if their respective territories are interspersed. This, however, should not have any influence on each individual village's ownership of water areas.[18] The *skifteslag* is a formal concept, relating only to the partition procedure; in law, it has no bearing on property rights.

The village occupied a central position in the Swedish-Finnish legal system from the standpoint of the ownership of land before the Great Partition. Ownership of water today is based essentially on the same principles as the ownership of land before the Great Partition. In this repect, the village is not a legal 'person' which can own land as an independent entity, as can the State or a commune. Legally, when talking of an area owned by a village, nothing more is meant than ownership of an area in common by the landowners of the village, each landowner having a fixed share. Where the areas covered by a fiscal village, area of common ownership, and unit of land partition correspond to the historical village, there is no problem in deciding the ownership of adjoining water areas. Where the fiscal village, area of common ownership, or unit of land partition differs from the historical village, it is the last that determines ownership of water areas in the absence of any other legal title. Each case must be investigated separately to determine the development of land-ownership rights.[19]

The opinion has sometimes been held locally that water bodies (especially lakes) remain common to several villages or even several parishes, as was often the case before the Great Partition. The Fishing Committee set up in 1895 reported, for example, that in a number of parishes in the Saimaa region the general view was that lakes and fishing-rights were owned in common by all the landowners of the adjoining parishes. According to Lang, this opinion is only valid if a specific agreement to this effect was recorded at the Great Partition or if a court judged that village boundaries on land did not affect water ownership.[20] Otherwise, by definition, once their boundaries on land are demarcated, separate villages cannot own water in common. This remains true even if there are no demarcated boundaries across the water and if the actual water boundaries are in dispute. Consequently, partitioning of water areas between different villages cannot normally take place on the basis of *mantal*, and the only valid land-survey operation is demarcation of water boundaries (Sw *vattenrågång*, Fi *vesirajankäynti*), which technically ascertains and marks boundaries already legally existing in theory.[21] The provision of the 1902 law making the marking of water boundaries between villages compulsory did not affect water-ownership rights but merely laid down how existing ownership should be made clear.

Since village boundaries on land are the prime determinant of water ownership, problems arise when land adjoining water is exchanged between villages. In southern and central Finland, in particular, the territories of many villages were already delimited by legal boundaries on land before the Great Partition, but exchanges occurred in certain cases to form unified village territories. Problems may arise if it was not specifically stated in the land-survey documents whether the water adjoining the exchanged land was included or not.[22] Similar problems may occur where land has been exchanged between villages after the Great Partition. Moring expressed the following opinion:[23]

> At property exchanges or the straightening-out of boundaries, shore areas may be transferred from one village to another. Even if the water boundary has not been demarcated before such a transfer takes place, it seems that, at least as a general rule, this does not have any significance for water-ownership rights. The land exchange or boundary straightening ought not to be considered to extend in effect any further than the land-survey operation specifies.

If the water is specifically included in the exchange, of course, this does not apply. A lake surrounded by the exchanged land is automatically included in the exchange. Furthermore, according to

Moring, effective change in water ownership occurs if each village concerned uses the water adjacent to its new shores without dispute.[24] Such problems naturally only arise where the water boundaries have not been properly demarcated.

Even after a demarcation has taken place, it does not always follow that the whole area respectively on each side of the boundary forms a single ownership area. A single peripheral water boundary may in certain cases enclose water areas owned by several villages, between which the water boundaries have not yet been demarcated. Moring explained:[25]

> A boundary indicates only that the land or water on each side belongs to different ownerships; but this does not mean the whole area on each side constitutes a single ownership. It can consist of several, between which the boundaries have not been demarcated because of uncertainty about ownership rights. Even if a boundary-demarcation map or the documents state that the water area within the established peripheral boundary is common to those owning shares in area, this ought to have no significance if the land-surveyor has not been specifically authorized to decide on the matter.

Where a village consists of several separate areas which are not *urfjäll* but are separated from each other by land belonging to other villages, then the village owns the water adjacent to all of its areas. Since all of the areas belong to the same village, the water adjacent to each of them is owned in common by all the landowners of the village, including those who do not own land in all of the areas in question.[26]

A demarcation of water boundaries between villages differs from the partition of a village's water area (Sw *vattenskifte*, Fi *vesialueen jako*) between individual landowners according to *mantal*. The partitioning of water areas, which can be requested by any individual if it is not to the detriment of the others in the village, has been undertaken fairly extensively in Finland's south-western archipelago, but is less common in Ostrobothnia. With the aim of retaining fishing-waters unpartitioned in larger, economically more efficient units, the Fishing Act of 1951 provided for the establishment of local fishing administrations (Sw *fiskelag*, Fi *kalastuskunnat*), composed of part-owners, to take care of commonly owned fishing-waters. With the exception of lakes falling entirely within a single land holding, which are regarded as part of that holding, water remains in the common ownership of the village in many parts of Finland. This is of particular significance for the ownership of emergent land.

Ownership Rights to Emergent Land

The principles of ownership for water areas apply similarly to land emerging from them. The basic rule is ownership by the adjacent village, except where the land has emerged from water which is owned by special legal title or adjoins *urfjäll*. The Law Code of 1734 contained the first reference in general legislation that ownership of the water area was decisive in determining ownership of emergent land. The Land Survey Ordinance of 1848 specified that *urfjäll* did not possess rights to emergent land, following a similar pronouncement in a royal circular of 1782. Seventeenth-century lawsuits concerning the Vaasa archipelago illustrate that the principle was already well established. A dispute taken to court in 1663 involved the emergent land round an island which had been purchased in 1603 from an owner in Vassor village (at that time in Mustasaari parish) by an inhabitant of Merikaarto (Merikart) village in Vähäkyrö (Lillkyro) parish: the latter's title was confirmed to the original island but not to the newly emergent land.[27] Disputes between mainland and archipelago villages over rights to emergent land sometimes came before the courts several times in the course of a century. Between 1675 and 1762, the archipelago village of Replot had on a number of occasions to assert its rights to emergent land around islands belonging to mainland villagers from Jungsund, Västervik and Smedsby (Sepankyla); it was judged that the islands were *urfjäll* within Replot's fishing-waters, and that the emergent land therefore belonged to Replot. Replot also had several disputes in the seventeenth century over land emerging in the channel which at that time separated it from its neighbour Vallgrund; the outcome was that the emergent land, which included small islands, was recognized as belonging to the village on the side of the sound to which it was nearest.[28]

The general rule is that emergent land belongs in common to the landowners of the village owning the water from which it has emerged. As in the forest and other outlying land before the Great Partition and in water areas before a water partition, each landowner owns a share in emergent land on the basis of his *mantal*. When a farm is subdivided among heirs, the *mantal* of the original holding is subdivided proportionally, and the new holdings come to own shares in common land and fishing-waters according to their individual *mantal*. Where a lot is sold or transferred to another owner, the *mantal* is divided between the original holding and the separated lot according to their respective land values. In the case of lots separated before 1895, the general rule was that they were assessed as consisting solely of the area separated, and did not receive a share in common land and water. After 1895, the law was subject to varying interpretations: the general practice was for lots to be accorded shares according to *mantal* unless anything was mentioned to the contrary in the deed of transfer.[29] Since 1916, the law has specified that this is the case if what is assigned to the new holding is not fixed in the deed of transfer; otherwise, the deed is decisive. This may stipulate that the share in common property is retained entirely by the original holding or allotted to one only of several separated lots; alternatively, shares may be divided in a different way from what the size and value of the holdings would normally warrant. It is possible that only one holding may be given a share in fishing-water, while shares in other common property, such as village roads, streams, forest and clay or gravel pits, may be divided among several.[30] It is obvious that where this occurs *mantal* is no longer the direct determinant of shares in common property. The *mantal* of holdings without common-ownership rights must be added to the *mantal* of the parent holding when the latter's share of water or emergent land is calculated.[31] In effect, such holdings come to assume two *mantal*, one indicating the value of the holding in relation to other holdings, and another directly determining its share in common property.[32] When talking of the ownership of water areas and associated emergent land, therefore, it is more convenient to refer to each holding's share (Sw *andel*, Fi *osuus*) rather than to its *mantal*. Since 1953, land-survey records concerning the separation of lots have had to specify whether or not the new holding has a share or not in common property.

The general rule is that every land-ownership unit in a village has a share in the village's water areas unless specifically excluded. A tenant holding, conversely, has no rights to water ownership, which remain with the parent holding, except where the tenant holding is a separate registered property run by a leaseholder. Crofts and cottages, therefore, had no share in water ownership and hence no claim to emergent land. Occupants of State-owned holdings possess the same rights as private landowners to common land and water, and are responsible on behalf of the State for dealing with ownership disputes and other questions which may arise. Rural communes, as legal 'persons', also have the same rights of water ownership as a private landowner if they own land in a village. In certain cases, a water area may be referred to as common to a parish or commune, but this does not mean that the commune as an independent legal entity owns it. Before the Great Partition, it meant simply that all the landowners of the parish owned shares. After the Great Partition, it must be interpreted as meaning that the water boundaries between the villages of the commune have not been demarcated.

An increase in the number of land holdings in a village has an important influence on the ownership of water and hence of emergent land. The effect of the post-independence land reforms, by creating a large number of new independent holdings, was substantial. In general, the new holdings were allotted shares in the fishing-water of the villages in which they were situated, and the shares of the parent holdings were rendered correspondingly smaller. According to the terms by which leaseholds were redeemed after 1918, crofters who had carried on fishing in water owned by the parent holding or in which the parent holding owned a share could be allotted a proportional share of the parent holding's water rights. If, however, this meant that the water area would be divided into meaninglessly small shares, no allotment was made to the new holdings. If several crofts were entitled to shares in the same water area, a separate water area could be marked off for them in common. Where crofts were allotted shares in water, emergent land or other common property, it had to be set down in the contract of sale. The rule was that they had no rights unless specifically stated. In the case of redeemed tenant farms which were whole holdings on lease, the new owner simply retained the share in water belonging to the holding. Land-settlement holdings set up after 1922 were entitled to a share in water ownership according to their *mantal*, except where the share was so small that a harmful splitting-up of the water area could result, or where other substantial disabilities might arise to the parent holding, which then retained its original share. Residential holdings were not entitled to shares without the agreement of the parent holding. Later land-settlement legislation provided generally for all but the smallest holdings to receive shares in common water and land areas; such a share could also be included in the purchase of additional land for a smallholding or farm.

Where the reforms (or ordinary processes of subdivision and sale) resulted in *urfjäll* becoming an independent holding, it retained its status as *urfjäll* and was therefore not entitled to a share in the water area or emergent land of the village within whose boundaries it lay, except by special legal title. Whether as an independent property it received a share in the water belonging to the parent holding's village depended on the terms of its formation into a separate holding.

The post-independence measures, by contributing to the fragmentation of land tenure, have produced a great increase in the number of part-owners of water areas and hence emergent land. The division of landowners into two categories, those possessing shares and those not possessing shares in common property, has made determination of the exact ownership of village waters and emergent land a highly complex issue. The matter is further complicated by the fact that shares in common land and water are recorded not by landowners but by registered properties which, it has been seen, are much more numerous than the landowners.

Where the water area of a village has been partitioned between individual landowners, the ownership of emergent land poses fewer problems, since it automatically belongs to the individual owners of the water. No special land-tenure arrangements need generally be made, and land use is a matter to be decided primarily by the individuals concerned. Where, as is more usual, water and emergent land are in common village ownership, the question of which landowners do and which do not possess shares is in itself a legal problem; it gains a geographical expression if the part-owners wish to partition the area so that it passes from common to individual ownership. Partition directly influences spatial patterns of land tenure and indirectly influences patterns of land use. Until such a partition takes place, the use and actual tenure of emergent land is a collective decision, made by the landowners of the village who own shares; such decisions may be determined or influenced by local customs and agreements or by legislation. Consequently, the human responses to land emergence in respect of land tenure can be divided into two groups: responses taking the form of land partition, and responses occurring before partition or where partition is not undertaken at all.

6

The Regulation of Emergent Land

The Partition of Emergent Land

A PRIME AIM of the Great Partition was to end the common owner-ship of land. Land emerging subsequently did not fit neatly into the pattern of land tenure which this partition established. The legal status of emergent land was the same as that of the fishing-waters from which it had emerged: it was owned in common by the land-owners of the village. Thus a category of land was continuously appearing which it had been one of the express intentions of the Great Partition to eliminate. Logically, therefore, emergent land should be dealt with according to the same principles which were behind the Great Partition. When a sufficiently large area of new land had appeared, it was graded and partitioned among the part-owners, whose respective shares were determined on the basis of *mantal*. In order to ensure rational integration into the existing land-tenure pattern, and to prevent disabilities in land use arising, the procedure followed was that, as far as was consistent with the allocation of shares according to *mantal*, each landowner was to receive his share adjacent to his holding, and no one whose land adjoined the coast was to be cut off from it. This procedure, the Partition of Emergent Land (Sw *tillandningsskifte*, Fi *vesijätön jako*), can be regarded as a periodic adjustment to the land-tenure pattern created by the Great Partition, necessitated by a constantly occurring and predictable physical phenomenon. The Partition of Emergent Land was regarded as a special land-survey operation, separate from both the partition of land and the partition of water.[1] It was concerned with the transfer of land, which had emerged through coastal uplift, sedimentation at river mouths, or other causes, from the realm of water legislation to that of land legislation.

The legislation enacted in the eighteenth century for the Great Partition contained no such specific provisions. The first reference in general legislation to the possibility of a Partition of Emergent Land was in the Land Survey Ordinance of 1848. A paragraph dealing with the 'division of sea fodder [ie reeds], emergent land or commonly owned arable land' provided that such partitions could be either provisional or permanent. In the former case, the area was dealt with in the same way as holdings provisionally subdivided among heirs: all part-owners were allotted individual parcels, whether their holdings were legally ratified as separate units or not. This allowed the individual part-owners of a farm which had been informally subdivided, without official ratification in court, to receive separate shares of emergent land. Informal subdivision of holdings was common in Ostrobothnia in the nineteenth century, and provisional Partitions of Emergent Land enabled individual owners to make full use of valuable pasture on such land. A permanent Partition of Emergent Land was permissible among holdings which were legally ratified as separate units; these were generally the holdings marked out by the Great Partition. Only holdings which had been formally subdivided by a ratified land-survey operation were otherwise entitled to separate shares; part-owners of an informally subdivided holding received their shares in common. A permanent Partition of Emergent Land, according to the 1848 Land Survey Ordinance, was to be carried out in accordance with the procedure for the Great Partition. The Land Survey Ordinance in fact merely formalized the procedure already established locally in the areas most affected by land emergence.

Local regulations dealt with the problem of land emergence long before national laws. Occupation rights to emergent land generally followed the rule that emergent land was awarded to the owner of the adjacent land. In cases of dispute, similar divisions between disputants were effected as in the case of intakes from the forest, based on the tax values of the respective owners' properties. Various court cases concerned with disputes over emergent land in Ostrobothnia in the seventeenth and eighteenth centuries illustrate the principles on which divisions were made.[2]

A lawsuit in 1633 involved two farms in the village of Palvis in Vörå, who were disputing the ownership of an area of reeds which 'formerly was covered by deep water but has now become dry land'. The court decided on the division of the emergent land 'according to *öre och örtug* [ie size and tax value of their existing properties, forerunner of *mantal*], as was earlier done with the other area of reeds which was under dispute'.[3] The phenomenon and its attendant human problems were clearly already familiar. In 1667, a dispute over emergent land involved all the villagers of Smedsby in Mustasaari parish. The court ruled that first 'the separation between the emergent land and the old meadows' must be ratified, after which the villagers should 'divide the emergent land in accordance with their taxes'.[4] The division of emergent land according to the owners' tax assessments in relation to each other was recorded in Lappfjärd (Lapväärtti) in 1621, when the villagers divided with the traditional measuring-rod the land 'which has now recently emerged from the sea, so that everybody may receive equivalent to his tax and tax value'.[5] In the Vörå village of Karvsor, which now has no coastline, it was recorded in 1643 that 'the emergent land which at the village's common . . . place has appeared between Hästnässkatan and Giessnäs' was 'adjusted among the neighbours according to their tax', using the measuring-rod to effect the division.[6] Similarly, a request was made in 1683 by the villagers of Kvevlax (Koivulahti), east of Vaasa, for impartial witnesses to assist in dividing emergent land according to *öre och örtug*.[7] The principle that if owners in one village had rights in another village's fishing-waters they were entitled to a share of emergent land, but that ownership of *urfjäll* in another village did not entitle them to a share, is illustrated by two court cases concerning Palvis's neighbour, the village of Bertby to the east. Around 1640, the inhabitants of Bertby divided among themselves a meadow on newly emergent land, without taking account of the fact that certain farmers in Miemois, an inland village of Vörå, possessed 'of old' a share in the fishing-water through inheritance. In 1641, the Miemois farmers brought a petition to court requesting that they receive 'in the said meadow land their right quota and share of emergent land'. The court ordered that the emergent land should be repartitioned so that everybody was allotted his right share on the basis of his tax assessment, and the Miemois farmers were accorded a share of Bertby's emergent land. A case in 1686, conversely, resulted in farmers from outside villages being excluded from a share in emergent land, when inhabitants of Karvsor and Rökiö villages of Vörå were ordered to mark off old meadows owned by them from Bertby's adjacent emergent land, which was then divided among the Bertby villagers according to *öre och örtug*.[8]

In the second half of the eighteenth century, the land-partition courts set up in the Vaasa area to supervise the Great Partition laid down rules concerning the procedure to be followed in an attempt to anticipate disputes over future emergent land. The widths of holdings along the shore were, relative to one another, to correspond, as far as possible, to the respective *mantal* of each landowner; partitions of land emerging later could then take place by the simple extension of the pre-existing land-tenure boundaries and still correspond to *mantal*. Where, however, the shore was irregular, boundaries between holdings and the sea were to be clearly marked, 'so that the present sea, where it may in future become meadow, may with certainty be distinguished and divided among the villagers', as the regulations for Vörå parish stated. The regulations, dated 1768, contained similar provisions for both Vörå and Mustasaari parishes. In the latter case, the document was unsigned, but it is perhaps significant that in Vörå it was signed on behalf of the land-partition court by E. O. Runeberg, and follows a common pattern which he seems to have drawn up beforehand.[9] He was keenly aware of the practical problems posed by the fact that 'the meadows along the sea shore are continuously expanding through annual land emergence', and it was specifically laid down that the first step in undertaking the Great Partition was to compare the maps made for the tax assessment a few years before with the existing position so as to note 'the changes which after the last measurement could have occurred both through the work of nature and the activity of the farmers'; the alterations were to be duly mapped and included in the area undergoing partition. The regulations were considered to have the same force 'as all other law and directions'.[10]

Land emerging after the Great Partition had been completed was periodically dealt with by the general procedure followed at the main partition. The 1848 legislation amplified this in certain respects but otherwise made little practical difference to the partition of emergent land; it codified in outline existing practice. A Partition of Emergent Land could be requested by any part-owner. Initially, the existing shore and islands were mapped and compared with the coast on the map drawn for the Great Partition. Where the old coastline formed a crooked boundary, this could be straightened by minor adjustments. The area between the two coastlines was then graded according to value, as in the Great Partition, and the part-owners were allocated shares of the total value in accordance with their *mantal*. Areas could be left in common ownership for roads, drainage ditches, boatplaces, sand and gravel pits or other purposes, and the value of these areas was subtracted from the total before partition. The new parcels were positioned as near as possible to the farms to which they were allotted — next to their existing holdings where this could be done — or were positioned by lot. Allocation of shares according to *mantal* ensured that each part-owner received the exact share of emergent land due to him, for under natural conditions one farmer might have adjacent to his holding a shoal or coastal shallows which had developed into a wide stretch of good-quality pasture, while another might only have an area of stony land of little value or, if his shores were steep, no significant area of emergent land at all. Compensation was to be paid where it was not possible to allot an individual landowner the exact value of land due to him.

The Land Survey Ordinance of 1848 reduced to six the maximum number of parcels that could be allotted to each holding at the Great Partition. This was not interpreted to mean that the allocation of parcels of emergent land could not increase the total number of the holding's parcels above six, but that the emergent land itself could not be allocated in more than six parcels per holding. However, the desirability of placing a landowner's share of emergent land adjacent to his existing holding echoes the expressed aim of the Great Partition that a farmer's holding should consist of as few parcels as possible. This applied in the procedure for the partition of a water area, regarding which the 1848 ordinance specifically stated that parcels should as far as possible be placed adjacent to landowners' existing properties. The aim was to integrate the newly partitioned area into the pre-existing land-tenure pattern. This was not always possible, however. Where, as a result of special legal title to the water or the existence of *urfjäll* on land, the water belonged to a different village from that on the adjoining shore, emergent land could easily cut the shore-owners off from the sea. Even within a single village, emergent land might be concentrated at one particular place, such as a shallow bay or river mouth, so that all would receive their parcels together in a group. Everybody, too, would desire a share in a particularly fertile emergent area resulting, for example, from sedimentation. In these cases, the principle of division according to *mantal* clearly took precedence.

It was first expressly laid down in a decree of 1868 concerning the lowering of lake levels that when emergent land was partitioned everybody was to receive as far as possible his share in conjunction with his other land and anyone owning land adjoining the water was not to be cut off from it. The difficulty of ensuring this while at the same time determining shares on the basis of *mantal* was recognized, as the paragraph continued with a provision enabling compulsory land exchange or purchase if the allocation of a parcel of emergent land to someone between another property and the sea would hamper land use. These principles applied in practice equally to land emerging along the sea coast; formal legal recognition of this was provided by the Law on Water Rights of 1902, which set out similar provisions for all emergent land.

These provisions were reiterated in the general reform of land-partition legislation in 1916. This reform also contained more extensive and detailed provisions for a Partition of Emergent Land than did the Land Survey Ordinance of 1848, and was designed to offset some of the anomalies arising and to create a more rational land use than often resulted from the existing procedure based on the Great Partition. A Partition of Emergent Land was, until 1916, restricted to land which had emerged after the completion of a Great Partition or Great Partition Adjustment and was regarded simply as a continuation of the main partition. The 1916 reform widened considerably the scope of partition. Where a suitable distribution of land tenure could not be brought about by land exchanges in conjunction with a Partition of Emergent Land, it became possible after 1916 to carry out a simultaneous New Partition of as much of the adjoining, previously partitioned emergent land as was necessary to bring about a satisfactory arrangement of parcels. Shares in newer emergent land were determined in the normal way on the basis of *mantal*, while reallocation of the land that had been previously partitioned depended on previous ownership according to the procedure for a New Partition. Until 1916, a Great Partition or Great Partition Adjustment had to embrace the whole village territory, which meant that emergent land had to be included. After 1916, it could be left out if it was not thought suitable to include it in the partition or if it could be more conveniently dealt with by a separate Partition of Emergent Land. The former applied where it was desired to retain the emergent land under common use or control. The latter was mainly applicable to emergent land resulting from a permitted lowering of a lake level, where others apart from the water-owners might also possess rights.

The 1916 reform set out a detailed procedure to be followed at a Partition of Emergent Land, which was to be a definitive regulation of ownership rights to emergent land; no provision was made for a provisional partition. The new regulations codified existing procedure while amending it to introduce greater flexibility. The basis of division remained as before: *mantal* after grading of the land. Provision was made for marking the boundaries of the emergent land in case of uncertainty; for straightening out its boundaries against adjoining properties; and for the exchange of former islands in certain cases.

The scope of compulsory land exchange and purchase was extended to include emergent land which was not being partitioned. If a landowner's property was cut off from water or its use was obstructed in other ways by adjoining emergent land, he could obtain possession in exchange for another area, or where there was difficulty in finding a suitable area for exchange, by purchase. When land exchanges took place, cultivated or cultivable land could be exchanged for an equivalent value of forest. Compulsory exchange was not permitted, however, if the area was used as a building plot or a garden, or for industrial purposes; in these cases, the agreement of the owner was necessary.

The 1916 legislation made the Partition of Emergent Land a completely independent operation, instead of simply a complement to previous land partitions. Alternatively, emergent land could be included in the redistribution of holdings at a New Partition, as before at a Great Partition Adjustment. In this case, the share of each holding in the emergent land is added to the allotment of land due at reallocation on the basis of previous ownership. The new, better consolidated holdings after the New Partition may not always actually include part of the emergent land, but their size will have been increased to take account of the share due to them. Smaller areas of emergent land, as with other common property, can also be partitioned and land exchanges made, with the agreement of the landowners, in conjunction with a Great Partition Complement.

Before shares in emergent land can be allotted, whether at a Partition of Emergent Land or a New Partition, it is necessary to determine which landowners in the village are entitled to shares. For naturally emergent land, the principles are the same as for determining shares in water ownership; it is necessary to examine the land records of each holding to determine whether it has a share or not. The date and method of formation are crucial factors in this respect. The post-independence land reforms and the rapid rise in the number of holdings in the twentieth century have greatly increased the amount of research necessary before emergent land can be successfully partitioned. A further complication is the fact that shares in emergent land are recorded on the basis of registered properties rather than by landowners.

The Land Partition Act of 1951 reiterated, with certain clarifications and additions, the provisions of the earlier legislation regarding Partitions of Emergent Land. Any part-owner was entitled to have his share of emergent land separated, even if the other part-owners did not desire a full partition. The possibility of a provisional Partition of Emergent Land was reintroduced. Owners of adjoining property were to be ensured some sort of connection with the water. Provisions designed to prevent the formation of minute shore lots included boundary adjustments, compulsory land exchanges and purchase, the inclusion of adjoining property in the partition, and the partitioning of water and emergent land as a single operation. It was specified that emergent land could be left in common ownership if this was the most rational solution.

The land-tenure patterns arising through Partitions of Emergent Land were, none the less, often complicated, reflecting the general complexity of land-ownership conditions. The traditional partition was often unsuitable for regulating ownership conditions on emergent land. Partitions of Emergent Land, with other land-survey operations, carried eligibility under a law of 1938 for State assistance to offset costs resulting from partition, such as road construction, land clearance and drainage. This ceased to apply when the 1938 law was replaced in 1960 by a new law designed to reduce the incentives favouring land partition.

In 1961, the Land Partition Act was amended to improve the possibilities of creating a rational land-tenure pattern at a Partition of Emergent Land. Land exchanges or the inclusion of part of the adjoining area in a New Partition are not always the best means of bringing about a convenient arrangement of parcels. If this is the case and an area of emergent land can be rationally used only by the adjoining landowners, or if the area is small and the number of part-owners large, the adjoining landowners can be compelled to purchase the emergent land adjacent to their holdings, whether they own a share in it or not, instead of a normal Partition of Emergent Land taking place. A part-owner can obtain emergent land adjacent to someone else's holding only if special circumstances warrant it. However, areas can be left in common ownership where necessary. The part-owners of the emergent land are entitled to shares in the total purchase price on the same basis as they previously owned shares in the emergent land. Owners of land on the coast who do not have rights to a share in the traditional Partition of Emergent Land, as for example many owners of summer-cottage plots, are represented at the proceedings in the same-way as part-owners, and the sale of emergent land to them ensures that their access to the sea is maintained. The emergent land is integrated into the pre-existing land-tenure pattern, while in return for giving up their ownership rights the part-owners receive financial compensation in proportion to their respective shares.

A second amendment extended the scope of purchase by adjoining landowners in the case of emergent land which is not undergoing a partition. The owner of an adjoining holding can request the purchase of commonly or privately owned emergent land which obstructs the use of his holding or which can only be rationally used in conjunction with it. However, this purchase can only take place where the difficulty cannot conveniently be solved by a land exchange. Several such purchases by summer-cottage owners have occurred in the Vaasa and Jakobstad areas. Initially, a problem of interpretation arose over whether the amendment was applicable to emergent land which had been partitioned previously. This was clarified by a circular from the National Board of Land Survey in 1971, which confirmed that previously partitioned emergent land could be purchased by the adjoining owner if this was the only rational way of using it. A recent interpretation of the law by V. Suomaa stated that privately-owned emergent land includes areas allocated by a Partition of Emergent Land undertaken subsequent to a Great Partition or New Partition. Purchase can thus take place in certain cases where a holding was cut off from the sea by emergent land allotted to another owner at an earlier partition.[11]

The question of what constitutes emergent land and when it should be partitioned ultimately depends on the views of the owners and on the discretion of the land-surveyor. Geographically, the distinction between land and sea is variable, owing to diurnal and seasonal water-level variations. Emergence is a gradual process; in the past, reeds were harvested and still today cattle may graze on areas that are more watery than dry land. The transition to more permanent land uses such as agriculture and forestry occurs at a later stage. Legally, sea does not become land until it has been subject to a land-survey operation such as a partition or boundary demarcation. The outer edge of the emergent land depends on whether reed swamp and water are included, as well as on the map used for the land-survey operation and the water level on the day of mapping. The inner edge of the emergent land is determined by the edge of the previously partitioned area, usually the former shoreline. The position of the old shore is determined initially on the basis of old maps, and may vary in accuracy. To the problems of surveying inaccuracies and the variable condition of the old maps, is added the difficulty of the varying water level. If the water level on the day of the old survey was extra low, land could be marked where there was water according to a later map drawn when the level was high. The position of the shore on the Great Partition maps was sometimes only approximate; small islands were frequently drawn in by eye, so that their positions or size did not always correspond to the later situation. Where old maps are obviously inaccurate, or they have been destroyed or lost, the position of the old shore is surveyed by other means, such as by levelling between known stretches of the old shoreline or on the basis of land-uplift values; in certain cases, vegetation has been used as a guide, on the estimation that it takes about 150 years for spruce forest to establish itself on emergent land. Once the old shoreline has been determined, the inner edge of the emergent land is frequently marked by drawing a series of straight lines between fixed points, so that minor irregularities are straightened out. Even after emergent land has been demarcated or partitioned, it still retains its status as emergent land for certain purposes, as is evident from Suomaa's interpretation of the 1961 amendment.

The involved nature of the ownership of emergent land is a direct and logical consequence of the highly developed system of legal rights first codified in the ancient Swedish provincial laws. Emergent land is not unowned land to be disposed of by administrative measures, but private land owned in common by a particular group of landowners. Just as those not owning shares in common village meadows or forest before the mid-eighteenth century were excluded, at least in principle, from using them, so those not owning shares in emergent land are similarly excluded. The development of land use on emergent land has been influenced by this fact. Instead of emergent land being used for the creation of new holdings or being incorporated automatically into adjoining holdings, it has been subject to complex procedures of division, unless left as a single unit of common ownership.

The increasing number of landowners and the increasing complexity of the land-ownership structure in Finland after independence has produced a corresponding increase in the complexity of the procedure to be followed when emergent land is to be divided among its part-owners. A Partition of Emergent Land involving several score landowners has become a time-consuming and costly process, frequently causing further fragmentation of an already fragmented land-tenure pattern and often giving only a small areal addition to each landowner. The importance of the changes in 1961 is that they reflect the greater emphasis being given in land legislation to measures promoting rational land use, and provide a means of obviating difficulties arising through strict adherence to the partition of emergent land on the basis of ownership.

The Regulation of Unpartitioned Emergent Land

It is not normally worth the expense of formal partition until a fairly considerable area of new land has appeared. Until a Partition of Emergent Land takes place, therefore, local customs and agreements determine to a large extent the human responses to emergent land, which remains in the village's common ownership. Responses vary: emergent land may be used by the villagers in common as meadow land or pasture; in many villages, local convention allows individual landowners the right to use land emerging alongside their property; alternatively, the village may let emergent land and divide the income among the landowners on the basis of *mantal*; in other cases, the emergent land may be divided among landowners within a village by local agreement. All of these arrangements determine only the rights of use, not ownership, which remains in common.

The use of emergent land has been regulated from early times. Natural meadows along the coast and around lakes and marshes were an important source of winter fodder, and 'on the gradually drying emergent land along the sea coast, new meadows continuously came into being without manual labour'.[12] In that relatively little preparatory work was required, the meadows were comparable to fishing-waters rather than to arable land. As G. Nikander noted with reference to Swedish-speaking Ostrobothnia, 'since fishing and cattle-rearing were the Swedish coastal inhabitants' main sources of livelihood, the village common areas were of greatest importance for the farmers' economic life.'[13] The use of meadows historically displayed features closer to the use of fishing-waters than to other land uses. The relationship between emergent land and water ownership seems to be significant in this respect. Nikander observed:[14]

> The use of common meadows exhibits many similarities to fishing in common waters. Between these different types of common property exists often a close connection, since the meadows to a certain extent arose from fishing-waters through land emergence and thereby have come to be subject to the same legal regulations as common fishing-areas.

Meadow land along the emerging coast could come also into private ownership. Often the owners lived considerable distances away, having established ownership before village boundaries were drawn up, when occupation of outlying common land was free; when the boundaries were established between villages, which was done relatively early in western Finland, these areas became 'out-village meadows' (Sw *utbysängar*, Fi *ulkokylänniityt*), a type of *urfjäll*, within another village's boundaries. Along the Ostrobothnian coast, meadows appearing on emergent land were taken into possession in this way by owners living often tens of kilometres away, whose rights came to be based on *urminnes hävd*. After village boundaries had been drawn up, it was no longer possible to occupy meadow within another village's boundaries, which testifies to the ancient origin of these out-village meadows.[15] The situation was similar in the case of fishing-waters: fishermen from inland villages and distant coastal villages often established rights to islands in the Vaasa archipelago and the surrounding fishing-water, and these rights were confirmed on the basis of *urminnes hävd* when water ownership became more closely determined by the drawing up of village boundaries. A. Luukko noted that fishermen from the villages of the middle Kyrönjoki valley, who were active in the inner Vaasa archipelago (as it then was) before the fourteenth century and who carried on fishing communally from temporary bases without establishing permanent occupation, generally lost their rights when the Swedes arrived and settled the coastal regions, establishing when they came the principle of coastal ownership rights to water. However, fishermen from inland villages nearer the coast, such as those in Vörå, Vähäkyrö and Laihia parishes, established individual rights to islands and fishing in the (then) outer skerries, especially after the fourteenth century, and these rights continued into much later times.[16]

Generally, meadows were in the common ownership of the landowners of a village in the same way as fishing-waters. Both of the medieval Land Laws forbade the taking of meadows into private ownership, but in practice this occurred and such ownership was later ratified by the local courts. Meadows on emergent land or flood land, however, could be owned in common before the Great Partition by several farms, all the farms in a village, or even by farms from several villages.[17]

Use of commonly owned meadows varied in different villages. Harvesting and grazing were arranged according to an agreed scheme drawn up by the village meeting. The schemes were generally based on centuries-old traditions. Three main types of method can be distinguished: communal harvesting and subdivision of the harvest; annual division of the meadow into strips which were distributed among the landowners according to a set order; and annual rotation of fixed plots. The three types of use represent successively younger developments, although in practice they were not so clearly differentiated; systems combining different methods were often found.[18]

Communal harvesting of meadows, the oldest method of use, was a feature in parts of Swedish-speaking Ostrobothnia until at least the mid-eighteenth century. The work of harvesting and afterwards the harvest were shared according to the tax assessment of each farmer. The villagers of Harrström in Korsnäs, for example, resolved in 1752 that emergent land at Skarvören should be harvested communally in this way until a proper division of the land could be made with the assistance of a land-surveyor. Another case of communal harvesting of meadows was recorded from Bergö on Söderstenarna and other skerries at the time of the Great Partition in 1757. Communal harvesting was a convenient method where a particular meadow gave an irregular or uneven yield. An example from the village of Karby in Pedersöre concerned a bog considered unusable at the land measurement of 1740; by 1759, it seems to have dried out somewhat, for the villagers agreed that it should be commonly harvested and the harvest shared according to tax assessment, although the area itself could not be divided on account of the uncertain grass growth.[19] Communal harvesting of commonly owned meadows in Molpe (Moikipää) village in Korsnäs and of hay from lake shores in Monå village in Munsala has been recorded in more recent times.

Annual division of meadow land into strips occurred at places in western Finland until relatively recently. An account from Närpes in the mid-eighteenth century referred to the division in Tjärlax village of the meadow, which was primarily on emergent land, into strips: the division was renewed annually, partly because the boundary markers were removed by spring floods, but also because the quality of the harvest varied in different places from year to year. The part-owners' shares in the emergent land were calculated in 1757–8 for a permanent partition, but the villagers rejected this solution and continued to redivide the area each year until 1890. By this time, the greater part had as a result of uplift dried out sufficiently for it to be permanently divided; the more marshy part continued to be annually divided into plots until the New Partition in 1928. A detailed description of the operation had been made five years earlier: the strips were measured with a measuring-rod of the type used for the partition of fields into strips before the Great

Partition; they were then distributed among the farmers in the order of the farms' positions in the village, beginning with a different farm each year, so that every farmer received his share in a new place.[20]

In Lappfjärd, meadows on emergent land were subject to periodic divisions among part-owners until the beginning of the present century. A partition of an emergent area known as 'Sundet', which took place in 1886, was made for ten years and later renewed for shorter periods. The reasons for the periodic renewal of the division were that the area was covered by annual deposits of river silt, and the boundary markers were disturbed each winter by ice, while the area which was dry enough to be harvested varied from year to year. The original farms of the village received fixed shares, which were then divided further in the case of farms which had been subdivided. A division of the meadow again in 1903, originally for ten years but virtually permanent as it was not renewed, was undertaken, allowing certain farms a regular placing of their shares in relation to their existing holdings, while others chose their strips by lot.[21]

Under the third system of use, the meadow was divided into fixed lots, the use of which was rotated annually among the share-owners. On Hailuoto, according to Stierwald's description from the 1760s, some of the meadows were in private use and others annually rotated among from two to more than ten farms before the Great Partition. There were two types of rotation: in the first case, each farm used the meadow in succession for a year at a time; in the second case, the meadow was divided into as many lots as there were part-owners, and the lots were rotated among them each year. Complicated rotations developed where shares differed in size, and as the number of owners increased. In Lappfjärd, for example, Storsjöträsk, a marshy lake, was divided into four blocks and the share-owners into four groups, among which the blocks were rotated; each block was subdivided among the share-owners within the group according to a set order established by drawing lots, each share-owner receiving thirteen or fourteen plots. Annual rotations of meadow land continuing to the twentieth century have been recorded in Kaarlela and Pedersöre. Rotation among groups of owners was frequently accompanied within the rotated blocks by common harvesting; in the case of Östensö village in Pedersöre, the harvest was divided by a complex system of drawing lots, which continued until the rotation system ended with the New Partition in 1917.[22]

The annual rotation of meadows had features in common with

similar rotations of fishing-waters among groups of owners within a village, for example in Bergö, Replot and Björköby,[23] and at places in Finland's south-western archipelago.[24] In Sundom, south-west of Vaasa, Jonas Cajanus described in the 1750s the annual rotation of fishing-waters and pasture in the skerry guard among three groups of owners, while a fourth group used the same area every year.

Systems of annually dividing meadows into strips or of annual rotation represented survivals on emergent land of formerly wide-spread customs regulating the use of commonly owned meadows. Development from common harvesting to annual division, rotation and subsequently to permanent occupation of fixed plots was seen by Nikander as a clear succession from common to individual land tenure. Mostly, the earlier customs disappeared when meadows were divided permanently among individual owners by the Great Partition. Significantly, however, certain features continued until relatively recently in local customs regulating the use of commonly owned emergent land in Ostrobothnia. Nikander explained this in the following words:[25]

> Land uplift is a geological factor which in Ostrobothnia has had a conserving effect on the farmers' way of life and their legal customs . . . Since the coast is flat and the coastal waters very shallow, considerable areas of land emerge in the space of a generation. These areas automatically become the common lands of the village. Both at the Great Partition in the 18th century and afterwards, these emergent areas have been surveyed and partitioned by State land-surveyors, but unceasingly new areas have emerged which could be used as meadows. To avoid costs, the farmers were accustomed to divide up these emergent areas themselves according to old legal regulations. Because of land uplift, many shallow lakes have also become land and been converted to meadow. The farmers have often hastened the process. These meadows are also often used according to extremely ancient methods.

Before the Great Partition, the unit which regulated the use of common meadows, as of other land uses, was the village. Land-owners met at the village meeting, where communal work and use of the commonly owned village lands and fishing-waters were organized in accordance with established local custom. The village was the traditional unit of Swedish community life: its functions were defined in the ancient provincial laws and in the medieval Land Laws; decisions involving a departure from normal practice required unanimity; and communal work and land use were determined in accordance with an established system or decided by casting lots. The village reached the peak of its organizational development in the eighteenth century, a model set of village regulations (Sw *byordning*, Fi *kyläjärjestys*) being drawn up by the government in 1742. Landowners chose a village alderman (Sw *ålderman*, Fi *kylänvanhin*, *oltermanni*) for one or two years, who could have one or two assistants (Sw *bisittare*, Fi *kylänlautamiehet*). The alderman was responsible for supervising the regulations concerning the open fields and the decisions of the village meeting concerning land use — when the harvest was to be undertaken and at what time cattle could begin to graze on the stubble or harvested meadows. Villages often had their own cash-accounts. Many Ostrobothnian villages, in particular, adopted written village regulations in the eighteenth century, and village regulations continued to be adopted throughout the nineteenth.[26]

The importance of the village organization was counteracted from the middle of the eighteenth century by the Great Partition which, by partitioning the village lands, removed the necessity of many of the village's functions. However, the size and concentration of many Ostrobothnian villages which resulted from the intensive subdivision of farms after the Great Partition, the retention of certain village lands in common ownership, and the development of community life in other directions meant that the village meetings continued to serve a purpose.[27] In particular, the retention of fishing-waters in common ownership, as well as sand pits, gravel pits and boatplaces, meant that the village meeting did not lose all its former functions. Common pastures and fencing, as well as bridge and road maintenance, were similarly matters of concern to the village as a whole. The gradual emergence of land along the coast provided a further category of land which fell under village management. Where local convention did not simply allow landowners to use the land emerging along their shores until it was partitioned, or emergent land was not regulated by ancient traditions concerning the use of meadows, it could be divided by local agreement, without official ratification. Another common procedure was to hold an auction at the village meeting, when meadows on emergent land (and often fishing-waters) were leased for a fixed period to the highest bidder. In Alakylä, a village in Ahlainen (Vittisbofjärd), north of Pori, an annual auction was held to sell the hay yield from an area of emergent delta land; elsewhere in the village, where a total of 667 ha had appeared between 1784 and 1894, the emergent land was used by the adjoining landowners.[28]

Individual landowners using commonly owned land in accordance with one or other of these customs are not allowed to sell or let it. This was not a major restriction in former times, when the chief value of emergent land was as meadow and pasture. However, with changing assessments of the value and potential use of coastal areas, which are now much favoured for summer cottages, this restriction can cause major difficulties. Such 'changing circumstances have produced changes in policy on the part of village communities towards the use and division of emergent land. In the nineteenth century, when there were relatively few landowners in each village, short-term temporary divisions of emergent land, followed eventually by permanent partitions, were favoured and practical solutions. Emergent land was an important source of pasture and fodder, providing both hay and reeds; in some cases, reed-filled water was partitioned, with a permanent influence on the pattern of land tenure later when the area emerged. The large increase in the number of landowners during the twentieth century and the rising value of coastal land, however, have been major factors favouring the retention of emergent land in common ownership, with special provisions for the organization and control of land use by the village.

Management of these often valuable areas, where they remained in village control, was difficult, however, since for many matters the unanimous agreement of the part-owners was required. It could be hard to unravel at a particular time exactly who were the part-owners of a commonly owned area and even harder to obtain unanimous agreement, especially if owners were absent or not known with certainty. The requirement of unanimity led to delays and allowed the possibility of obstruction by an individual owner. The principle that a part-owner could not use common land for cultivation or other purposes without the agreement of the other part-owners was old-established and had been set out in the Law Code of 1734 — if the other part-owners wanted to leave the area unused or if they disagreed on its use, an individual could request his share to be marked out for his own use; frequently, however, common areas (including emergent land) were too small, or for other reasons could not be conveniently divided among part-owners. A further problem arose because of the lack of clear provisions as to how part-owners should be represented in the event of legal action over their land. Disputes frequently arose over the ownership of common areas, both among part-owners and between them and outside interests; where such disputes came to court, all the part-owners had to co-operate in the proceedings. This was often difficult and sometimes impossible. All of these problems became more difficult as the value of common areas rose and the number of part-owners increased.

The old institution of village meetings had become unsuited for administering common areas. Furthermore, the regulations that existed only applied to common areas of villages: virtually no provisions existed for the care and administration of other types of commonly held land, such as that owned by a smaller group of landowners. A new institution to look after common areas was needed which could make decisions binding on a minority. In 1940, therefore, the Act on Common Areas was passed to regulate the use and administration of land and water areas owned in common by a village or by smaller groups of landowners. The Act aims at ensuring that common areas are not left unused where unanimity cannot be achieved, but will instead give the best return to the part-owners.

The Act provides for areas left specifically in common ownership for a particular purpose, such as sand, gravel and clay pits or common forest areas; land areas (for example, small islands) left out of the Great Partition and hence automatically remaining in common ownership; common fishing-waters; and both natural and artificially drained emergent land which has not been partitioned. The Act concerns only the administration and use of common areas and the rights and benefits due to part-owners: it is not concerned with actual ownership rights, and applies only in cases not covered by other laws. The Act provides for the establishment of formal administrations for common areas. The basic decision-making organ is the meeting of part-owners (Sw *delägarstämma*, Fi *osakasten kokous*), which can be convened by any part-owner. Every part-owner has voting rights corresponding to his share in the common area: thus a landowner with a large share has a proportionally greater number of votes than one with a small share. Uncertainty over who owns shares or how large shares are can be resolved by a land-surveyor. The part-owners' meeting is responsible for the case of the common area and may decide on its disposal by sale or lease. The meeting may also establish a permanent administration to take care of day-to-day matters where the area is of reasonable economic value; a set of written regulations, which has to be legally ratified, is then drawn up and establishes the procedure for regular meetings of the part-owners, for the periodic election of one or more permanent administrative officers (Sw *sysslomän*, Fi *toimitsijat*), for planning the use of the common area to the best advantage, and for dealing with income and expenditure. The income can be used for purposes serving the common interests of the part-owners or be divided according to their respective shares.[29] By the 1961 amendment to the Land Partition Act, the part-owners' meeting or the elected officers are responsible for the income from emergent land sold to adjoining landowners where the value is insufficient to divide among the part-owners directly; if there is no administrative organ, the sum is deposited with the county council for safe keeping, falling to the State if not claimed within ten years.

Normal decisions concerning use of the common area can be made by a simple majority of the recorded votes at the part-owners' meeting. If, however, it is proposed to let part of the area for more than five years or to sell it, this must be accepted by a qualified majority consisting of at least two-thirds of the recorded votes and two-thirds of the individual owners taking part in the voting. Individual owners can demand the separation of their share before transfer takes place. If the State or Church owns a share in the common area, its consent must be obtained before a sale can take place. Any part-owner can appeal within thirty days to the district court if he disagrees with a decision of the meeting on the grounds that it was not lawfully arrived at, infringes the law, was outside the meeting's authority, or results in disability or economic loss for the part-owner.[30] In common with the traditional village meeting, the part-owners' meeting does not constitute a legal person and hence cannot own property of itself. It is simply the means of organizing and regulating the interests of the part-owners of a common property, while the elected officers act as their representatives in administrative and legal matters.

The 1940 Act provides a means of overcoming the problems arising in the use of commonly owned land where agreement among part-owners is difficult to obtain. It represents the final departure from the ancient principle of unanimity, which had become completely unrealistic, and allows more rational use to be made of common areas. Although the Act concerns a variety of types of common property, in coastal areas of western Finland emergent land is the most extensive type (apart from water) to which it applies. To a large extent, emergent land has been regulated by local customs and agreements. Certain general principles can be distinguished, but the regulations vary in detail from village to village. The 1940 Act, which in part formalized existing procedure, contains for the first time in general legislation provision for the regulation of unpartitioned emergent land on an organized basis.

A Model of Human Response to Land Emergence

As far as land use is concerned, the human response to land

emergence can be seen to operate at three levels: that of the State, of the local community, and of the individual. The State responds by legislation; the local community responds by local regulations, agreements, and customs or traditional practice not formally established by law, which can be collectively referred to as 'local conventions'; the individual (and sometimes also the State and local community) responds by creating spatial patterns of land use. Legislation and local conventions can be termed the *socio-cultural response*, concerned with the formulation of a code of behaviour to deal with the problems arising from the predictable, constantly occurring change in the environment brought about by land emergence. The creation of spatial patterns of land use can be thought of as the *geographical response* and depends partly on assessment by the individual or group and partly on the application of laws and local conventions, for 'traditions and the local laws in which they are codified . . . become an integral part of the modes of thought of the men to whom they apply'.[31] The nature of the response in its various stages is summarized in Table 7.

Table 7   THE NATURE OF THE RESPONSE TO LAND EMER-
            GENCE

1 Socio-cultural response (formulation of code of behaviour to deal with problems arising)		2 Geographical response (creation of spatial patterns of land tenure and use)
(A) General legislation	(B) Local conventions (regulations, agreements, customs)	Individual or group assessment; application of general legislation and local conventions
Concerned with applying general principles of land use to emergent land	Deal with factors not taken into account by legislation	

SOURCE: Jones, *Terra* (1970), 2.

Emergent land is primarily used by individuals, operating within the framework of certain restraints. The individual's response to the problems presented depends on his assessment of the situation in terms of his views on land use; this assessment is conditioned by his cultural background and by his receptivity to new ideas and innovations. Conflicts between the interests of individuals give rise to customs and local agreements enforced by the local community. The traditional unit is the village, within which decisions concerning the village community as a whole are made. These decisions affect the way in which the individual makes use of the land. In the past, customary law played a significant role in Finland, but its importance has been greatly reduced with the increase in the scope of statutory law, which takes precedence. Legislation is passed where the State wishes to impose a certain uniformity of practice. Historically, land legislation has been influenced by local customs: the ancient provincial laws and the medieval Land Laws were built on the ancient legal customs of the farmers. In codifying a multiplicity of local customs, legislators select those which are most suited to the policies and principles they wish to develop, since legislation is a means of regulating a situation according to certain ideas and principles held by society (or the State). Legislation is thus another factor affecting the way in which the land is used. The geographical response to land emergence depends, therefore, on individual reactions conditioned by local conventions and legislation.

During the last two centuries, land legislation has aimed at rational land use within a framework of private ownership. The laws pertaining to emergent land can be considered as a set of instructions designed to apply these principles to the new land. (It should be noted in this connection that Finnish law does not depend on precedent in the same way as law in England and other common-law countries; courts in Finland are under no compulsion to follow judicial precedent, although in practice lower courts tend to adopt the views of superior courts.[32]) The instructions are intended to put into effect what may be regarded as a 'model solution' of the problems presented by land emergence; the model solution provided by the procedure for the Partition of Emergent Land involves (a) division on the basis of *mantal* to maintain the principle of private land ownership, and (b) measures to ensure integration into the existing land-tenure pattern to maintain the principle of efficient land use. To discover whether the legislation has produced the desired results, the model solution can be compared with a series of actual solutions, provided by the spatial patterns of land tenure and use on emergent land. These actual solutions, when compared with the model solution, fall into three groups: those which are the same as the model solution; those which are a modified form of it; and those which are based on alternative solutions.

Where the actual solution corresponds to the model solution, the intentions of the law have been achieved. The instructions for the Partition of Emergent Land have been followed correctly, with no irregular patterns of land tenure and no land disputes arising. The emergent land has been partitioned according to *mantal* and at the same time integrated into the pre-existing patterns of land tenure and use.

The actual solution may be a modified form of the model solution where errors have occurred owing to incorrect application of the law, as when the land has not been partitioned strictly according to *mantal*. A modified form of the model solution may also occur where, although the instructions were followed correctly, complications have arisen so that the intended aims of the laws were not fully achieved. It may not always be possible both to partition the emergent land on the basis of *mantal* and to integrate it successfully into the existing land-tenure pattern. Complications of this nature arise owing to factors not taken into account when the laws were formulated. Two types of complication may be envisaged:

(1) Complications arising from unperceived circumstances already existing. Legislators often have an incomplete view of the problem, owing to inadequate knowledge or to simplified perception.
(2) Complications arising from changing circumstances. These include unforeseen social and economic changes, such as population changes and changing assessments of the potential use of the emergent land.

A common type of unperceived circumstance causing complications has occurred where land in one village adjoined fishing-waters owned by another. Where, for historical reasons, a holding in one village owns *urfjäll* within another's boundaries, the former is not entitled, as has been seen, to a share of the latter's fishing-waters nor, therefore, to the land emerging from them. As a result, *urfjäll* situated on the coast has often become cut off from the sea by a strip of emergent land, which was difficult to integrate into the existing land-tenure pattern. Cases exist of a holding in one village owning an island within the fishing-waters of another and finding in time that its property has become entirely cut off from the sea by land emergence.[33] Elsewhere, fishing-waters have come to be owned by a different village from that on the adjoining shore, and land emergence has gradually separated the latter from that stretch of coast. To avoid inconveniences, such coastal strips have often been left out of a Partition of Emergent Land.

Simplified perception frequently results from the fact that legislators are usually making laws for a whole country. A series of related problems often shows variations in detail at the local scale, while legislation represents a general solution which may not be entirely suitable for every case. Helmfrid's suggestion that the *storskifte* legislation set out a model plan for land distribution which, when put into practice, had to be modified through a series of compromises,[34] applies also to the Partition of Emergent Land.

The most important changing circumstance causing complications has been population change. As the number of landowners in a village increases, the smaller is the share received by each when emergent land is partitioned. In the mid-nineteenth century, there were relatively few landowners in each village and the partition of perhaps half-a-century's emergent land resulted in a substantial area being allotted to each. It has been seen that the rapid growth in Finland's population in the second half of the century caused increasing subdivision of land holdings and contributed to the development of the crofting system; combined with the post-independence land reforms, this has brought about a rapid rise in the number of independent landowners. Consequently, the traditional Partition of Emergent Land has become impracticable if time and expense are not to be wasted in allocating minute areas in accordance with the principle of *mantal* and further fragmenting the land-tenure pattern. Complications arising from both changing circumstances and unperceived factors may also be a cause of actual errors in a Partition of Emergent Land.

Complications reveal the shortcomings of the legislation. Where the geographical response (the actual solution) does not accord with the intentions of the laws (the model solution), other factors besides the laws have been influential; such factors can be identified by examination of the complications, which can also indicate contradictions in the principles on which the laws were founded. Where the laws are not sufficiently complex to deal with the situation brought about by changing or unperceived circumstances, compromises, dictated by competing factors, are necessary. The need for compromise means that certain principles are partly disregarded. In Finnish land legislation, the principle of private ownership has tended to prove stronger than that of efficient land use based on rational land tenure where the two have become incompatible. This situation is reflected in the legislation concerning emergent land.

Apart from actual solutions which are the same as or modified forms of the model solution, there is the third type of actual solution, where the model is replaced by an alternative. Alternatives are provided by the local community: local conventions include unwritten consensus of opinion, established usage or custom, which may change according to circumstances; short-term written agreements; and regulations laid down by local bodies such as courts of law and administrative authorities. Examples are the ancient customs regulating the use of meadows on emergent land; the convention in certain areas that landowners can use land emerging alongside their properties until a formal partition is made; agreements elsewhere between landowners informally partitioning emergent land; and the regulations of the land-partition courts concerning emergent land at the Great Partition. Local conventions are better able to take into account unperceived local differences and changing circumstances where these are not dealt with by legislation. Conventions may provide a code of behaviour between the time of emergence and the application of the legal solution, or may provide an alternative to the legal solution if this is not acceptable or applicable. Where there is no legislation, as with many aspects of land use, the socio-cultural response may occur at the local level only. Local conventions may be the embodiment of traditions older than laws. Thus, while in some respects local conventions may be more flexible than legislation, they can also be an impediment to change, to overcome which legislation may be needed. Local conventions can help identify some of the factors not dealt with by the laws.

The influence of legislation and local conventions on spatial patterns of land tenure and use is illustrated diagramatically in Fig 22. Legislation may itself be influenced by the spatial patterns, as a result of increasing knowledge of the complications resulting from its application. Since, in practice, the principle of private land ownership has tended to dominate and act in some cases to the detriment of that of rational land use, a number of changes in legislation have been made in an attempt to strengthen the latter principle. In 1868, the possibility of compulsory land exchange or purchase was introduced if the allocation of emergent land at a partition would be detrimental to land use. The increasing difficulties of satisfying the principles both of partition according to *mantal* and of integration into the existing land-tenure pattern were eased by the reform of land-partition legislation in 1916. This legislation was replaced in 1951 by the Land Partition Act, which was amended in 1961 to extend the provisions for purchase of emergent land, with the aim of maintaining as rational a land-tenure pattern as possible while ensuring that part-owners received their shares of the income on the basis of their former shares in the emergent land. The reform of 1916 replaced the Great Partition Adjustment, introduced in 1848, by the New Partition, which greatly facilitated the reallocation of holdings in a village. The inclusion of commonly owned emergent land in a New Partition

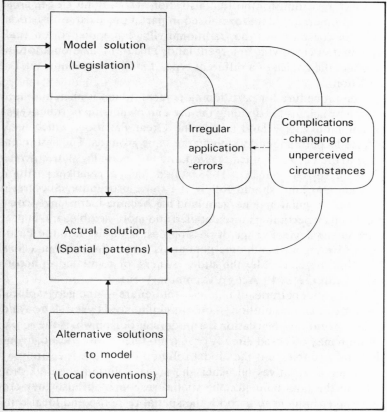

Fig 22   Interaction between different elements of the response to the problem of land emergence.
SOURCE: Jones, *Terra* (1970), 7

provides an additional form of the model solution alongside the Partition of Emergent Land.

Local conventions also influence the model solution, since legislation has frequently codified existing procedure. Much of the legislation concerning emergent land was based on what was already established procedure in the areas primarily affected, particularly Ostrobothnia. The pattern for the Partition of Emergent Land was established here long before general legislation came into being. This is a continuing process. Unpartitioned emergent land was regulated by local conventions in the form of long-established customs and local agreements until the 1940 Act on Common Areas;

this Act, providing for the administration of commonly owned areas such as emergent land, formalized in part a pre-existing situation, since in coastal areas the traditional village meetings often dealt with matters involving emergent land. This formalization afforded in effect the choice of a different type of model solution instead of partition.

The procedure for partitioning emergent land is ancient, based on the principles for dividing the use and ownership of other types of common village land before the Great Partition, which itself effected a permanent division on the same grounds. The first reference to the Partition of Emergent Land in general legislation, in the Land Survey Ordinance of 1848, stated that a permanent partition of emergent land should follow the same procedure. Successive legislation regulating emergent land has become increasingly complex, in part becoming more detailed and more flexible, and in part introducing a wider range of possibilities: in addition to the Partition of Emergent Land, emergent areas may be included in a New Partition, purchased by the shore-owners, or regulated in accordance with the 1940 Act on Common Areas.

The spatial patterns of land use and tenure — the geographical response or actual solution — are thus influenced by legislation and local conventions: legislation is a model solution on which the actual solution may be based directly or in a modified form; local conventions may supplement the model solution or replace it entirely by providing alternatives on which the actual solution is based. Not only do the laws influence the spatial response but also they are themselves influenced by both the spatial response and local conventions, so that the model solution changes and becomes more complex.[35]

The model of human response to land emergence provides a conceptual framework within which detailed land-tenure and land-use patterns may be examined. The geographical response to land emergence in the Vaasa area, as one of the main areas affected, provides numerous examples to illustrate what has happened in practice. Examination of these allows assessment to be made of the influence of legislation on the land tenure and use of emergent areas, and indicates the types of complications and local conventions which have been reflected in legislative change.

7

The Ownership and Use of Emergent Land in Practice: Examples from the Vaasa Area

The Historical Antecedents

THE DOMINATING IMPACT of land emergence on the geography of the Vaasa area arises from the rapid rate of uplift, the flat shore and the existence of the Vaasa archipelago. The $8 \cdot 6$ mm isobase passes through the archipelago (Fig 3, p. 24); with allowance for the eustatic rise in sea level, the observed rate of uplift at the present time is almost 80 cm a century. The skerry-guard coast occurs where the old worn-down peneplain of hard crystalline rock forming the Fennoscandian Shield meets the sea at a shallow angle. The Pre-Cambrian bedrock, comprising predominantly granites, was subject to pre-glacial erosion of long duration. Glacial action added to the undulations of the bedrock surface. The archipelago and adjoining mainland coast are mostly covered by uneven morainic deposits which emphasize the local irregularity of the surface, while exposures of the bedrock occur in places. The irregularity is reflected in the indented coastline and numerous islands; the length of shore along which land emergence is effective is consequently considerable. Another important contributory factor affecting land emergence is river sedimentation. Alluvium transported by the Kyrönjoki and smaller rivers is channelled between the islands, while the lack of tides or strong currents hinders its removal. These various factors, assisted by vegetation colonization, bring about a continuous transformation of the area's physical geography. Islands coalesce with each other and with the mainland; the channels once separating them are preserved in the landscape as depressions

143

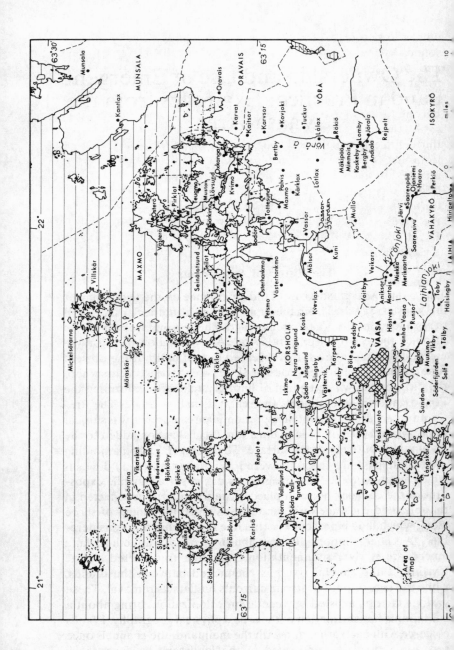

followed by small streams and ditches, and the former islands stand out as low, forested hills surrounded by cultivated land. Inlets, sounds and bays become shallower and eventually dry up, with lake and marsh representing an intermediate stage. Seawards, irregularities on the sea bottom emerge as rocky islands, heralding the appearance of a new skerry guard to replace the old that has become joined to the mainland.

At the end of the prehistoric period, which lasted until the thirteenth century, the archipelago had a completely different form from that of the present. The inner archipelago included areas now attached to the mainland, while the present outer islands were still largely submerged. The archipelago was unsettled, used as *erämark* for fishing, hunting and grazing by the early Finnish inhabitants of the river valleys. Permanent settlement by the Finns in the Kyrönjoki valley, with its fertile floodlands, is thought to date from the twelfth century or the beginning of the thirteenth. A northern extension occurred in the valley of the Vörå å, while a smaller outpost existed in the Laihianjoki valley.[1] The rivers, at that time navigable, provided routes to the coast and archipelago. The Finns farmed the valley clays and silts down to the contemporary coast. The archipelago and the forested coastal areas between the main valleys remained unsettled. Evidence of their use as *erämark* is provided by the marked Finnish influence on the placenames of the coastal belt later settled by Swedes. Common placename endings are *-lot* (Fi *luoto*, skerry), *-sar* and *-sor* (Fi *saari*, island), *-lax* or *-laks* (Old Fi *laksi*, modern *lahti*, inlet, bay). A number of names in the Vaasa archipelago indicate fishing, hunting and summer pasturing, such as Satmalot (Fi *satama*, harbour), Majlot (Fi *maja*, hut), Ritalot (Fi *rita*, trap), Karjalot (Fi *karja*, cattle), Heplot (Fi *hepo*, horse), Järlot and Oinaslot (Fi *jäärä, oinas*, ram).[2]

Swedish colonization began in the thirteenth century. The question of whether there was some continuity of settlement from the assumed Germanic population who occupied southern Ostrobothnia, centred on the Kyrönjoki valley, before the ninth century, has aroused lengthy academic dispute; present-day scholars are mostly of the opinion that the arrival of the Swedes occurred completely in historical times. Närpes, Korsholm and Pedersöre are thought to be the oldest Swedish settlement centres in Ostrobothnia; Oravais may also have been an early centre of colonization.[3] From points situated in what was then the inner archipelago, the Swedes appear to have spread along the coast, establishing settlements on the Finnish *erämark*, and infiltrated into Finnish-settled river valleys such as the Kyrönjoki and Vörå å. The valleys provided the Swedes with a way inland just as they provided the Finns with a route to the coast. Placenames in the Kyrönjoki valley suggest Swedish penetration which was later absorbed by the Finnish population.[4] In Vörå, on the other hand, the Swedes in time absorbed the Finns. The southern villages of Vörå, which originally constituted a chapelry of the Finnish-speaking Kyrö (Kyro) parish, are characterized by Finnish placename elements indicating permanent settlement. In the coastal villages and inner archipelago, the Finnish name elements are nature names recording former inlets and islands, and indicating seasonal occupation rather than permanency. The northern villages of Vörå, with their chapel at Oravais, belonged to the predominantly Swedish-speaking Mustasaari parish until the sixteenth century, when north and south Vörå were united to form an independent ecclesiastical and administrative unit.[5] The Finnish inhabitants of southern Vörå were largely assimilated by the Swedes in the sixteenth century,[6] although the area seems to have been still bilingual at the beginning of the seventeenth.[7] Between the main valleys, Swedish penetration inland was hindered by forest, marsh and sandy wasteland. Only the coastal belt itself was suitable for settlement, the inner islands of the archipelago and small inlets and river mouths of the mainland shore providing sites where some agriculture could be carried on. The limited possibilities of cultivation meant that stock-rearing, fishing and sealing provided the main sources of livelihood. The Swedes joined the Finns in using the skerry guard for grazing cattle and sheep and for fishing.

An idea of the distribution of land and sea at the time of the Swedish colonization can be obtained by comparing relative heights above sea level. The 5 m contour represents the approximate coastline of the fourteenth century, allowing for a present uplift rate of 86 cm per century and retardation of one per cent per hundred years. Closer dating requires detailed information on eustatic sea-level variations, although Lamb has suggested that the sea level was as high as or even slightly higher than it is now at the end of the Middle Ages' warm epoch in the thirteenth century.[8] Moreover, land emergence can vary considerably over time and place because of river sedimentation. A general impression, however, is gained from Fig 24.

The oldest documentary evidence for the existence of individual villages is found in legal and tax records from the fifteenth and sixteenth centuries. From Fig 24, it can be seen that the villages mentioned at this time fell into two groups: those situated at scat-

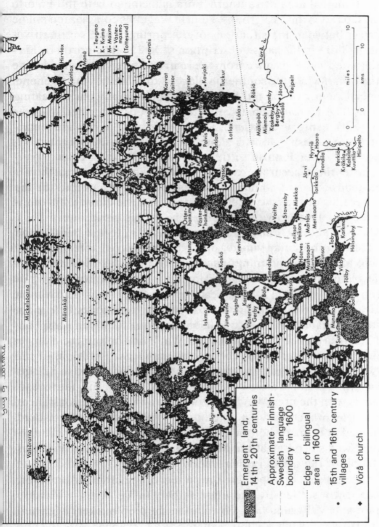

Fig 24 Land emergence and settlement in the Vaasa area, fourteenth to sixteenth centuries. Approximate fourteenth-century coastline based on present 5 m contour; language boundary according to *Atlas of Finnish history* (1959), 18–19; fifteenth- and sixteenth-century villages according to Karsten, *Svensk bygd*, II (1923), 60–189.
SOURCE: Jones, *Hist Tidskr för Finl* (1971), 149

tered locations on inlets along the coast and on sounds in the inner archipelago, and those situated close to one another along the river valleys. The language boundary between Swedes and Finns in 1600, if the bilingual area of southern Vörå is included with the Finnish area, separates the two groups. Henric Wegelius commented on the contrast between the situations of the northern and southern villages in Vörå in his parish description of 1825.[9] The northern ones are situated some distance from the river and lie entirely on one side or the other, while the southern villages extend across the river and, formerly, many of the old farmsteads stood closely packed alongside it. The transition between the two types coincides with the fourteenth-century coastline. The northern villages were established by Swedish colonists along the sea shore; the southern villages were older Finnish settlements along the river bank.[10]

The earliest accurate evidence for the position of individual farmsteads is found on farm and village maps dating from the last two decades of the seventeenth century and the early years of the eighteenth. Two active land-surveyors of this period were Jonas Gädda and Petter Uhmijn. Gädda completed in 1696 a hand-drawn atlas of Ostrobothnian villages on a scale of approximately 1:5,000, which, although containing inaccuracies, provides the first large-scale picture of many villages. Uhmijn's maps, drawn mostly between 1705 and 1712 on a scale of 1:4,000, show remarkable accuracy. These maps show the position of farmsteads before the destruction caused by the Russian occupation of Finland from 1714 to 1721 (during the Great Northern War), and before the changes brought about later in the century by the Great Partition. Fig 25 shows the position of farmsteads in Maxmo and Kärklax villages according to maps drawn by Uhmijn in 1709. The farmsteads coincide with the present 5 m contour, the approximate coastline of the fourteenth century; it is quite possible that the farmsteads remained at or near their original locations established at the time of the Swedish colonization. Maxmo and Kärklax are by no means untypical of the area in this respect.[11]

In the present archipelago, only a few of the larger islands were permanently settled by the end of the Middle Ages. Björköby, Replot and Vallgrund had grown up in the Replot skerry guard in the north-west, while Kvimo, Teugmo and Oxkangar were the only villages in what was the Vörå archipelago in the north-east; in the southern Vaasa archipelago lay Bergö. These villages are probably younger than the mainland settlements.[12] Traditions recorded at the tax assessment of 1753 in Oxkangar relate that the island was

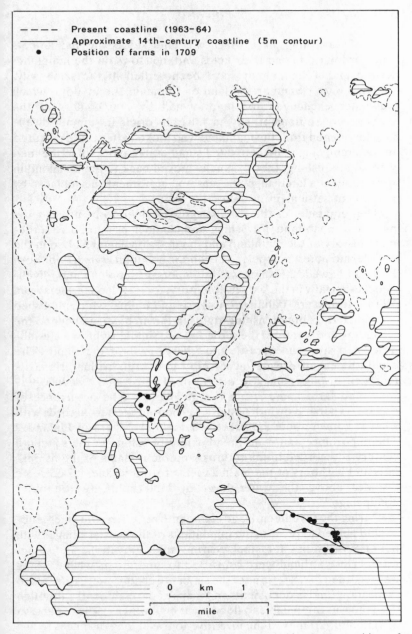

0   km   1

0   mile   1

Fig 25   Approximate fourteenth-century coastline and oldest known positions of farmsteads in Maxmo and Kärklax villages.

SOURCE: Jones, *Hist Tidskr för Finl* (1971), 151

originally a fishing-place which was later settled by mainlanders who for long retained their fields and meadows on the mainland. Kvimo and Teugmo may have been settled in the same way. Teugmo once owned arable land on the mainland in Vörå, which was later exchanged for land owned by mainlanders in the archipelago. Settlement may have had its origin in summer dwellings for women from the mainland who looked after cattle pastured in the archipelago and cultivated small arable plots while the men were at sea, fishing; they originally moved back to the mainland in winter, but at a later stage this seasonal movement was replaced by permanent settlement in the skerry guard.[13]

The remainder of the archipelago continued to be used by the mainland inhabitants for fishing and summer pasture. The settlement history of the mainland and inner archipelago resulted in the middle and outer archipelago becoming common *erämark* for both Finns and Swedes. Fishing was an important supplementary livelihood, especially in the sixteenth century, for mainland farmers from Vörå, Mustasaari, Vähäkyrö, Isokyrö and Laihia, who established individual or common fishing-rights in the archipelago beyond the village-owned waters of the settled areas. Similar rights were established to pasture sheep, cattle and other animals on the islands. The establishment of private ownership rights to individual islands is recorded in placenames incorporating Finnish and Swedish personal and farm names from the mainland.[14] The occurrence of private ownership by individuals or groups of farmers accords with what is known about *erämark* ownership elsewhere in Finland.[15] The importance and widespread extent of fishing in the sixteenth century is recorded in tax returns, and the remains of the fishing-huts and harbours of the mainlanders are still visible, raised some distance above the water level by land uplift, in the outer archipelago.[16]

During the seventeenth and eighteenth centuries, the emergence of land helped to provide the inhabitants of the coastal villages with better possibilities for stock-rearing and cultivation, as fishing-waters close at hand were converted to land. Inlets where fishing was recorded in tax returns of the sixteenth century were referred to as meadow land in documents and maps of the eighteenth, although this land was often liable to flooding at high water.[17] The expansion of agriculture removed the incentive to travel long distances to fish in the outer archipelago. For the inhabitants of the inland villages, the outer archipelago offered the only possibility for fishing, since the waters of the inner archipelago and mainland coast were owned by the coastal villages. The sixteenth-century tax records for the villages of southern Vörå mentioned only Baltic herring, which were caught in the outer archipelago. Inland inhabitants gradually ceased in the eighteenth century to make the long journey, especially as land uplift caused the Vörå å, Kyrönjoki and Laihianjoki to become less easily navigable. Although both Swedes and Finns continued to own fishing-waters and pasture in the archipelago until the eighteenth century, their value decreased for the distant Finnish owners as agriculture developed inland and the rivers became unnavigable, and the Finnish rights gradually passed over to the coastal Swedes.

As late as the seventeenth century, there was no permanent settlement in the archipelago apart from the few villages established during the Middle Ages. If pasture and fishing-waters had not been firmly established in the ownership of the mainlanders, to whose livelihood they were a necessary supplement, it is possible that seasonal fishing-places would have developed into permanent settlements earlier than was the case.[18] Royal directives of the sixteenth century urging settlement of *erämark*, furthermore, were hindered in practice in the following century by restrictions on establishing crofts and cottages.[19] Consequently, the cultural landscape of the archipelago is largely a creation of the eighteenth and nineteenth centuries.[20] Land uplift indirectly contributed to the settlement of the archipelago from the eighteenth century onwards. The disappearance of navigation channels, the extension of agricultural land on the mainland, the decline of fishing and the reduced need for pasture in the skerries led to a weakening of the ties between the mainland and the archipelago.[21] Crofts were established in the first half of the eighteenth century on the archipelago possessions of Crown holdings, such as the Tottesund military estate in Maxmo (the seat of the commander of the Ostrobothnian Regiment) and the Crown farm of Korsholm (leased by Ostrobothnia's provincial governors), which were not subject to the restrictions applying to ordinary farmers before 1757. The main period of croft development began on the island holdings of the mainland villages after 1757. The process of new settlement on Särkimo, involving the reclamation of emerging land, was recorded in detail in 1791 (Fig 26).

The settlement history of the Vaasa area up to the eighteenth century is basic for understanding responses to land uplift since then. While reconstruction of the geographical effects of uplift before the 1700s is possible through archeological, toponymical

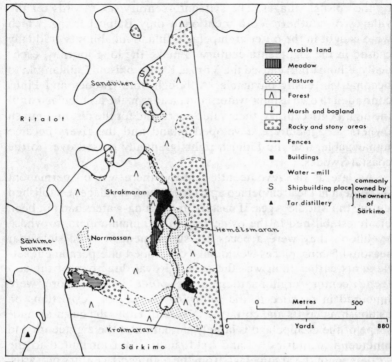

Fig 26   A new settlement in the Vaasa archipelago—Anders Spets' farm on Särkimo, 1791. The Great Partition documents of 1791 record that the first settlement on Särkimo was established seventeen years earlier by Anders Spets from Maxmo, who had cleared nearly 1 ha each of arable land and meadow and drained 5·9 ha of pasture. The arable land was described as emerged sea bottom, of which a further 0·4 ha had been drained ready for cultivation at Norrmossan. The pasture at Krokmaran and Hemåtsmaran and the meadow at Skrakmaran consisted of drained marshland.
SOURCE: National Board of Land Survey, Helsinki

and documentary evidence, the evidence is sparse and sometimes contradictory. It allows the influence of land uplift on human activity to be discerned in general rather than detailed terms. From the middle of the eighteenth century, when the maps and documents of the tax assessment and Great Partition become available, human responses to land uplift can be followed in detail.

Emergent Land at the Great Partition in the Eighteenth Century

The mapping and tax assessment of land in Ostrobothnia was instituted in accordance with the decree of 1749. Little progress was made with the Great Partition, however, until the decree of 1757 ordered it to be set in motion in the parishes where the tax assessment was ready. The work of partition began almost immediately in the inland Finnish-speaking parishes of the Vaasa area. The only coastal village in which the Great Partition was undertaken during this initial phase was Kvevlax, where it was completed in 1764 and ratified in the following year. Instructions for initiating the Great Partition in the Vaasa area's three eighteenth-century coastal parishes of Vörå, Mustasaari and Malax were set forth by their respective land-partition courts in 1768. The instructions laid down the procedure to be followed in reallocating arable land and meadows, and were followed in 1773 and 1774 by further instructions for the partition of the forests. Exchanges among villages were also to be arranged: *urfjäll* and out-village meadows were to be moved where possible to within the boundaries of their owner's village or, if this could not be done, they should be situated as close to the owner's village as possible and reallotted in the minimum number of parcels. As has been seen, the instructions included regulations designed to anticipate disputes over future emergent land.

The partition documents for certain villages in Mustasaari referred to the application of the provisions dealing with emergent land. In Böle and Smedsby, note was taken of the places where land had emerged between the mapping of the villages in 1757 and the commencement of the Great Partition in 1768, and the seaward boundaries of holdings were drawn accordingly. In the neighbouring village of Singsby, which in 1769 still had a short shoreline at the head of Infjärden, it was decided to mark off emergent land and leave it in the villagers' common possession until sufficient had emerged to be worth partitioning.

The maps and documents of the tax assessment describe some of the problems resulting from land emergence. Jonas Cajanus was responsible for most of the village descriptions in Mustasaari, while Gullic Wislander described the villages of Vörå. The difficulties arising from the low-lying situation of the fields and meadows in the coastal villages of both parishes were a recurrent theme. The descriptions of Kaitsor, Bertby and Maxmo villages noted that the arable land was situated for the most part on areas that had emerged from the sea. Because it was low-lying, frequently situated close to inlets and marshes, and often difficult to drain, the arable land in the coastal villages suffered from cold and frost. The meadows were mainly on emerged sea shores and inlets, with the result that they were wet and subject to flooding. The description of Kärklax in 1763 mentioned that 'the meadows, which are partly spread out around the village, consist for the most part of wettish land, while the remainder adjoin the sea and are difficult to harvest in some years as they are covered at harvest by flood water.' In Bertby, the meadows on the former bay known as Bertbyfjärden remained mostly unharvested in wet summers. The descriptions of Kovjoki, Tuckur and Lålax, which in the previous century were situated at the mouth of the Vörå å, indicate that in the 1750s the meadows on the former estuary were still liable to flooding from the sea. G. A. Piper, the governor of Ostrobothnia, mentioned the problem of flooding on emergent meadow land in his official report of 1748. The flooding damaged grass growth and hindered harvesting. He recommended that farms should not be taxed for these emergent areas until the sea had receded further.[22] Wegelius commented in his description of Vörå in 1825 that the only drainage undertaken on meadows consisted of a single outlet ditch.[23]

A further problem in sandy areas was declining fertility as the land rose. The description of Bertby, dated 1757-9, included the observation that 'the meadows are also to a greater part emerged from the sea, and in recent years have much declined in hay growth.' In Karvsor, it was noted that the meadows were formerly productive, but were largely on sea sand and declining in fertility, with poorer grasses replacing 'sea fodder'. The villagers of Karvat relied on continued land emergence to replace older meadows as they deteriorated, but by 1753 they were finding themselves faced with a new problem, as the land-survey description makes clear:

> The meadows around the village have all lain under water, and at the time of first emergence yielded much hay; but as they consist of sea sand, and sandy soil, they are annually declining . . . ; the expectation that had hitherto prevailed, that they would always annually expand and increase at the sea shore, has cast the peasants in doubt, since the shores, it now appears, are of sand and gravel, and steeply sloping and deep.

The impact of land emergence was greater in the archipelago villages than on the mainland. The description of Kvimo in 1760 stated that 'this island about 500 years ago was only a fishing-place', and that gradually fields and meadows had come into being on the emerging shores and bays. Frost owing to the low-lying situation of the fields and to the existence of many inlets and marshes was a problem in both Kvimo and Teugmo. Kvimo's meadows along the sea shore were 'often damaged by flood water', while in Teugmo the meadows, entirely on low-lying marshes and dried-out lakes, were insufficient for local needs. The forest in the two villages was broken up by inlets, lakes and marshes. In Kvimo, it was further split up by former islands owned by other villages as 'out-village islands', which had become joined to Kvimo. The coalescence of islands brought problems to both Kvimo and Teugmo, since there was nothing to stop animals put to graze by other villages on their own islands from wandering on to neighbouring ones. In Kvimo, it was observed that 'the pasture could easily be sufficient, but as the out-villagers bring more than their islands can provide fodder for, the village suffers great harm before the meadows are harvested, and if no separation is made in the future the pasture can only be considered as poor.' In Teugmo, too, 'the pasture could well be good, but as the inhabitants from further inland usually bring more animals to their islands than can be fed there, they tend to look for fodder on this farm's property and outlying land, so that the pasture is rather poor.'

Disputes arising from land emergence caused uncertainties in land ownership, delaying the carrying out of the Great Partition. The economic deputation for Ostrobothnia, charged with initiating the Great Partition and dealing with land disputes, referred to this problem at length in its report of 1760. When new land had first begun to appear, according to the report, no particular attention had been paid to it, but it had been regarded as common property and taken into occupation by anyone who liked. As more land emerged, confusion arose over the position of property boundaries. Property-owners interpreted old court judgements as if the shore had remained unchanged, even although it had completely altered and islands had become joined to the mainland since the judgement had been given. Conflicting claims led to expensive and protracted lawsuits.[24]

One cause of dispute was the existence of out-village meadows, the incidence of which was widespread in Vörå and Mustasaari and which had probably arisen through the taking of emergent meadow land into private possession at scattered places before firm boundaries had been established between villages. At the Great Partition, extensive exchanges occurred between different villages in an attempt to rationalize the situation. Where possible, exchanges of out-village meadows were arranged so that owners received meadows in their home village in compensation for meadows owned in another. Exchanges often involved several villages at once. Where it was not possible to exchange out-village meadows so that they were transferred to their owners' home villages, attempts were made to consolidate them and place them in a position that caused least inconvenience to the village within which they were situated. In Vörå, for example, upstream villages owned strips of meadow land at the old mouth of the Vörå å in Tuckur village, where they had formerly possessed common fishing-waters;[25] these out-village meadows, which were intermixed with the Tuckur villagers' meadows, were consolidated by land exchanges. Farms from eleven different villages in Vörå, Mustasaari and Vähäkyrö owned meadows on the valuable emergent land at the mouth of the Kyrönjoki and at the southern end of Vassorfjärden, within the village of Vassor. Kärklax was the main owner, possessing more than twice as many parcels as the other villages together. In 1689, a dispute had arisen when Kärklax laid claim to the emergent land adjoining its meadows at Vassorfjärden. Vassor contested this on the grounds that the land had emerged from its private fishing-waters. The Kärklax villagers stated that they had fished in Vassorfjärden of old, and that no village boundary had been demarcated either on land or water. It was ruled in 1691 that Kärklax would retain most of the land which had already emerged, and that a boundary fence was to be erected. The rights of the Kärklax villagers to fish smelt at Degsundet, where they shared traditional fishing-rights with Vassor, Mullo and Miekka, were upheld, but the Kärklax villagers were excluded from fishing in the remainder of southern Vassorfjärden, as were the Vassor inhabitants from Kärklaxfjärden, the water adjoining Kärklax.[26] At the Great Partition in Vassor, it was resolved 'that the said *urfjäll* meadows be consolidated into as few parcels as possible'. The number of parcels belonging to Kärklax was reduced from 138 to 27. The meadows belonging to the other villages were also reduced in number.

The partition documents for individual villages sometimes included agreements among villagers concerning the use of emergent land. When the forest was being partitioned in Maxmo village in 1795, an agreement among the villagers concerning the positioning of their allotments concluded with what was in effect a prototype Partition of Emergent Land. The relevant paragraph concerned primarily the land which had emerged since the village had been mapped for the tax assessment in 1763. The principle was followed of allotting shares, as far as consistent with *mantal*, adjacent to the owners' existing holdings. However, the partition of the emergent land was not put into effect because of disagreement over how much emergent land was to be included. It was decided instead that 'the emergent areas are of such a nature and situation that they can later be divided among the villagers separately.' By leaving the emergent land out of the partition, the additional costs of mapping and dividing it were saved. Instead, a detailed agreement was drawn up regulating the use of emergent areas. For the most part, owners were to retain emergent land adjacent to their meadows, allowing individual farmers unimpeded use, although the emergent land remained in common ownership.

One of the most complex parts of the Great Partition in the Vaasa area involved the archipelago, where a multitude of conflicting interests had to be resolved, land exchanges arranged, and the final partition undertaken. The traditional status of the archipelago as *erämark* was reflected in the widespread distribution of the villages from which owners came before the Great Partition to fish and pasture their animals. Farmers from almost every village in Vörå, as well as from villages in Mustasaari and Nykarleby parishes and the Finnish-speaking Vähäkyrö parish inland, possessed rights in the Maxmo skerry guard, then part of Vörå (Fig 27). The complicated ownership situation made it necessary for the greater part of the Vörå archipelago to be dealt with at the Great Partition as a separate operation. The archipelago was not the common property of a group of villages (as was often the case with forest on the mainland), but instead individuals or groups of individuals from various villages had independently established ownership over particular islands. In a memorandum to the governor of Vaasa County in 1793, Petter Trana, the land-surveyor responsible for the Great Partition in the Vörå archipelago, noted that the archipelago possessions of farms in the mainland villages had not been included in their tax assessments but were considered as 'separate properties or *utjordar*'. An independent *utjord* (Fi *ulkopalsta*) is a holding separately assessed for taxation but used in conjunction with another main holding, which is usually situated in another village; although *utjord* is assessed separately, it is without *mantal* and because of its nature is usually unsettled.[27] In most cases, *utjordar* do not carry rights to water ownership,[28] although it is evident that in the case of the Vörå archipelago they did. The situation was equally complicated in the remainder of the Vaasa archipelago.

While the old-established villages in the skerry guard were dealt with in the same way as the mainland villages, the first stage of the Great Partition elsewhere was the recording of each island or island group and its owners. The shares of individual part-owners in an island belonging in common to several owners were in most cases noted as a proportion of the total number of sheep the island could

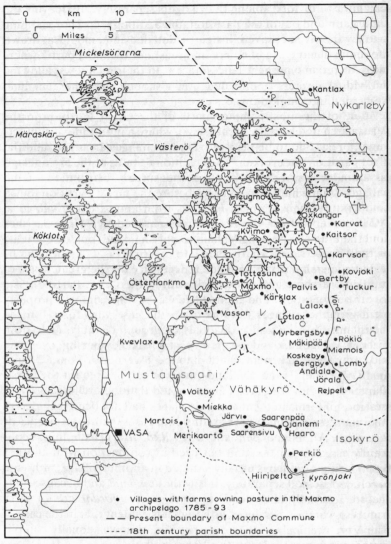

Fig 27   Villages with farms owning land in the Maxmo archipelago, 1785–93, immediately before the Great Partition.
SOURCE: National Board of Land Survey, Helskini

carry. The value of pasture per sheep tended to vary on different islands, since the total sheep-carrying capacity of each island was derived from tax assessments and court judgements of varying dates. Islands with only one owner were valued without reference to sheep pasture, while on certain islands shares were expressed as simple fractions. Previous ownership on each island or group and not *mantal* formed the basis of partition. This reflected the fact that the archipelago was not in common ownership but consisted of a mass of private properties owned by individuals or groups who derived their rights from court awards or *urminnes hävd*. In some cases, small islands belonged to individual farms; more commonly, several farms often from different villages and even different parishes, shared pasture rights on an island. After ownership rights had been recorded and the land graded according to use and quality, a series of exchanges designed to bring about more convenient positions or consolidated holdings was arranged before the final partition took place. Where possible island properties in Mustasaari belonging to farmers from Vörå were exchanged for the possessions of Mustasaari owners in the Vörå archipelago. As far as could be done, shares owned in different islands by a single owner were consolidated into one parcel, or as few parcels as possible.

Partition of the archipelago helped to overcome some of the problems of ownership which had arisen owing to the islands joining together as a result of land emergence. The tax-assessment documents for Mickelsörarna, for example, had recorded in 1766 that the islands of Villskär and Håkonsskäret 'now both form one land, without any boundary'. The problem of out-village islands which had become joined to Kvimo was partially solved by exchanging a number of them for land owned by Kvimo on the neighbouring island of Jenäsör. Boundary adjustments in Teugmo included the straightening of a former fishing-water boundary which crossed the emergent land joining Teugmo to the island of Långholmen. Recorded in the partition documents was an agreement of 1730 mentioning the ownership of emergent land at Långholmen, which belonged to a number of farms in mainland Vörå. The agreement, concluded with Teugmo, stipulated that the mainland owners, in accordance with their 'ancient rights', were to retain the island, with its forest, pasture and emergent land, as their private, inalienable property. The fishing-waters around Långholmen and two smaller islands to the north were to be used and owned in common with Teugmo. The smaller islands and the adjoining emergent land were recognized as belonging exclusively to Teugmo. In 1792, the boundary around Långholmen and the commonly owned fishing-waters was demarcated in accordance with a boundary agreement of 1759. In conjunction with the land exchanges made at the partition of the Vörå archipelago, the number of mainland farms with property on

Långholmen was reduced from eleven (in five different villages) to seven (in three villages), the others receiving compensation in land elsewhere in the archipelago. The documents gave no indication, however, of the implications of the land exchanges for the ownership of water and emergent land at Långholmen and in the rest of the archipelago.

The Great Partition in the archipelago and in the coastal villages of the Vaasa area established the basic land-tenure pattern into which later emergent land was to be incorporated. Responses to land emergence in the ensuing period were influenced both by the experience of the Great Partition and by patterns of use existing earlier. The responses depended in part on varying assessments of the value and importance of emergent land, in part on the extent to which the partition legislation was found to be applicable, and in part on the strength of older traditions of use.

Partitions of Emergent Land

Land which had emerged before the Great Partition was, as a general rule, included automatically in the partition. The Great Partition was based mainly on the mapping undertaken for the tax assessment decreed in 1749, however, and there was often a considerable lapse of time between the mapping and the partition. Mapping in the coastal parishes of Mustasaari and Vörå was undertaken largely in the 1750s and 1760s, while the Great Partition did not begin in most villages until 1768 and continued in the area for the remainder of the century. In certain cases, significant areas of land emerged in the intervening period. Where the maps were not revised, it was sometimes considered expedient to carry out supplementary Partitions of Emergent Land as adjuncts to the Great Partition.

Some earlier divisions of emergent land were carried out in conjunction with the tax assessment in the 1750s and 1760s. E. O. Runeberg's notebooks, preserved in the archives of the National Board of Land Survey in Helsinki, contain references to several such partitions in the Vaasa area. Most of these were concerned with dividing emergent land among villages in association with the demarcation of village boundaries, although there were also cases of farmers receiving their individual shares. The Partitions of Emergent Land carried out after the Great Partition were, with some exceptions, among individual owners within a village. The average amount of new land received by individual farmers varied considerably in different villages, depending on the total area of emergent land and the number of part-owners (Table 8): in certain cases, other minor commonly owned areas were partitioned at the same time. The emergent land was valuable as a source of fodder in an agricultural economy highly dependent on animal husbandry. A typical holding of 100 ha in a coastal village of Vörå, for example, might have in the mid-eighteenth century 1–3 ha of arable land and 10–20 ha of meadow land, with the remainder forest. An additional half hectare, or sometimes much more, of emergent land, most of which would provide a harvest of hay or reeds, meant a useful supplement to a farm's resources. Numerous divisions of emergent land took place in the Vaasa area during the period of the Great Partition and in the first half of the nineteenth century, after which they became less frequent. Many were unratified and of limited duration, and must be considered as local agreements of a temporary character. Table 8 shows Partitions of Emergent Land which received official ratification. Land-survey operations were ratified by the district courts until 1917, when entry of a completed land-survey operation in the land register superseded legal ratification in court.

The general rule followed in the partitions was as far as possible to allot to each owner his share so that it adjoined his existing holding, or otherwise at the most convenient place; the position of parcels was determined in certain cases by drawing lots. The amount received by a particular farmer depended on his *mantal* in relation to the total village *mantal* and on the graded value of the land. The farmers agreed among themselves how much they wanted to include in the partition, and on the grading of the area. In some cases, considerable areas of reed-filled water and other areas still in the initial stages of emergence were included. The emergent land partitioned in Kvevlax in 1803 was divided into four categories: the most valuable was already under cultivation; the second grade was sedge-covered and free from flooding; the third category consisted of sedges and rushes and was subject to floods; while the fourth grade comprised reeds and rushes in water-covered areas about to emerge. At the partition undertaken in Runsor in 1787, on the contrary, the emergent land was considered to be of even quality, and could be divided directly among the part-owners without being graded according to value. In many cases, part of the emergent land was left in common ownership for roads and other purposes, although the size of the area was not always recorded in the documents. In Kaitsor, ½ ha was left in common in 1787 to give access

Table 8 LEGALLY RATIFIED PARTITIONS OF EMERGENT LAND UNDERTAKEN IN THE VAASA AREA AT THE TIME OF THE GREAT PARTITION AND LATER

Village	Date of ratification of partition	Approximate dates of emergence	Area partitioned, ha*	No of part-owners receiving separate shares	Average area received per part-owner, ha	Area left in common or for other purposes, ha
Voitby	1773	1757–73	140·00	14	10·00	
Palvis	1784	1759–84	32·58	12	2·71	
Vassor	1785	1757–78	22·98	7 (incl. Mullo)	0·77	
Kuni	1785	1757–85	17·88	5	3·58	
Kaitsor	1787	1733–87	4·16	11	0·38	0·43 common
Österhankmo	1787	1762–87	53·56	11	4·87	0·57 to Kvevlax chapel
Runsor	1787	1736–87	29·62	7	4·23	
Petsmo	1788	1761–8 1761–81 1761–88	66·22	20	3·31	
Västerhankmo	1791	1758–91	32·80 emergent land + 180·37 reeds	14	2·34 +12·88	
Kärklax	1796	1762–96 1772–96 1778–96	6·09	23	0·26	
Österhankmo	1797	1787–97	12·58	12	1·05	
Kvevlax	1803	1764–1801	170·20	48	3·55	2·11 to parish clerk
Koskö	1807	1758–1806	5·67	14	0·41	
Smedsby, Kråklund	1816	1757?1776?–1815	20·90	2 villages	Smedsby 16·19 Kråklund 4·71	
Toby, Karkmo, Vikby, Norra Hälsingby, Södra Hälsingby	1827	1779–1811	194·13	5 villages	Toby 37·32 Karkmo 32·07 Vikby 25·01 N and S Hälsingby 99·73	
Toby	1827	1779–1811	8·08	22	0·37	
Västerhankmo	1827	1804–26	16·49	19	0·87	
Karperö	1832?	1803–31	84·84	38	2·23	2·65 to military croft
Vassor, Mullo	1837	1778–1837	26·30 emergent land (+138·91 water)	2 villages	Vassor 22·01 (+116·27) Mullo 4·29 (+22·64)	(2·54 water common)

Södra Vallgrund	1842	1828–41	58·78	16	3·67	
Kärklax	1842	1796–1840	45·10	35	1·29	3·14 common
			emergent land			(including 2·98
			+51·01		+1·46	disputed)
			rushes and reeds			c.2·90 to parish clerk
Voitby	1843	1757–1837	68·86	14	4·92	
Vassor	1843	1768–1838	41·37	43	0·96	
			emergent land			
			+98·72		+2·30	
			emerging and reeds			
Karvsor	1843	1753–1843	20·33	29	0·70	
			+39·94		+1·38	
			repartitioned			
Västerhankmo	1844	1804–44	27·61	26	1·06	
Maxmo	1845	1763–1844 1792–1844	161·11	6	26·85	0·12 common 0·96 to Maxmo chapel
Finne	1845	1763–1844 1792–1844	25·13	3	8·38	
Oxkangar	1845	1786–1844	57·69	14	4·12	
Petsmo	1846	1781–1844 1788–1844	52·88	19	2·78	1·60 to village smith
Österhankmo	1873	1787–1871	160·29	22	7·29	0·19 common 1.15 to school master
Replot	1910	1758–1905 1815–1905	838·37	15	55·89	15·37 common
Böle	1915	1758–1914	4·22	24	0·18	
Gerby	1921	1757–1915	63·85	52	1·23	1·22 common
Vikby, Tölby	1927	1826–1926	96·60	2 villages	Vikby 28·28 Tölby 68·32	
Maxmo	1927	1763–1915 1791–1915 1844–1915	34·21	21	1·63	13·50 common 4·09 unspecified
Corrected	1937	1844–1915	34·05	21	1·62	4·09 unspecified
Bertby	1934	1905–31	72·78	62	1·17	2·71 common
Petalax	1934	1760–1932	634·38 (including 68·66 older estuarine land)	368	1·72	26·53 common

*Areas partitioned may include other minor commonly owned areas which were included in the partition. Emergent land partitioned with larger areas of other commonly owned land, in which the emergent land constituted a minor part or was not distinguished, is not included in the table.

SOURCE: National Board of Land Survey, Helsinki, and Vaasa County Land Survey Office.

for fodder collection. When the former inlet on which Kaitsor was situated was partitioned in 1843, the village boatplace and a channel through the partitioned area were left in common ownership. On occasion, villagers who had given up land from their holdings for common purposes such as new roads received compensation at a partition in the form of additional emergent land. Partitions of Emergent Land also gave opportunities for a village to provide extra land for the support of the parish priest, parish clerk, village smith or local schoolmaster.

Exceptionally, partitions involved more than one village. Mullo farm in Vähäkyrö, for example, possessed a share in part of Vassor village's water on the basis of ancient ownership rights and was allotted 1·7 ha when the emergent land was partitioned among the Vassor villagers in 1785. In 1837, the water area and newer emergent land in which Mullo owned a share was partitioned between the two villages on the basis of *mantal* after a court judgement recognizing Mullo's rights. A partition of nearly 200 ha of emerging land at the mouth of the Laihianjoki, completed in 1827, involved five villages, which owned the water at the river mouth in common. An adjoining area of reed-covered water and emergent land, amounting altogether to nearly 100 ha, belonged one-third to Vikby and two-thirds to Tölby and was partitioned between them in 1926. The common ownership of fishing-waters at the mouths of rivers by groups of villages occurred elsewhere and was similarly reflected in the land-tenure pattern when the land emerged.

The Partitions of Emergent Land carried out in the Vaasa area provide a series of actual solutions to the problems of land emergence which can be compared with the model solution set out by legislation. Detailed study of the land-tenure patterns arising from individual partitions shows how successfully the model was applied. It is difficult to find cases where the intentions of the legislation were put into operation with complete success, with the emergent land being partitioned on the basis of *mantal* and achieving at the same time full integration into the existing land-tenure pattern, but examples with a fair measure of success can be noted. Into this category falls a partition completed in Maxmo village in 1845 (Figs 28 and 36). Over half of the emergent land fell to the former military estate of Tottesund (leased out by the State after the incumbency of the last commander of the Ostrobothnian Regiment ended in 1826), which accounted for 3$\frac{5}{24}$ of the total village *mantal* of 5$\frac{1}{12}$, while 77·33 ha were divided among the other 5 farms of Maxmo, which received an average of 15·47 ha each, an increase of

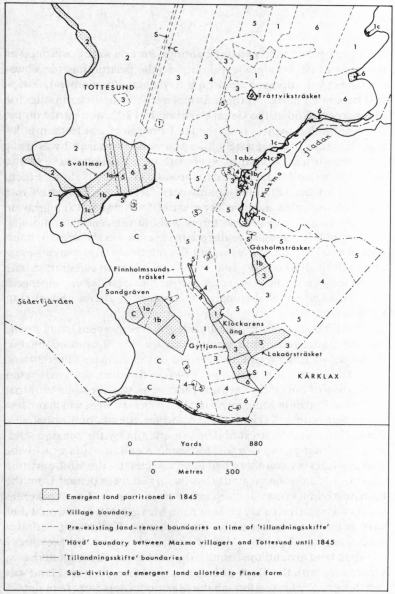

Fig 28   The Partition of Emergent Land in part of Maxmo village, 1845. Numbers are property register numbers in Maxmo village. Numbers with letters identify parcels allotted separately to the three part-owners of Finne farm, who subdivided their share according to *mantal* after the main partition. C = Church land; S = commonly owned land. The partition boundaries are shown in relation to the existing boundaries of the holdings at the time of the Partition of Emergent Land (*tilland-ningsskifte*). Before the partition, Tottesund had, like the adjoining holding, *de facto* possession (*hävd*) of the northern half of Svältmar, but surrendered this area to the Maxmo villagers in 1845.

SOURCE: National Board of Land Survey. Helsinki

8·71 per cent on their existing holdings. Parcels were positioned on the basis of *de facto* possession before the partition as far as was consistent with division according to *mantal*. Previous possession had depended partly on the informal agreement allocating the use of emergent land at the Great Partition in 1795, and partly on the convention that owners used the land emerging next to their holdings. Because of the estate's long shoreline, Tottesund was using more than it was entitled to, even with its high *mantal*, and had to surrender some emergent land to the villagers. Mostly the emergent land fell to the adjoining landowners, becoming integrated into their holdings, although two larger areas, Svältmar and Sandgräven, were divided among several farms without reference to adjoining properties. They remain as distinctive features in the present land-tenure and land-use patterns, but the relatively large parcels present no difficulties of use. Two other exceptions to integration with the adjoining holdings were in the archipelago, where emergent land adjoined *urfjäll* belonging to owners in Palvis and Tuckur villages within Maxmo's fishing-waters.

The difficulties of successfully integrating emergent land into the existing patterns of land tenure and use are illustrated by two Partitions of Emergent Land carried out in Kärklax (Figs 29 and 32). The first took place in 1796, only thirteen years after ratification of the Great Partition there. This was the same year that the Great Partition was completed in Maxmo village, which possessed *urfjäll* within Kärklax on the former islands of Bodholmen, Furuholmen and Svärtesholmen. An attempt by the Maxmo villagers to exchange their *urfjäll* for some meadows adjacent to the Maxmo-Kärklax boundary had been rejected by the land-partition court in 1772 on the grounds that the *urfjäll* were distant from the farmsteads in Kärklax and separated from them by forest, whereas access was relatively easy by boat from Maxmo; Kärklax would thus have been inconvenienced by the exchange. Kärklax agreed as a concession to allow the Maxmo farms to retain the previously emerged land around the former islands, but the court ruled that in accordance with the Code of Land Laws future emergent land was to belong to Kärklax, although the Maxmo owners were to maintain rights of access to their land. On other grounds the court overruled the aim of the Great Partition to exchange *urfjäll*. It is probable that in 1796 the Kärklax villagers were anxious to secure their rights to land which had emerged adjacent to the islands since 1772. About 5 ha had appeared, which were shared among 21 landowners, partially cutting off the land belonging to Maxmo from the sea and producing a highly fragmented pattern of land tenure. Parcels were positioned by lot. The partition also included 1½ ha of emergent land elsewhere in Kärklax; this seems to have been included in the adjoining holdings, although no map exists. The total area was partitioned according to *mantal* among 23 landowners, giving an average increase to their holdings of 0·22 per cent.

The 1796 Partition of Emergent Land was exceptional owing to the circumstances of division and the small area involved. A second Partition of Emergent Land was completed in Kärklax in 1842. Between 1796 and 1840, when the new land was mapped, about 96 ha of emergent land and reed growth had appeared. The partition included in addition 5½ ha which had been left in common ownership at the Great Partition. A small island allotted to two farms at the Great Partition was also included, a mistake that apparently passed unnoticed. An area of 3 ha, disputed with Finne farm in Maxmo village, was excluded. The partition was based on *mantal* and gave an increase of 2·74 per cent to the villagers' existing holdings. Parcels were allotted as far as possible to the adjoining landowners. At Bodholmen, Furuholmen and Svärtesholmen, parcels were placed next to the small lots of the 1796 Partition of Emergent Land (Fig 29). At Kärklaxholmarna, more than half of the partitioned area consisted of reed- and rush-filled water. Everybody received a separate share of the reed and rush beds, although where possible parcels were allocated in conjunction with the lots of emergent land (Fig 32). The disputed area, on the southern side of Maxmo fladan (Fig 34) was used by Finne, as the adjoining owner, under the 1795 agreement regulating the use of emergent land in Maxmo. The Kärklax villagers, however, regarded Finne's possessions south of Maxmo fladan as *urfjäll*, without rights to emergent land, and pointed out that the map used for the Great Partition drew the boundary between the two villages along the middle of Maxmo fladan. To avoid the heavy costs of submitting the dispute to the land-partition court, it was decided in 1841 not to include the disputed area in the partition. Later the same year, however, the Kärklax villagers petitioned the district court to order Finne to vacate the disputed land. The case was terminated in 1842 after one of the part-owners of Finne agreed to surrender the area to the Kärklax villagers, who agreed in return to drop the case and not hold him liable for legal costs.

The two Partitions of Emergent Land in Kärklax provide examples in which the model solution was modified owing to complications resulting from unperceived local circumstances. In 1796, the

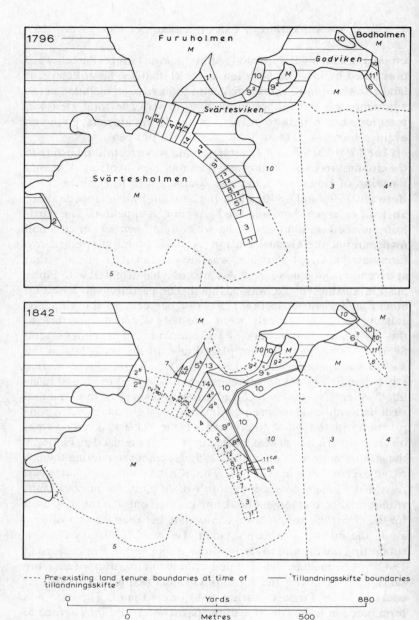

Fig 29 The Partitions of Emergent Land at Svärtesviken and Godviken in Kärklax, 1796 and 1842. Numbers are property register numbers in Kärklax; those in italics indicate pre-existing holdings at the time of each Partition of Emergent Land (*tillandningsskifte*). Number with letters show parcels allotted separately to part-owners of informally subdivided holdings. *M* denotes land within Kärklax owned by Maxmo villagers

SOURCE: National Board of Land Survey, Helsinki

emergent land was partitioned according to *mantal* but there was almost complete lack of integration owing to the existence of *urfjäll*. The 1842 partition was partially successful; with the exception of one minor mistake, the land was divided according to *mantal*, while integration occurred in some places but not everywhere. The impact of the partitions on land tenure and use is most striking at Svärtesviken (Fig 29), where minute parcels remote from the village farmsteads present particular problems of use. At Kärklaxholmarna, the separate partition in 1842 of the reed and rush beds, which have since largely emerged, is reflected in the land-tenure pattern long after the original purpose of the partition, to share out reed fodder, has been forgotten (Fig 33). Former fishing-water boundaries also retain an expression in the landscape. Sounds where reeds were harvested 130 years ago and fish caught until thirty or forty years ago have recently been transformed from swampy ground to good-quality meadow; the main drainage channel, following the village boundaries, corresponds to the old fishing-water boundary (Figs 30 and 31).

Fig 30   Kärklaxholmarna and Maxmoholmarna — mid-eighteenth century land use. Skadaholmen, Röislot and Matilot constitute Kärklaxholmarna (The Kärklax Islands); Kockholmen and Essesholmen are the main islands of Maxmoholmarna (The Maxmo Islands). The boundary between Kärklax and Maxmo villages is marked. The islands are situated in the Kyrönjoki estuary, where land emergence is accelerated by river sedimentation.
SOURCE: National Board of Land Survey, Helsinki

Fig 31   Kärklaxholmarna and Maxmoholmarna — present land use. The influence of land emergence on land use can be seen by comparing this map with the 1762 map. The present forested areas correspond closely to the former islands. The arable land is on the natural meadow of 1762 or on more recently emerged shores. The rush and reed beds partitioned in 1842 (Fig 32) are still boggy, hindering land access to Matilot. Former fishing-water boundaries are reflected in the landscape by drainage channels, which follow village boundaries.
SOURCE: National Board of Land Survey, Helsinki

Fig 32   Kärklaxholmarna — the Partition of Emergent Land, 1842. Numbers are property register numbers in Kärklax; those in italics indicate pre-existing holdings at the time of the Partition of Emergent Land (*tillandningsskifte*). Numbers with letters identify parcels allotted separately to part-owners of informally subdivided holdings
SOURCE: National Board of Land Survey, Helsinki

Fig 33   Kärklaxholmarna — present pattern of land tenure. The fragmented land-tenure pattern, due in part to the subdivision of holdings, also reflects the Partition of Emergent Land in 1842. In particular, the separate partition of reeds has had permanent results in the land-tenure pattern long after the original purpose has been forgotten.
SOURCE: National Board of Land Survey, Helsinki

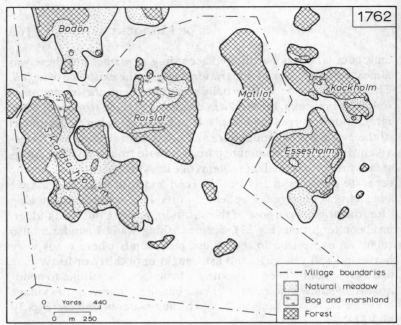

Fig 30

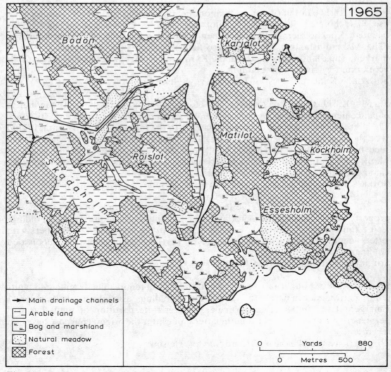

Fig 31

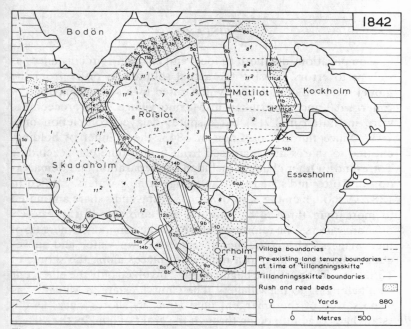

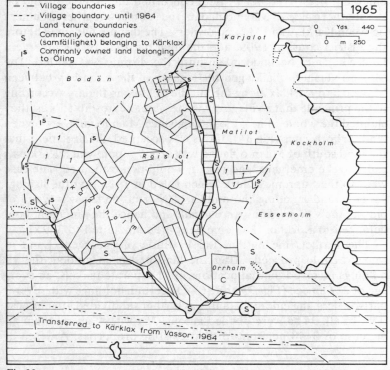

Fig 32

Fig 33

Complications due both to local and changing circumstances as well as to errors, causing the actual solution to differ from the model solution, are admirably illustrated by a second Partition of Emergent Land undertaken in Maxmo village. The proceedings were instituted in 1912, but disputes delayed completion until 1937. Since the first partition in 1845, the number of holdings entitled to shares had increased from five to nineteen (excluding Tottesund). Other changes included the separation and demarcation of Tottesund's share of the village fishing-waters, ratified in 1887. Although on the basis of *mantal* Tottesund's share amounted to more than three-fifths, this did not embrace all the estate's offshore waters. The remainder stayed in the common ownership of the villagers, who consequently came to own water and subsequently emerging land at a number of places along the shores of Tottesund. The partition begun in 1912 involved only the emergent land belonging to the villagers. The Church estate in Maxmo was dispossessed of the emergent land along its shores since, as the estate had come into being through the grant of land by the village and did not have its own *mantal*, it was not entitled to a share in the emergent land. Another dispute concerned the emergent land on the southern side of Maxmo fladan, the subject of earlier argument between Kärklax and Maxmo owners. The dispute had gone before the district court in 1909, and the final partition of the emergent land could not be undertaken until the dispute was settled. The Maxmo villagers challenged the legality of the boundary between Maxmo and Kärklax along the middle of Maxmo fladan. According to the principle that a village owns the water nearest its shores, they claimed the whole of Maxmo fladan, since Maxmo villagers owned land on both sides (Fig 34). If this was accepted, the argument that the land south of Maxmo fladan was *urfjäll*, upon which Kärklax's claim to the emergent land rested, would be invalidated. The case went to the Supreme Court, which ruled in 1923 that the fishing-water boundary along the middle of Maxmo fladan was 'valid of old', Finne's possessions were *urfjäll* and hence the emergent land belonged to Kärklax. The emergent area amounted to 3·95 ha.

The verdicts meant that the Partition of Emergent Land in Maxmo could proceed. After the land had been graded, the 19 holdings received their allocations in 41 separate parcels, an average of 2·2 apiece (Figs 35 and 36). On certain holdings with several part-owners, the emergent land was further subdivided after allocation. In all, 34 ha were divided among 21 owners, giving them an increase of 3·48 per cent to their existing properties. An area of

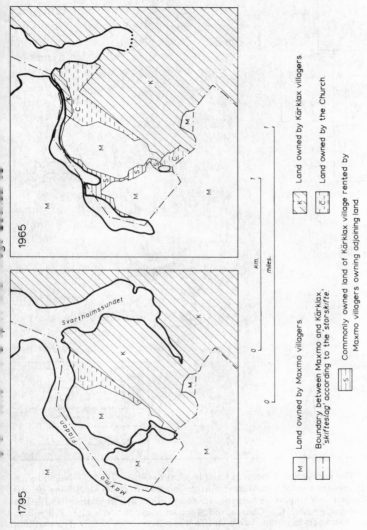

Fig 34   The maps show the boundary between Maxmo and Kärklax villages at the Great Partition. The land belonging to Maxmo villagers and the Church on the Kärklax side of the boundary are *urfjäll*, without rights to emergent land. The 1795 shoreline is reflected in the land-ownership boundaries on the 1965 map
SOURCE: National Board of Land Survey, Helsinki

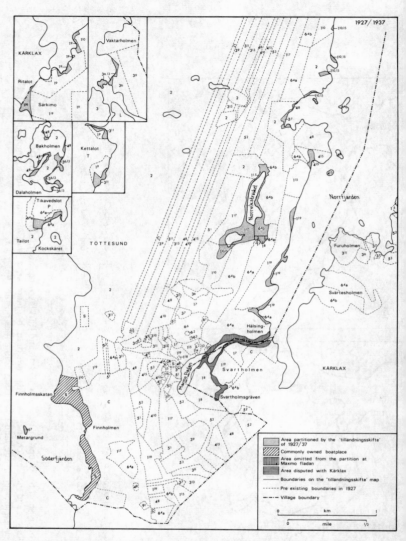

Fig 35   The Partition of Emergent Land in Maxmo village, 1927/37. Numbers are property register numbers in Maxmo village, those with letters identifying parcels allotted separately to part-owners of informally subdivided holdings in 1927. The Tottesund estate is no 2. C = Church land; S = commonly owned land; L, P, T = land belonging to owners in Lotlax, Palvis and Tuckur villages respectively. The partition boundaries are shown in relation to the existing boundaries of the holdings at the time of the Partition of Emergent Land (*tillandningsskifte*) in 1927. Insets show Maxmo village's archipelago holdings. The partition at Maxmoholmarna is shown in Fig 36.
SOURCE: National Board of Land Survey, Helsinki

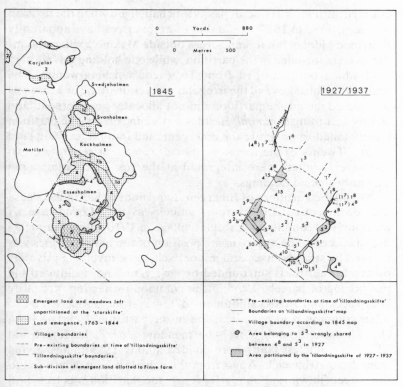

Fig 36   Maxmoholmarna — the Partitions of Emergent Land, 1845 and 1927/37.
Numbers are property register numbers in Maxmo village. Those with letters identify
parcels allotted separately to the part-owners of Finne farm in 1845 and to part-
owners of informally subdivided holdings in 1927. Where changes occurred between
1927 and 1937, the 1927 allocation is indicated first in brackets.
SOURCE: National Board of Land Survey, Helsinki

13½ ha, adjoining the Church estate, was left in common as a
boatplace. The partition was entered in the land register in 1927,
but a revision became necessary after the discovery that a privately
owned former islet, covering 0·16 ha, had been mistakenly
included. The correction involved returning the former islet to its
rightful owner, and four land exchanges were made to compensate
the two owners to whom the area had been wrongly allotted (Fig
36). Strictly, every holding's allocation of the emergent land should
have been diminished, but since the areas that would have been
involved in land adjustments between every parcel would have been
minute, the changes were made on paper only. The solution

adopted, although irregular, passed unchallenged when the revision was completed in 1937. A number of other errors have apparently remained hidden. Some small areas outside Maxmo's village boundaries were included in the partition, while one holding was allotted land which had emerged from Tottesund's fishing-waters. The undetected mistakes and the irregular correction of the one that was discovered meant the partition did not allocate the emergent land strictly according to *mantal*. Besides containing errors, the partition largely failed to integrate the emergent land into the existing land tenure. Twenty of the forty-one parcels remain as separate plots, and several others were integrated at the cost of creating some curiously shaped holdings.

Not all the Partitions of Emergent Land undertaken in the Vaasa area during this period were as unlucky as the Maxmo case. A partition was completed in Replot village in 1910 with a fair measure of success. The approximate position of the old shorelines was marked by straight lines, and minor exchanges, involving privately owned former islets surrounded by emergent land, facilitated the positioning of parcels. Land left in common ownership, primarily boatplaces and roads, amounted to 15 ha, while about 1½ ha of other common land were included in the partition. Nearly 840 ha (8·37 ha arable land, 576·74 ha meadow, 207·87 ha forest and 45·39 ha valueless land) were divided among 15 holdings, giving from 26 to 70 ha each. Apart from the valueless land, which fell to the parcels in whose boundaries it lay, the partition was based on *mantal*. In the case of one owner who found that the partition had included an islet in his private ownership, the land-surveyor ruled that he should have appealed against the demarcation of the emergent land within the legally allotted period. An area of ½ ha accidentally excluded from the partition was purchased by the owner of the adjoining parcel, the price being paid into the village cash-account. Owners who gave up arable land in the emergent area received financial compensation. The partitioned land was largely integrated into the existing land-tenure pattern. Four landowners received part of their allocation in parcels not adjoining their existing holdings. The only major difficulty was caused by a number of islands and former islands belonging as *urfjäll* to owners in Norra Jungsund, Smedsby and Västervik villages. A demarcation of the emergent land surrounding the islands had been ratified in 1902. The demarcation had been difficult because the maps from the Great Partition were tattered and defective, and in some cases the emergent land had only been distinguished by subtracting the areas of the islands at the Great Partition from their areas in 1901. The emergent land was allotted to the nearest holdings in Replot, consequently cutting the *urfjäll* off from the sea. Otherwise, the division of a large area of emergent land among relatively few holdings contributed to the comparative success of the partition.

The rapidly increasing number of holdings resulting from the post-independence land reforms and continuing subdivision led to increasing complications when emergent land came to be partitioned. In the 1930s, often little attempt was made to integrate parcels of emergent land into the existing land tenure. In mainland Bertby, for example, emerging land was divided in 1934 among 62 holdings; most of the lots remain as separate parcels in the present-day land-tenure pattern.

Also completed in 1934 was a partition in Petalax.[29] Besides 587·4 ha which had emerged since 1760, when the map used for the Great Partition was completed, 73·5 ha of estuarine pasture and small islands left in common ownership at the Great Partition were involved. After 26·5 ha had been marked off for roads, harbours and other common places, 634·4 ha remained for partition among 368 owners in Petalax and Nyby villages. Slätan, the delta plain at the mouth of the Petalax å, was divided into some 150 parcels, which remain a characteristic of the present land ownership. After the partition, most of Slätan was brought into cultivation, although the damp sedge land nearest the shore remains as pasture. Integration of the parcels into the existing land tenure was impossible, owing to the large number of owners and the situation of most of their farms along the banks of the Petalax å rather than along the coast. The emergent land comprised the large, compact delta plain and strips along the shores of the mainland and skerry guard, including some areas surrounding *urfjäll* islands belonging to holdings in Malax. It was partitioned correctly according to *mantal*, although the procedure was complicated by the fact that two villages were involved. Nyby village had come into being in 1795, after the establishment of new farms on surplus land surrendered by Petalax to the Crown for settlement; these farms had received rights to fish in Petalax's fishing-waters but not to other common property. The right of the Nyby villagers to shares in the emergent land was upheld in 1878 by the Finnish Senate, at that time the supreme court, which overruled an earlier decision of the Vaasa County governor that the new settlement established in Petalax after the Great Partition had no rights to emergent land. In 1887, an unratified partition, valid for thirty years, was concluded on the basis of *mantal* between the two villages (see Table 9, p 187); the emergent land, providing principally meadow and pasture, was not at this time divided among individual holdings. Land emerging around the islands belonging to Malax had been recognized as belonging to Petalax by court judgements of 1705 and 1746, although Malax possessed rights to fish with certain equipment in part of Petalax's water known as 'Domvattnet' (The Judgement Water); these rights did not convey a share in water ownership, although Malax disputed this for centuries. In 1934, the Nyby owners received their due shares of Petalax's emergent land, but were not entitled to shares in the older land of the estuarine plain, which had been left as Petalax's common property at the Great Partition and was partitioned among the Petalax villagers only.

Many of the complications arising over emergent land in the Vaasa area derive from the preservation of ancient property rights, in particular *urfjäll* and old-established ownership of water areas. It has been seen that the owners of *urfjäll* normally possess no rights to adjoining emergent land while, conversely, owners of fishing-waters own land emerging from them, even when adjacent to another village's land. The existence of *urfjäll* has been a primary cause of complications in Partitions of Emergent Land, since division according to *mantal* and the allocation of emergent land to the adjoining holdings are mutually exclusive. The law contained insufficient provision to prevent anomalies arising. The only provisions for the compulsory exchange of *urfjäll* to bring about a more convenient land-tenure pattern were in conjunction with the Great Partition (when it did not always occur or was not always possible), or later in conjunction with a Great Partition Adjustment, which had its own attendant difficulties until replaced by the New Partition in 1916. Fishing-waters owned by owners in one village next to another village's land occurred at several places. Legislative provisions made possible the exchange or purchase of emergent land in certain circumstances, but again these did not always occur or were not always possible. The complications arising from such local circumstances were compounded during the course of the twentieth century by complications arising from the increasing number of owners. The problems were foreshadowed by the Partition of Emergent Land among nineteen holdings in Maxmo village between 1912 and 1937. By August 1970, the number of registered properties entitled to shares in Maxmo village's emergent land had reached ninety-six. The lack of integration when large numbers of owners are involved was indicated by the partitions concluded in

1934 in Bertby and Petalax. Such partitions can only have any value if the area involved is comparatively large and reasonably compact, to ensure that holdings receive usable parcels. While the New Partition provided an alternative in certain circumstances, it was not until the 1961 amendment of the Land Partition Act that the traditional Partition of Emergent Land according to *mantal* was supplemented by more flexible forms of parcelling to facilitate integration of emergent land with the adjoining land tenure.

The New Partition

The solution provided by the Partition of Emergent Land to the land-tenure problems resulting from land emergence sought to regulate the situation in relation to the existing land-tenure pattern. The alternative afforded by the New Partition integrates emergent land into a reformed land-tenure pattern by dividing emergent land on the basis of *mantal* in conjunction with a general reallocation of holdings; at the same time difficulties such as those caused by *urfjäll* can be overcome by land exchanges.

It was natural that the earliest reallocations of land should take place in Ostrobothnia, where the Great Partition began and where the subdivision of holdings was most intensive during the nineteenth century. The early date of the Great Partition meant that mistakes and compromises had produced a land-tenure pattern which was not always the best possible, while in some villages the partition had been incomplete. The frequent subdivision of holdings informally among heirs, who tended to divide all their parcels to ensure absolutely equal shares, had the result that farms were internally fragmented, and confusion often reigned over the location of boundaries. The problem was particularly severe in the coastal parishes, where holdings were small in comparison with those further inland. The need for the reallocation of holdings in the second half of the nineteenth century in the Vaasa area was generally brought to official attention when an individual landowner in a village requested a legal subdivision of a farm or a boundary demarcation. The confused land-tenure pattern resulting from the informal subdivision of holdings meant that such a request could often not be satisfied until a Great Partition Complement had been undertaken, involving the re-marking of the legal farm boundaries dating from the previous century. In these circumstances, land-surveyors frequently decided that a reallocation of all the land in the village would be a more practical undertaking and would help to promote more efficient agriculture. The forerunner of the New Partition, the Great Partition Adjustment, required a special decree of the Senate unless there was unanimity among the villagers. Unanimity was rarely forthcoming, and the Senate's decision usually depended on whether a majority were in favour of or against reallocation. Most landowners tended to be opposed to reallocation during the nineteenth century, and holdings were reallocated only in a few villages; in other cases, the old boundaries were redemarcated. A change of attitude became apparent towards the end of the century, and at the beginning of the 1900s a series of reallocations were set in motion by the Senate in accordance with the wishes of the majority of landowners.

One of the first reallocations to be ordered began in Vassor village in 1851. This, however, did not include any previously unpartitioned emergent land. In fact, the reallocation excluded 89 ha of 'sea fodder and waterlogged emergent land' which had been partitioned earlier. The excluded area embraced part of the reeds and emerging land included in the Partition of Emergent Land in 1843, as well as the water area allotted to Mullo in 1837; the latter area was exchanged at the reallocation, together with the other possessions belonging to Mullo in Vassor, for a more suitably located piece of land adjoining Mullo's boundary. The reallocation in Vassor provided a particularly unfortunate example to surrounding villages, since disputes delayed its completion for fifty-nine years.

Another early reallocation took place in Björköby, where the Great Partition, ratified in 1774, had only dealt with arable and meadow land. Proceedings began in 1844 for a 'New Great Partition' of the whole village. This was four years before the Great Partition Adjustment was introduced in legislation. The procedure followed that laid down for the Great Partition, except in one detail. Normally the allotment of arable and meadow land depended on previous ownership, while other land was partitioned so that each owner received what was still due to him according to *mantal*. In Björköby, the villagers agreed that only the arable land was to be reallocated according to previous ownership, while the meadow was to be partitioned on the basis of *mantal*, along with the forest and other outlying land. This procedure was upheld by the Senate in 1861 after being overruled by the local land-partition court. Possibly the villagers' decision was motivated by the importance of emergent land as a source of hay. The documents stressed that the meadows consisted mostly of 'stony emergent land which has appeared from the sea and a limited amount of sedge meadow', although no clear distinction was made between the meadows partitioned in 1774 and meadows situated on land which had emerged subsequently. Disputes and appeals against the repartition delayed the final transfer to the new holdings until 1873. In that year, arguments between those who wished to harvest their old meadows and those who wanted to harvest their new lots caused such an uproar in the village that extra police were needed and the county governor had to make an appearance to calm the situation.[30]

The costs and time involved in the redistribution of holdings led to an attempt by the villagers of Södra Vallgrund to shorten proceedings by excluding emergent land from the reallocation instituted there in 1880. The villagers had originally requested a re-demarcation of the Great Partition boundaries; the land-surveyor appointed to the task in 1877 recommended a reallocation of holdings which, despite opposition among the villagers, was ordered by the Senate. The villagers agreed among themselves to include in the reallocation the area divided by a Partition of Emergent Land in 1842, but to exclude most of the land that had emerged since then, which they had informally divided in 1871. In 1895, however, the county governor ordered the inclusion of the latter, which amounted to 121·27 ha of meadow and 1·95 ha of forest and wasteland. It was shared according to *mantal* among 11 holdings, giving them an average addition of 11·2 ha each. The reallocation was ratified in 1900.

A large number of reallocations took place in the Vaasa area beginning in the 1890s. In a few cases, for example Lålax, Smedsby, Munsmo and Norra Vallgrund, the villagers were in unanimous agreement, but in most cases decrees of the Senate were necessary. After the introduction of the New Partition by the reform of 1916, one of the main barriers to setting a reallocation in motion was removed when it became possible at the request of a single owner. In the coastal villages, the reallocations provided an opportunity to share out the emergent land. The value of the emergent land due to each of the village landowners on the basis of *mantal* was taken into account in the reallocated holdings, often together with other land owned in common. The additional area varied considerably from village to village. The reallocation completed in Munsmo in 1906 divided 358.65 ha of emergent land, predominantly meadow, among 45 holdings, giving an average increase of 7·97 ha each. Of the total, 327·75 ha had previously been in private occupation through informal division. In Västerhankmo, 333·78 ha of emergent land, two-thirds meadow, was divided among 32 holdings at the reallocation ratified in 1914, giving each holding an average of 10·43 ha. In this case, 224 ha of meadow had been in private use beforehand. In Iskmo, also ratified in 1914, 95·2 ha of emergent land gave an additional 3·97 ha on average to the 24 holdings involved. In Vikby, where the reallocation was completed in 1916, there were only 16·65 ha of emergent land which, divided among 27 holdings, amounted to an average of 0·62 ha each. The reallocation completed in Bertby in 1912 included for the first time 34·3 ha of commonly owned land, while an area of 21·4 ha of previously partitioned emergent land was excluded because it was found to be under water; the gain for each of the 63 holdings involved was insignificant. In the archipelago village of Oxkangar, 243·86 ha of commonly owned, mostly emergent, land were shared according to *mantal* in the repartition ratified in 1919, giving an average addition of 7·17 ha each to 34 holdings. This included all the land that had emerged since the Great Partition, even though part had already undergone a Partition of Emergent Land in 1845. At the New Partition completed in Kaitsor in 1939, 38 holdings out of 70 in the village were entitled to shares in the emergent land; the area involved was 79·73 ha, giving an average of 2·09 ha each. These examples, in which the emergent land was easily identifiable in the documents, give a general impression of the varying significance of emergent areas as a source of additional land.

The New Partition in Kvimo village, undertaken between 1921 and 1931, is illustrated in Fig 37. Substantial changes had occurred since the Great Partition: 104·2 ha, more than one-tenth of the village area, had emerged between 1760 and 1922, while new cultivation and settlement (the original 2 farms had increased to 32) had further transformed the landscape.[31] A repartition was necessary since the land was only informally subdivided: the average number of parcels per landowner was 15, two having their land split into 33 parcels; while the emergent land had been included in the subdivision of adjoining holdings. The New Partition permitted land exchanges to eliminate the anomalies brought about by land emergence in the vicinity of *urfjäll*: generally, the owners of the *urfjäll* retained the emergent land in return for surrendering an equivalent area of their holdings to the Kvimo owners. The reallocation of holdings was arranged so that each owner retained his cultivated land (including that on the emergent area), and the remaining share of the older and emergent land due to each farm was then allotted according to *mantal*. The removal of nine farm-

Fig 37 The New Partition in Kvimo village, in the Maxmo archipelago. The area of emergent land labelled 'Vörå tillandning' was not included in the New Partition (*nyskifte*). Its exact status is undetermined, and it has been informally divided between the two adjoining landowners.
SOURCE: National Board of Land Survey, Helsinki

steads out of the tightly packed village centre facilitated the distribution of the land into fewer parcels, generally one per farm. The inconvenience of the location of much of the meadow on emergent shores distant from the village centre was reduced. In the 1920s, one-third of the emergent land consisted of meadow, compared with one-tenth of the older land, while the meadows on the emerged areas accounted for a quarter of all the meadow in the village. Each landowner received on average in his new holding the equivalent value of 3·24 ha of emergent land, which was successfully integrated into the land-tenure pattern. The land which has emerged since 1922 customarily provides supplementary cattle pasture for the adjoining owners although continued land emergence has caused difficulties for common boatplaces marked off at the New Partition.

Where emergent land was considered of little value, the owners sometimes agreed at a New Partition simply to incorporate the emergent land in the adjoining holdings instead of working out shares according to *mantal*. This was done in Karvat village, where all the farms bordered the shore and the extent of the emergent land was difficult to determine. When the New Partition began in Palvis in 1922, it was noted that the commonly owned property consisted only of an insignificant area of emergent land, which was included in the adjoining holdings. In 1931, however, the land-partition court found that a division of emergent land completed in 1863 was unratified, and that it was necessary to undertake a formal partition. This, involving 122·86 ha, was carried out by allotting the emergent land to the holdings which previously possessed it, so that no change in the reallocated holdings was necessary. At a New Partition in Petsmo, the inclusion of emergent land in the value of the adjoining holdings already using it, instead of shares being determined by *mantal*, was among errors which led to the partition's annulment by the Supreme Court in 1949. Many of the landowners had been dissatisfied with the original reallocation proposal made in 1928, but the land-partition court had ordered only minor changes, the partition being entered in the land register in 1931. After the successful appeal to the Supreme Court, proceedings recommenced in 1957. A complete repartition was impossible because of uncertainties concerning ownership before the reallocation. The Land Partition Act laid down that where the costs and inconveniences of redoing a land-survey operation were greater than the value to be derived, the mistakes were to be corrected by financial compensation among owners; other mistakes were to be corrected by adjustments on the ground. The corrections were completed in 1972.

The examples indicate that the New Partition has been generally successful in integrating emergent land into the land-tenure pattern while maintaining ownership rights in accordance with *mantal*. The cases where division on the basis of *mantal* was not strictly adhered to were either the result of local agreements among villagers or of errors and oversights on the part of land-surveyors. The main drawback of the New Partition is that it is not a convenient method of dealing with emergent land unless a reorganization of all or part of the existing holdings is desirable. Most of the problems arising, however, appear capable of solution in accordance with the 1961 amendment of the Land Partition Act.

Unpartitioned Emergent Land: Traditional Agricultural Uses

When land first emerges alongside a holding, the normal convention in the Vaasa area has long been that the owner uses the emergent land as if it were part of his holding, thus establishing rights of *de facto* use but not legal ownership. Where the emergent land became fairly extensive or was detached from the rest of the village, as well as for various other reasons, it could be subject to special regulation, without being formally partitioned. In some cases, agreements existed among villagers distributing the use of different areas of emergent land among themselves. In the nineteenth century, unratified divisions of emergent land among part-owners were common. Such divisions were generally of limited duration. In the twentieth century, in particular, it has become more usual for emergent land to be retained in common by the part-owners, who are most frequently the landowners of a village.

References to the use of emergent land by the adjoining land-owners occur in land-survey descriptions of the mid-eighteenth century. In Björköby, it was recorded in 1760 that 'the villagers have divided the emergent land among themselves so that everyone uses that before their plots; but when the emergent land increases, both on the home island and in the skerry guard, it will be divided according to their future *mantal*.' The convention whereby individual landowners used the emergent land next to their holdings could lead to inequalities. The description of Vallgrund, again from 1760, stated that 'the villagers have until now each used the emergent land before their meadow plots, and those whose meadows do not adjoin the sea have gone without'; in compensation, the latter were allowed, with the other villagers' consent, to clear commonly owned areas as hay land. Future emergent land was to be divided on the basis of *mantal*. On the mainland, the villagers of Smedsby, according to the land-survey description of 1757, had already come to an agreement to share out use of the emergent land in proportion to their taxes, except for one farm which received as its share the land emerging at a particular place.

Private agreements among villagers concerning the use of emergent land can be found among the documents of the Great Partition and later land-survey operations. They were often designed to save the costs of a formal partition. The agreement made in 1795 at the Great Partition in Maxmo, distributing use of land emerging after the mapping of 1763, lasted until the Partition of Emergent Land in the village in 1845. The emergent areas provided both meadow land and reeds and rushes for fodder. The agreement is an example of a local convention determining the use of emergent land in the period before the model solution, a formal partition, was applied. An agreement made in Karvat in 1805 divided among 6 farms 3·20 ha of sedge- and rush-covered emergent land and an indeterminate area of reed fodder where the water was too deep to permit mapping and measurement. The sedges and rushes were allotted mainly to the owners of the adjoining meadows, while the yield of reeds was shared by the cartload. A private agreement, to be valid for thirty years, was made in Björköby in 1886 to save the 'enormous costs' of a Partition of Emergent Land which had been requested in 1877, but which was suspended at the unanimous request of the villagers, who instead agreed among themselves to make some adjustments to the existing distribution of the emergent land.

Informal divisions of emergent land could be carried out either with or without the assistance of a land-surveyor. Frequently, his services were used to map and divide emergent land equitably among villagers without the partition being formally ratified in court. These cases were not recognized as official land-survey operations, although many of the documents are preserved in the land-survey archives (Table 9). Generally, the procedure adopted was similar to that at a Partition of Emergent Land, with shares being allocated on the basis of *mantal* and lots positioned to allow each owner to retain, as far as his share permitted, the emergent land he had already been using, generally adjacent to his holding. Often, informal divisions were made for a stipulated period only.

An informal division of 9 ha of emergent land was made among 25 owners in Gerby in 1836 for a period of 8 years. Earlier owners had simply extended their boundaries to include the emergent land, and old maps were used to determine where the old land ended and the new land began. The emergent land was graded into three classes, one unit of the best quality being regarded as equivalent to two units of the second quality and three units of the third quality. The class of each area was determined by agreement among the villagers, who were familiar with the land through 'many years' use'. Once graded, the emergent land was divided on the basis of *mantal*. Areas which 'are not yet fully emerged, but covered with water, and thus cannot conveniently be graded or divided, are left until the

Table 9   UNRATIFIED DIVISIONS OF EMERGENT LAND CAR-
RIED OUT WITH THE ASSISTANCE OF LAND-
SURVEYORS IN THE VAASA AREA, EIGHTEENTH TO
TWENTIETH CENTURIES

Village	Date	Approximate dates of emergence	Area partitioned	No of part-owners receiving separate shares	Average area received per part-owner	Area left in common or for other purposes
			ha		ha	ha
Sundom	1778	1756–78	757·48	45	16.83	5·43 common 3·38 to military crofts
Koskö	1826	1806–26	21·45	15	1.43	
Bertby	1830	1759–1830	105·78	16	6·61	
Gerby	1836	1757–1836	9·00	25	0·36	1·97 common
Osterö	1837	1785–1837	6·32	12	0·53 ·	
Österhankmo	1844–8	1787–1844	147·79	25	5·91	0·09 common
Klemetsö	1848	1759–1848 1809–48	13·80	16	0·86	
Palvis	1860–3	1784–1860	71·67	22	3·26	
Norra Vallgrund	1867–9	1828–67	73·85	8	9·23	1·98 common
Södra Vallgrund	1871	1841–71	16·90	17	0·99	
Petalax, Nyby	1886	1760–1886	351·90	2 villages	Petalax 195·81 Nyby 156·09	6·83 common
Böle	1890	1758–1890	8·57	27	0·32	5·83 common
Österhankmo	1895–7	1787–1895	247·98	30	8·27	1·75 common
Vassor	1911–19	1853–1912	128·11	73	1·75	3·08 common

SOURCE: National Board of Land Survey, Helsinki, and Vaasa County Land Survey Office.

future in common for the village; and the yield from it is for the time being leased and the funds to be deposited in the village cash-account'. A division in 1890 of 8·57 ha of emergent land at Pitkälahti (Långviken) in Böle village was valid for 15 years. The area was shared among 27 holdings on the basis of *mantal*. A provisional partition of emergent land in Vassor was requested in 1911. This was only a year after the completion of the Great Partition Adjustment in the village, but since the mapping for this had been undertaken between 1851 and 1853, a substantial area of new land had emerged. It was agreed that natural meadow, consisting of arrow grass, sedges and rushes, and certain areas of reed growth would be divided, but that stony shores were to be excluded. The basis of division was to be a combination of existing possession and *mantal*. After 3 ha had been left in common ownership for a

boatplace, a road and a paddock for the village school, 128·11 ha
were divided among 73 part-owners. The division was to remain in
force for 25 years. The parcels were marked out in 1919, but the
partition was not entered in the land register.

Some informal divisions of emergent land were unconventional.
One, of temporary duration, occurred among twelve holdings on
the island of Österö in 1837, involving 6 ha of land which had
emerged since mapping for the Great Partition in 1785. At that
time, pasture rights on the island had been partitioned among
owners from several mainland villages in Vörå, many of whom
subsequently leased or sold their shares to crofters settling Österö
as fishermen. The mainland owners decided to leave the division of
emergent land to the tenants at the latters' cost; the basis of division
was according to sheep pasture, as for the Great Partition, rather
than *mantal*. Another unconventional division occurred in 1897 in
the village of Österhankmo, at the mouth of the Kyrönjoki, where
the combination of river sedimentation, vegetation colonization
and land uplift has produced particularly rapid land emergence.
Thirty owners shared nearly 250 ha of emergent land, of which
160 ha had been previously included in a partition ratified in 1873.
The division of 1897, although based on *mantal*, was unratified. It
lasted until a New Partition took place in Österhankmo between
1918 and 1924, when the area was included in the reallocated
holdings on the basis of existing possession; a further 145 ha which
had emerged since 1897 were divided according to *mantal*.

An eighteenth-century unratified partition of a special nature
came to have a long-lasting effect on the land-tenure pattern of
Söderfjärden, south of Vaasa. At the Great Partition in the 1760s
and 1770s, most of Söderfjärden still consisted of shallow water, but
154 ha of emergent land around its fringes were included in the
main partition of meadows in Sundom, Munsmo and Solf (Sulva)
villages. After the completion of the Great Partition in Sundom in
1770, an agreement among the villagers permitted shore-owners to
harvest rushes and sedges adjoining their property, while reed-
covered inlets, swamps and emergent land were divided into areas
to be harvested by two or three farms in common. In 1778, the
Sundom villagers divided the whole of their share of Söderfjärden
as well as other small emergent areas and swamps. The emerging
bay was given the same value all over, since the growth of reeds and
grass varied considerably from year to year; furthermore, a dam had
been built across the entrance of the bay a couple of years earlier to
regulate the water level and control flooding in order to improve the

quality of grass growth, and it was expected that this would promote rapid and even emergence. A drying-place for 'sea fodder', left in common at the Great Partition, was included in the division as it was no longer needed, since the dam allowed parts of Söderfjärden to be kept dry when necessary. After areas were set aside for soldiers' crofts, roads, and compensation for owners who had otherwise received poor or too little land, shares were allotted to the forty-five holdings in Sundom according to *mantal*. Owners received their parcels next to their existing property in all but three cases. The swamps were allotted to the holdings in which they lay, although fishing in them remained in common. In Söderfjärden, each holding received three parcels. Around the edge of the bay, the length of shore allocated to each holding was determined as closely as possible by *mantal*. The boundaries of the parcels radiated out from the centre of the bay, and the method of division became known as a 'fan partition'. Since the centre of the bay was still virtually open water and the reed and grass growth improved steadily towards the shore, this form of partition ensured an equitable division.

The fan partition of Sundom's share of Söderfjärden in 1778 was not at the time officially ratified. During proceedings for a Great Partition Complement in 1876, however, the Great Partition maps were found to be so poorly legible that it was agreed that the boundaries recognized by the landowners as those in customary use would serve as the basis for demarcation; thus the fan-partition boundaries were followed in Söderfjärden. The land-surveyor recommended a reallocation of holdings, but this was turned down by the Senate in 1879. The ratification of the Great Partition Complement in 1880 thus gave legal recognition to the boundaries of the fan partition drawn in 1778. However, the fan had become more complex through time owing to informal subdivisions of holdings during the nineteenth century. Land-surveyors were often called to help divide farms into two or more equal parts, and the normal practice was for every parcel to be divided. The documents are in the Vaasa County Land Survey Office, but none of the subdivisions undertaken in the nineteenth century received official ratification. By the beginning of the twentieth century, the narrow, tapering parcels, often 3 km long and only a few metres wide at the narrow end, were proving a hindrance to rational use. Söderfjärden provided natural meadow and reeds at this time, but the narrow parcels did not make it worth harvesting the reeds in the centre of the bay, which was knee-deep in water and had poor-quality growth. At about this time, efforts to improve the situation were made under the auspices of the district agricultural society, which, in order to promote agriculture, urged farmers to arrange for proper, legally ratified subdivision of their farms. The first of these in Sundom took place in 1900, others following suit. The original farms were repartitioned, allowing consolidation of the scattered parcels. This facilitated the cultivation of Söderfjärden after it was drained in the 1920s, since the parcels were less narrow than the earlier ones. None the less, inconveniences remain and will not be removed until the New Partition, begun in Sundom in 1956, is completed. The proposed underdraining of Söderfjärden in conjunction with this will further improve the situation, since the radial surface drainage follows the pattern of the old parcels. The land-ownership pattern in the segments of Söderfjärden belonging to Solf and Munsmo villages, where fan partitions had also been undertaken, was regulated somewhat in connection with reallocations ratified in 1903 and 1906 respectively, when the fan partitions were replaced by wider, although still long, parcels.

Informal or unratified divisions of emergent land among village landowners during the nineteenth century represented one stage short of a formal Partition of Emergent Land. Legally the land remained in common ownership. Informal divisions allowed individual owners use but not ownership of specific parcels of emergent land. Since the divisions were unratified, they were less binding, and could relatively easily be replaced by another division or a different form of regulation as circumstances changed. As the main value of emergent land at this time was for its hay and reed harvest, individual use of specific plots was a practical arrangement; otherwise, unless the emergent land was simply left at the disposal of the adjoining landowners, its use was regulated by the village meeting.

Most villages in the Vaasa area adopted village regulations, based on the model of 1742, from the mid-1740s onwards, although many were not ratified in court until some time later. Energetic in promoting the adoption of village regulations in Ostrobothnia was G. A. Piper, the provincial governor from 1746 to 1761; he had earlier farmed in southern Sweden, where village regulations and aldermen had become common in the sixteenth century.[32] The functions of the village meeting were extensive:[33]

> The village council had, among other things, to decide on the cultivation and crop sequence within the common fences, on when the fields should be opened for grazing and when the grazing ought to end, on when hay-harvesting and reaping should be begun; on the regulations for timber-felling; on the inspection of ditches, fences and gates; on the

repair of road sections between the dwellings and the properties; on fire inspection, and much more.

The village alderman was empowered to levy fines on villagers who did not observe the regulations. Villages were able to add paragraphs to the model set of regulations to take into account local conditions, as well as to decide on the amounts of the fines, although in theory the rulings had no legal force until ratified in court. A number of the functions of the village meeting ceased to be applicable after the Great Partition. Most villages, however, retained some land in common, and common grazing of the forest during the summer and meadows in the autumn after the hay harvest continued to be customary. Henric Wegelius, in his description of Vörå in 1825, referred to the existence in every village of regulations providing for the annual election of an alderman, who with two assistants was responsible for checking the maintenance of fences, fire hearths, drainage channels and roads, and for the supervision of pasturing regulations. The alderman called village meetings to discuss economic and other matters by sending round the *budkavle*, a short staff passed from farm to farm in a set order.[34] It was common for the main meeting of the year to be held on 13 January (unless this fell on a Sunday). This meeting was called the Twentieth-Day Council (13 January being the twentieth day of Christmas in Scandinavia), and at it the alderman was elected, the village accounts for the previous year presented, the use or disposal of common property decided, and other matters of general concern to the village community discussed. Commonly owned areas were often leased out at the village meeting, which also took care of the income. In coastal villages, fishing-waters and emergent land were frequently involved. By the beginning of the twentieth century, the village regulations had lost much of their force in many villages as their provisions had become outdated. This was particularly true in inland villages, where the reallocations of land which began towards the end of the nineteenth century eliminated most categories of common land and replaced the typical agglomerated Ostrobothnian village by dispersed settlement. After the reform of local government in 1865, furthermore, commune administrations took over certain responsibilities of the village communities such as road maintenance. While regular village meetings ceased to be held in many inland villages in the early decades of the twentieth century, the need to regulate fishing-waters and emergent land meant that village meetings continued to function in most coastal villages.

Village records, in particular the minute books of village meetings, are often valuable sources of information on the regulation of unpartitioned emergent land. The traditional use of emergent land for natural meadow, reed fodder and pasture continued well into the twentieth century. Ancient customs of communal village labour were maintained on emergent land in Kärklax. The work of draining and fencing an emergent lake was shared out on the basis of *mantal* according to records of the later-nineteenth century. The minutes of a village meeting in 1919 record that to thatch a hay barn on emergent land one sheaf of straw from the rye harvest was to be given for every ½ *mantal* owned. The leasing of emergent land provided a source of income for village communities. During the 1800s in particular, it was often the landless population who leased the land, while the village landowners, who were the only ones represented in the village meeting, disposed of the income. As early as 1793, the village meeting in Replot submitted to the district court for ratification an agreement which included a provision forbidding cottagers to graze animals on common pasture and meadows without payment.[35] Accounts kept in Kärklax in the 1860s record the leasing of reed- and hay-harvesting rights on emergent land to both farmers and crofters, while a record from 1842 refers to the leasing of the emergent land on the southern side of Maxmo fladan to the owner of the adjoining *urfjäll*.

A series of disputes involving an area owned by Kärklax at the mouth of the Kyrönjoki illustrates some of the problems arising from land emergence. The former island Mälsor and the fishing-waters on its northern side belonged, according to court judgements of 1548 and 1631, half each to Kärklax and Vassor villages. Kärklax's half of the island was delimited at the Great Partition, and its share of the fishing-waters was demarcated in 1821 after a dispute with Vassor. By the mid-nineteenth century, the water was becoming overgrown by reeds. The Kärklax village accounts record the leasing of the reed and rush harvest to inhabitants of Vassor by auction in 1869 and later years. In 1881, the Kärklax villagers sued the crofters on Mälsor for allegedly damaging the reed fodder by sailing their boats through it in various directions. The crofters argued that the only way to reach open water was to pass through the reeds which, at this time, provided almost the only winter fodder for the poorer landless, who had no meadows of their own and were too poor to rent any. In 1910, Kärklax's land on Mälsor was exchanged at the land reallocation in Vassor for a strip of land adjoining the Kärklax boundary, but the water area at Mälsor was unaffected and the reed fodder continued to be auctioned to the Vassor villagers. Kärklax temporarily lost possession of the area when a demarcation of water boundaries completed in 1914 awarded it to Vassor, but on appeal won the area back five years later. The two villages failed to agree on an exchange of the area for water elsewhere because Kärklax was unwilling to lose the value of the reed fodder. Disputes continued to arise. In 1920, Kärklax sued eleven Vassor inhabitants who 'unlawfully from spring 1920 until last midsummer had grazed their cows and horses on the said water area', and in 1924 Kärklax brought to court a farmer from Vassor for unlawfully cutting thirty-three alder trees from the emergent land at Mälsor. A firm boundary was established in 1935 when the old shoreline was demarcated, indicating that Kärklax owned 26.16 ha of emergent land, 63.34 ha of reed growth and 10·26 ha of water. The boundary was highly irregular and ran through the farmyards of the adjoining Vassor owners living along the old shore. The problem was finally solved when most of the area was exchanged at a New Partition in Vassor in 1964. Kärklax received instead a water area and an area of artificially reclaimed land. The latter was sold in 1968 to the State to provide additional land for farm enlargement.

The auctioning of rights to use common property was formerly widespread in the Vaasa area. In Kärklax, where the system has continued to the present time, the leasing of emergent land is related to five-yearly auctions of fishing-waters, at which specific areas are leased to the highest bidder. Village documents from the 1930s in Björköby record the annual auction of commonly owned land, smaller islands being used for sheep pasture and the emergent shores of larger islands for hay harvesting. Tottesund adopted an annual auction of emergent land and fishing-waters when the village meeting was instituted in 1930, after the redemption of crofts on the Tottesund estate. All the crofters had possessed rights to use the estate's fishing-waters, which passed into the common ownership of the forty-one new holdings which came into being. Tottesund provides an unusual example of the late adoption of the traditional system, including the election of an alderman and the institution of the procedure of calling meetings by sending round the *budkavle*, which remained the practice until the late 1950s.

Auctions were frequently held at the Twentieth-Day Councils. An account from Västerhankmo described these annual meetings as one of the major events of the year. Payments for the right of harvesting commonly owned land and rents for fishing-waters were paid into the village cash-account, the property was auctioned for the next year, and the landowners agreed on disposal of the income. The meetings were lively occasions. Coffee, and earlier, spirits, were provided from the village funds.[36] The rising price of spirits can be charted from the village accounts of Kärklax in the 1870s and 1880s. Besides rents, a further income is recorded in Kärklax, Maxmo and Tottesund from periodic sales of timber from emergent land. Generally, the alderman was responsible for organizing the cutting, and the wood was sold by auction. On occasion, it fell to the alderman to compel payment from individuals who had cut wood without permission. In most villages, the income was periodically divided among landowners on the basis of *mantal*. The villagers decided at the meetings whether to share out the income and what to allocate for general village purposes. The account book for Kärklax between 1865 and 1926 is representative: the income helped to pay the costs of court cases involving the village; land-survey costs; the construction, roofing and upkeep of hay barns on the emergent land; road construction and maintenance; bridge repairs; the upkeep of the village school and church buildings; the fencing of commonly owned land, and general costs of administration. Later expenditure included periodic grants to the youth club and prayer-house society (the latter after providing the village meeting with coffee), and during World War II food and money were sent to villagers at the front. In Björköby, where the income was not shared out, it was used to provide loans to individual villagers and co-operative enterprises such as the village saw- and flour-mill and the electricity co-operative. In some villages, it was traditional to employ a smith, who received payment from the village and rights to use certain areas of commonly owned land. The village chest of Björköby contains a contract of this nature dated 1825, while in Maxmo the village supported a smith after World War II. In Kärklax, an emergent area and the adjoining rush growth were leased to the village smith in 1860 for a small rent, one of the conditions being that he should work for the Kärklax villagers in preference to outsiders. The agreement seems to have held good until 1884, when the minutes of the village meeting record that, as the smith had moved to Tottesund, legal measures were to be taken to recover the emergent land. At the ensuing court case, a copy of a contract renewal of 1869 was produced, showing that the villagers had guaranteed the smith regular payment for his services, agreed to build him a house and smithy, and allowed him rent-free use of the emergent land, reed harvest and an area of arable land and meadow. The smith claimed that the villagers had not fulfilled their side of the contract by ending his payment after his removal to Tottesund, while the villagers claimed they had been deprived of his services. The smith was found guilty of breach of contract, and had to surrender the emergent land as well as pay costs.

Besides providing hay and reeds, emergent land was valued as pasture. The traditional pasturing system in much of the Vaasa area was for livestock to graze the forests during the summer and be transferred to harvested meadows from August until October. Formerly, spring grazing of the meadows for a few days in mid-May was usual; it was forbidden in the model village regulations of 1742 because it damaged grass growth, but the practice continued in many places after this. In coastal villages, it was often customary in the autumn for the more extensive areas of emergent meadow land to be grazed in common. In Västerhankmo, where a large part of the meadow was on recently emerged sea bottom, cattle were pastured in common after the hay harvest on Fjärden, a former bay at the mouth of the Kyrönjoki, until the reallocation of holdings in 1914.[37] Fjärden had been mapped as water in 1758, but the harvesting of reeds and rushes had led to a partition of the emerging land in 1791. In Sundom, common grazing continued in the autumn on Söderfjärden until the farm structure began to be improved by the proper subdivision of holdings in the early decades of this century; cultivation began to encroach on the natural meadows of the bay even before the draining of Söderfjärden in the 1920s. In Björköby, old pasturing customs have continued in attenuated form until the present day. Cattle and horses are still permitted to graze freely in the forest and on the natural pastures of the emergent shores. The former system of pasturing in Björköby and other island communities was described by Smeds in 1950:[38]

> The old system, still persisting to some extent, has been to reserve a fenced-off part of the main islands exclusively for summer pasturing. Here no meadow clearings are made, and here cattle graze until haymaking is finished in the rest of the island, when the gates are opened and the cattle are allowed to pasture everywhere.

The north-eastern part of Björköby's main island, the part that emerged first, was known locally as 'Öjen' (=Ön, The Island) and consisted of stony forest and poor grazing land; this was the area reserved for summer pasturing. The hay land was situated in the south and west of the island, where there were extensive meadows on the emergent shores and former lakes. On these, simply referred to as 'Ängarna' (The Meadows), cattle grazed from May to mid-

June, when the order was given by the village alderman to move them to Öjen to allow the hay to grow. The cattle were allowed back into Ängarna in August after the hay harvest. Horses were restricted to Öjen until August, when they too were allowed into Ängarna. The alderman supervised the arrangements and was responsible for seeing to the upkeep of the fence and gates between the two areas. In the 1930s, owing to intakes from the forest for cultivation and the increasing number of cattle, Öjen was enlarged by moving the fence southwards. Farmers who lost the use of meadows as a consequence were allotted in compensation the use of the emergent meadow land on another island called Luvören. Until the 1950s, hay from emergent meadows was an important part of the local economy. The general practice was for landowners to harvest the hay on the emergent land adjoining their property. They could also cut wood for their own use, but not for sale. The boundaries across the emergent land were not always simple extensions of property boundaries in a straight line, but by local custom followed the line of former inlets lying between holdings. The old system of grazing on the main island came to an end by agreement at the village meeting in 1951, when the fence was removed and the whole island became common grazing throughout the summer. The harvesting of hay on unfenced emergent land ended largely at the same time. In recent years, common grazing of livestock has declined as greater interest has been shown in forest improvement, and in 1969 the village instituted a grazing-fee for the remaining cattle and horses pastured in common.

The system of common grazing in Björköby and the other villages of the Replot archipelago had been recognized in agreements made at the Great Partition in the 1770s to leave most of the forest and pasture unpartitioned. When in Björköby these areas were partitioned among the individual landowners in the mid-nineteenth century, the villagers agreed that common grazing of their forest holdings would continue. The smaller islands and skerries, which mostly remained in common ownership, provided summer pasture for sheep. Sheep-pasturing had been abandoned on the main island in Björköby after a verdict of the provincial governor in 1766 had restricted sheep to the smaller islands because there was insufficient pasture on the main island for sheep as well as cattle and horses. An undated document in the village chest, apparently predating this verdict, refers to an attempt to restrict grazing on the meadows to milch cattle; one villager complained to the district court that not all the villagers were keeping the agreement, but that sheep and horses had broken fences and trampled the meadows, resulting in insufficient hay. Similar problems evidently occurred in Replot, where an agreement of 1833 included a provision forbidding the grazing of sheep and horses on the main island before haymaking.[39] Sheep-pasturing on the smaller islands was not unaccompanied by disputes. While at first shores acted as natural barriers, enabling animals to be kept without supervision or fencing, the gradual coalescence of islands owing to land emergence allowed animals to pass from one island to another. In the 1870s the inhabitants of Björköby were involved in several disputes with the mainland owners of other islands in the vicinity, because sheep put to graze by the mainlanders on their own islands were crossing to islands belonging to Björköby, and damaging meadows there. In one case, the Björköby inhabitants auctioned forty-two sheep belonging to owners in Höstves, who had ancient grazing rights on the island of Börsskäret (Stora Björkarskär). The sheep had wandered across to Hålörarna, where Björköby farmers harvested sedges on the emergent land. The case reached the Senate, which in 1878 confirmed the decision of the lower court that the Björköby villagers had acted legally but were to reimburse the Höstves owners with the remainder of the auction sum after the damage had been compensated for.

The system of pasturing sheep on the skerries in Björköby is related both to the traditional rotation of fishing-waters among groups of farms and to the harvesting of hay from the emergent shores of larger islands. The farms are grouped into three divisions, each of which is divided into two arms. The waters of the outer skerry guard undergo a six-year rotation, each arm using the same area every sixth year, while the inner waters, under an agreement of 1878, undergo a three-year rotation among the three divisions. Earlier, according to a document of 1763, a three-year rotation seems to have applied to the fishing-waters as a whole. The sheep islands are also divided into six groups and rotated. The old system is now becoming less binding than earlier. Fishing has declined in the shallowing or emerging inner waters, while new fishing-grounds farther away lie outside the rotation. With the agreement of the village owners, who established a fishing administration in 1953, the remaining professional fishermen tend to be independent of the rotation. The keeping of sheep has also declined, and in 1972 a three-year rotation of the islands was instituted on an experimental basis. The sheep are taken to the skerries in May, where they stay until haymaking on the unfenced emergent meadows of the islands of Lappörarna and Slåttskäret is completed; the sheep are then moved to these islands until October, when they are communally rounded up and brought home. Formerly, there were separate round-ups on Lappörarna and Slåttskäret, but owing to the reduced number of sheep the round-ups since 1964 have alternated between the islands. The old systems of pasturing and of harvesting hay on emergent land have gradually declined in response to economic changes favouring intensive rather than extensive farming.

Towns, as well as rural communities, find themselves beset by problems of emergent land. At the beginning of the present century, Vaasa (then Nikolaistad) expropriated 1·85 ha of new land, including docks, jetties and quays, and 83·59 ha of water around Palosaari. While the town owned most of the island, the water and emergent land belonged to Gerby. The corporation has followed a policy of expropriating or purchasing water areas within the town boundaries owned by outside villages, enabling it to regulate the use of both water and emergent land and to control shore development.

Where emergent land adjoins *urfjäll*, leasing can often secure integration of land use despite differences of tenure. After the dispute between Maxmo and Kärklax over the emergent land south of Maxmo fladan was settled in 1923, it became customary for the Maxmo villagers owning the *urfjäll* to lease the adjoining emergent land at the auctions. Another dispute between Kärklax and two Maxmo villagers arose in 1920 over the use of the emergent land adjoining the latters' *urfjäll* at Bodholmen. Kärklax successfully petitioned the county governor to order the two villagers to surrender the emergent land which they had been 'unlawfully occupying and using'. An agreement was then reached allowing the two villagers to lease the land. Apart from the areas at Maxmo fladan, the traditional leasing of emergent land for pasture came to an end in Kärklax in the 1950s. From 1959 onwards, emergent land, especially small islands, was leased for summer cottages. A demarcation completed in 1972 has permitted the village to regularize the position of users of emergent land by drawing up lease contracts. Policy has been to restrict the leasing of emergent land to the village's inhabitants or landowners.

The gradual disappearance of the traditional uses of emergent land regulated by long-established customs, and the appearance of new uses, has been accompanied by the replacement of the old village meetings in the Vaasa area by part-owners' meetings provided for under the 1940 Act on Common Areas. In practice, this has meant the adoption of new regulations and the modification of the village meeting and administrative system to meet the requirements of the 1940 Act. Many coastal villages of the Vaasa area set up 'an ordered and permanent administration of common property' during the 1950s and 1960s. This has provided a practical solution to the problems caused by the increased number of landowners which, while making the rational management of commonly owned emergent land increasingly difficult under the old requirement of unanimity, also rendered the traditional form of partition unsuitable as a means of dealing with emergent areas. In Replot, formal administrations were established not only for the village as a whole but also for two groups of holdings owning areas in common as a result of the Partition of Emergent Land in 1910.

The patterns of land tenure and use that have developed on unpartitioned emergent land are examples of actual solutions which depend on local conventions functioning as alternatives to the model set out by the land-partition legislation. Although often influenced by the legislation, the application of local conventions has also reflected the strength of customs and traditions. Traditions of use regulated by the village community, which were widespread before the Great Partition, have often remained in existence on emergent land long after they disappeared elsewhere. Owing to changing circumstances in recent years, administration by the local community has been facilitated by the establishment in most villages of formal administrations for common areas under the 1940 Act, so that local conventions now operate in these cases within the framework of an additional type of model solution provided for by legislation.

Disputed Fishing-waters and Emergent Land in the Vaasa Archipelago

The partition of a large part of the Vaasa archipelago at the Great Partition among a multiplicity of owners from numerous mainland villages created a land-tenure pattern which is unparalleled in other parts of Finland. The partition, regulating a complexity of private fishing and pasture rights in a largely uninhabited skerry guard, had a profound influence on later settlement and ownership rights. The settlement of the archipelago by crofters in the eighteenth century rapidly expanded during the nineteenth in response to continued population growth and increasing pressure on land. In the Maxmo and Vörå skerry guard, there were some 100 crofts and cottagers' holdings by the early twentieth century.[40] In Replot, Vallgrund and Söderudden, the number of crofter and landless households reached a peak of 261 in 1900.[41] When by the post-independence land reforms the crofters purchased their holdings, these continued to be registered within their original villages (Fig 38). The settlements that grew up after the Great Partition are not separate villages for purposes of land registration. The land belonging to a group of farms or even a single farm is, as a consequence, frequently divided among holdings registered in different mainland villages. This circumstance leads to a fundamental difference between the young settlements of the archipelago and the old-established villages in respect of ownership rights to water and emergent land.

According to the normal interpretation of water-ownership rights, the village owns the water lying nearer its shore than another village's, unless the water is owned by some other specified legal right. Within each village, the water belongs in common to the village landowners. In normal circumstances, the boundaries laid down at the Great Partition between the possessions of the mainland villages in the skerry guard would have automatically determined water ownership. The water, and hence emergent land, adjoining a holding allotted to an owner in a particular village would belong in common to all the landowners of that village. This would mean, however, that farms which have never possessed fishing-rights nor owned land in the archipelago would none the less own shares in the water and emergent land.

An alternative interpretation is that the unique historical development of ownership rights and the unusual nature of the Great Partition in the Vaasa archipelago render it a special case. Before the marking of village boundaries on the mainland, which automatically determined village ownership offshore, the land (except in the case of meadows and fields), and hence the water, was frequently in the common ownership of all the landowners of several villages. This was not the case in a large part of the Vaasa archipelago, where islands were generally not the common property of villages or groups of villages at all; each island was owned by an individual landowner or, usually, in common by a group of land-owners, often from different villages. At the Great Partition, each owner's share depended on previous ownership; had the archipelago been regarded as common property, it would have been divided as a whole between villages on the basis of *mantal*. The individual parcels had the status of *utjordar*, independent properties belonging to farms on the mainland. That most of these properties carried rights to offshore waters is evident from their historical

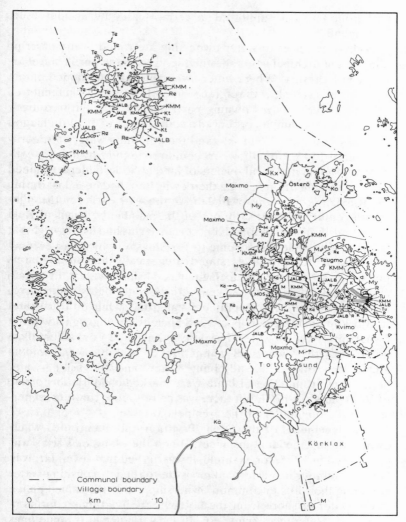

Fig 38   Village boundaries in Maxmo commune. Villages: B = Bertby; JALB = Jörala, Andiala, Lomby and Bergby; K = Kvimo; Kar = Karvsor; KMM = Koskeby, Miemois and Mäkipää; Ko = Kovjoki; Kr = Kaitsor; Kt = Karvat; Kx = Kantlax; Kä = Kärklax; L = Lotlax; Lx = Lålax; M = Maxmo village; MOS = Mullo, Ojaniemi and Saarensivu; My = Myrberg; O = Oxkangar; Or = Oravais; P = Palvis; R = Rökiö; Re = Rejpelt; T = Tottesund; Te = Teugmo; Tu = Tuckur.
SOURCE: National Board of Land Survey, Helsinki

background and is supported in certain cases by ancient court judgements.

Some references to water ownership are found in the descriptions of the archipelago made for the tax assessment in the mid-eighteenth century. Where water ownership was mentioned, it was in most cases stated, with reference to earlier court judgements, as belonging to the farms owning particular islands. Farmers from Vähäkyrö, for example, produced a court record of 1711 indicating that they had owned Finnskat and the adjoining water at Söderudden since 1545. Not all owners could prove their ownership conclusively: some mainland owners of land at Söderudden explained that the documents indicating their ownership had been lost during the Russian occupations of Finland in the wars earlier in the eighteenth century. The descriptions of the mainland villages of Böle and Smedsby also mentioned that certain farms had fishing-rights at their islands, while the documents for Singsby, which had become virtually cut off from the sea, stated categorically that only the farms possessing land in the archipelago owned fishing-waters. In certain cases, mainlanders possessed land without water rights, for example the owners of *urfjäll* in Replot and Vallgrund, while on Börsskäret in Björköby mainlanders possessed ancient grazing-rights without ownership of land or water. The description of the Vörå archipelago noted that the owners of a number of islands in the middle archipelago owned the adjoining water, and the fishing-water boundaries around these islands were marked on Wislander's map of Vörå parish in 1767, but there was no reference to water ownership in the remainder of the archipelago.

The documents of the Great Partition only mentioned water ownership in individual instances. When the island of Värlax was partitioned in 1795, for example, it was agreed that seven farms in Petsmo and four in Västerhankmo were to retain the fishing-water adjoining their lots in common ownership, while the same applied to the water offshore from the holdings received by six farms in Jungsund. References made to old legal judgements sometimes included statements relating to fishing-waters. The agreement of 1730 concerning Långholmen made it clear that the surrounding waters were owned by a group of landowners from different villages, not by the villages as a whole. The owners of Muston, south of Teugmo, also had exclusive ownership of the adjoining waters. Muston had originally formed part of Teugmo, in which village a three-tenth's share had belonged to a number of mainland owners by legal judgements of 1555 and 1583. When their share was marked out in 1723, they were allotted Muston 'with the surrounding islands, fishing-weirs and fishing-waters'. In several other cases where fishing-waters around islands were clearly demarcated, the Great Partition documents indicated that the water was in common ownership. However, it was left unclear how the ownership of water and future emergent land was affected by the land exchanges undertaken in conjunction with the partition. The fishing-waters around Köklot, for example, were in the common ownership of the island's part-owners, who included farmers from Vörå, Mustasaari, Vähäkyrö and Isokyrö. As a result of the Great Partition, part of the Vörå owners' land on Köklot was exchanged for land owned in the Vörå archipelago by farmers from Mustasaari and Vähäkyrö. However, no specific mention was made of any change in water ownership. Similarly, within the Vörå archipelago, water ownership was not mentioned in the exchanges involving islands such as Lövholmen, to which belonged 51 · 89 ha of fishing-waters according to the Great Partition documents; before the partition, Lövholmen belonged to holdings in the villages of Tuckur, Rejpelt (Rekipelto) and Lotlax, and afterwards entirely to holdings in Tuckur.

One of the few exchanges specifically mentioning fishing-water occurred in 1789 between Kvimo and Oxkangar villages. Kvimo's holding on the former island of Jenäsör, which had become joined to Oxkangar, was cut off by a boundary change from the shore, and it was agreed that the ownership of water here would be transferred to Oxkangar. Ownership of Jenäsör and the surrounding fishing-waters had been awarded to 'Kvimo village and its partners' (the latter being farmers from Tuckur) by a court judgement of 1478, after a dispute with Teugmo. A complaint against Oxkangar, which had tried to claim fishing-rights here, was upheld in 1658. Kvimo's share of Jenäsör amounted to nine-tenths, but this was reduced by the exchange of out-village islands within Kvimo for land on Jenäsör in 1779. Except in two cases, there is no record that these out-village islands owned water rights. In 1792, Kvimo requested from the land-partition court a clarification of ownership to emergent land and fishing-waters around Jenäsör and other islands belonging to outside villages. The court found, however, that Kvimo's claims to the fishing-waters and emergent land at these places were no hindrance to the Great Partition, since the question of water ownership was not inseparable from land ownership, and that therefore the case was outside its jurisdiction. The court also failed to give a ruling on whether or not water ownership was affected by the land exchanges undertaken at the Great Partition in the Vörå archipelago, despite a request by the land-surveyor in 1792 for a decision as to 'whether the parts of the farms which by legal judgement have fishing-waters at their skerries and islands can be transferred from these places to the other skerries and islands'.

As a land operation, the Great Partition was not concerned with water ownership and, as the Kvimo case made clear, a dispute over water ownership which did not hinder the carrying out of the partition on land was of no concern. Consequently, no complete inventory was made of water-ownership rights, which stayed in the same confused state as prevailed on land before the Great Partition. Much of the Vaasa archipelago lay outside village boundaries and was subject to special ownership rights. Between 1904 and 1924, fishing-water boundaries in the Vaasa archipelago were demarcated in accordance with the 1902 law. In Maxmo and Vörå, the boundaries marked were those appearing on Wislander's map of Vörå parish in 1767 (Fig 39). The islands which had their own water boundaries were regarded as constituting separate areas of common ownership, within which the water belonged to the owners of the islands. The remainder of 'Vörå and Maxmo parishes' common archipelago' was regarded as forming a separate area of common ownership, within which it was not necessary for the time being to mark other than the peripheral boundary. The demarcation in fact did little to clarify water ownership in the archipelago. As Moring pointed out, a demarcation of water boundaries merely distinguishes areas belonging to different ownerships and does not mean that the whole water area within a boundary is common to all those owning property there, even if this is stated in the demarcation documents.[42]

The confused water ownership in much of the archipelago applied equally to emergent land. At the time of the Great Partition, land which had already emerged was included in the partition, while land which might emerge in the future was scarcely considered. In practice, the emergent land has subsequently been dealt with in different ways, depending on the interpretations of different land-surveyors. Where their solutions have been ratified without appeal by the landowners, they have come to have legal force.

Mainland owners showed little awareness of land emergence in the archipelago during the nineteenth and early twentieth centuries. Many of the mainland villages had lost their coastal location by the time of the Great Partition, while others became cut off from the sea during the nineteenth century. Pasture and fishing-rights on distant island possessions gradually declined in importance for the main-

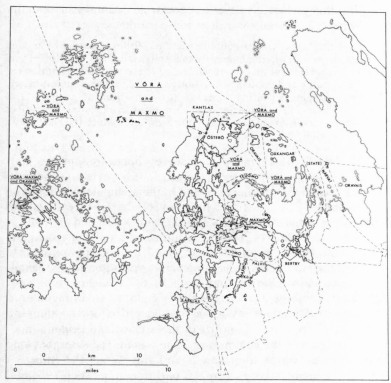

Fig 39   Ownership of fishing-waters in the Maxmo, Vörå and Oravais archipelago. The fishing-water boundaries are those marked on Gullic Wislander's map of Vörå Parish in 1767 (redemarcated 1904–14), with the addition of the water boundaries demarcated around Österö and the adjoining part of northern Västero in 1971. Underlined names are commune names and indicate that the fishing-waters have not been partitioned among individual villages or groups of owners. Abbreviations: K = Kvimo; Kr = Kaitsor; Kä = Kärklax; M = Maxmo village; MOS = Mullo, Ojaniemi and Saarensivu; O = Oxkangar; Tu = Tuckur. Village names indicate which village the owners of the water area are registered in; this does not imply in every case that the water area belongs in common to the whole village.

landers, whose archipelago holdings were occupied by crofters or began to be worked for forestry. Crofters generally used the land emerging at their holdings without hindrance. Contracts from the early twentieth century for crofts situated on Lövholmen (belonging to Tuckur) and Muston (on land belonging to Andiala) specifically stated that the crofters enjoyed the right of using the emergent land. Many of the mainland owners were uncertain of the exact location of their land in the archipelago and never visited it.

The situation was vividly described by Gustav Alm, in a short story set probably in Mickelsörarna at this period:[43]

> Up on the higher points could be seen old fishing-boat harbours and patterns of stones, reminders of men who laboured and toiled and procured themselves rights out here ... There were also traditions of land disputes and conflicts over outlying land, which resulted in one stone belonging to a farm long distant to the south and another to a farm equally far away to the east, and in the mainlanders knowing themselves to be the owners of land and water, the location of which they had only a vague notion.

The way in which many land-survey operations in the late-nineteenth and early twentieth centuries were carried out suggests that the ownership of emergent land in the archipelago aroused no special interest at this time. In many of the land reallocations undertaken in the villages of Vörå, the land which had emerged in the archipelago since the Great Partition was not distinguished, but simply included in the holdings it adjoined; no attempt was made to partition the emergent land among part-owners according to *mantal*. In two cases, Bertby and Rejpelt, the villagers specifically decided that emergent land in the skerry guard would be included in the adjoining holdings, as it was considered of little value and difficult to demarcate. As crofts in the archipelago became independent holdings, the common practice was for the emergent land to be included within their new boundaries. When the emergent land on the mainland of Bertby was partitioned between 1931 and 1934, the emergent land in the archipelago was excluded because it had been included by the deeds of purchase in the newly redeemed holdings. In Jörala, Andiala, Lomby and Bergby, which jointly instituted a New Partition in 1932, the parts of the original holdings which had been sold or redeemed were demarcated at an early stage in the proceedings. Although the documents clearly stated whether or not the new holdings in the archipelago had shares in common property belonging to the village or parent holdings, the adjacent emergent land was nevertheless included within the boundaries of the new holdings. From the maps of the new holdings on Muston, Jenäsör and Särkimo, it can be calculated that 42·27 ha had emerged between 1792 and 1935, an average of 1·32 ha for each of the 32 holdings involved and a total increase in area of 10·94 per cent. Moreover, more than 20 per cent of the arable land and more than one-half of the meadow on these holdings were situated on the emergent land. No appeal was made within the stipulated period against the way in which the emergent land was dealt with.

In a few cases, emergent land at holdings belonging to mainland villages in the archipelago was demarcated and left in common, although it was not always clear whether the part-owners were all the village landowners or only those with land in the archipelago. A few land reallocations included emergent land in the archipelago with other commonly owned land in the village, and shared it among all landowners according to *mantal*, as occurred at the reallocations completed in Västerhankmo in 1914, Jungsund in 1916, and Böle in 1930. Böle owned water in common with Smedsby offshore from the two villages' holdings at Söderudden. A partition of Smedsby's land at Söderudden, based on *mantal*, was ratified in 1894 and included the adjoining emergent land. When Böle's land at Söderudden was partitioned a few years later, it was observed that the emergent land should have been partitioned between the two villages first. The Böle owners remained content with demarcating the emergent land next to their own holdings, amounting to nearly 90 ha, and straightening the boundary by minor exchanges. A request for a Partition of Emergent Land in Böle led in 1917 to a New Partition being initiated. During the proceedings, the Smedsby villagers claimed a share in the emergent land adjoining Böle's holdings at Söderudden on the grounds that the water was common to both villages. This was rejected by the land-surveyor, who ruled that the boundary between Smedsby's and Böle's emergent land had been in effect demarcated in 1894 when the partition in Smedsby had included the adjoining emergent land. The land-surveyor's decision was finally accepted after a series of court cases, including two appeals to the Supreme Court.

In some land-survey operations, archipelago holdings (with their emergent land) were treated implicitly or explicitly as independent of the mainland villages. A repartition of the island of Västerö, ratified in 1878, included 25 ha of meadow and 30 ha of forest on land which had emerged since the mapping for the Great Partition in 1788. At land reallocations ratified in Hälsingby and Vikby in 1915 and 1916 respectively, the archipelago holdings were treated separately, being simply subdivided among their part-owners according to *mantal* without distinguishing emergent land. The procedure was similar at the New Partitions concluded in Karperö and Koskö in 1932 and 1933 respectively. At the New Partition in Singsby, concluded in 1928, the emergent land was mapped and included in a division of the archipelago holdings among their owners on the basis of *mantal*. The holdings consisted of two areas in the Replot archipelago which were dealt with separately from each other. In one case, there were 9·05 ha of emergent land, amounting to 30 per cent of the total area, which was divided among 12 owners; in the second case, the 12·78 ha of emergent land accounted for 41 per cent of the total area, which was shared among 4 owners.

The first Partition of Emergent Land in the archipelago outside the old-established villages was in combination with a New Partition on Ulot, in the Maxmo archipelago, in the 1930s (Fig 40). Ulot and the surrounding fishing-waters, which were clearly delimited, had been left at the Great Partition in the common ownership of six farms in Vähäkyrö parish. The island was partitioned in 1853, each farm receiving one-sixth, but the land which had emerged since the Great Partition was not included. Since the mid-eighteenth century, Ulot had been settled by Swedes from the neighbouring villages in Vörå and Maxmo; the Swedes leased the land from its Finnish-speaking owners, although the latter continued to fish at Ulot until about 1870. Ulot passed into the ownership of its Swedish-speaking inhabitants by the post-independence land reforms, although remaining in the original villages in Vähäkyrö for land registration. At the New Partition, the two northernmost holdings retained their old properties with the addition of their shares of the emergent land. The basis of partition for the emergent land was the same as for the whole island in 1853: the land was divided by value into six equal parts, corresponding to the original six holdings. The two northernmost holdings received their allocation along their shores, although the boundaries reflected the old coastline in certain places, making the holdings somewhat irregular in shape. The remainder of the emergent land was included in the reallocation of holdings on the rest of the island, each owner receiving his share of the value both of the old holdings and the emergent land on the basis of *mantal*. Finally, part of the irregularity in the shape of the holdings caused by the combination of a New Partition and a Partition of Emergent Land was eliminated by a land exchange. The island was divided into twelve parcels, although there were only eight farms; some landowners owned shares in more than one land-registration village, but in these cases their parcels were placed contiguously. The emergent land amounted to 26·98 ha, an increase in the island's area of 25 per cent. The average increase per landowner was more than 3 ha. The partition can be regarded as a successful example of an actual solution corresponding to the model solution of legislation.

A recent New Partition began in 1966 on Österö and part of

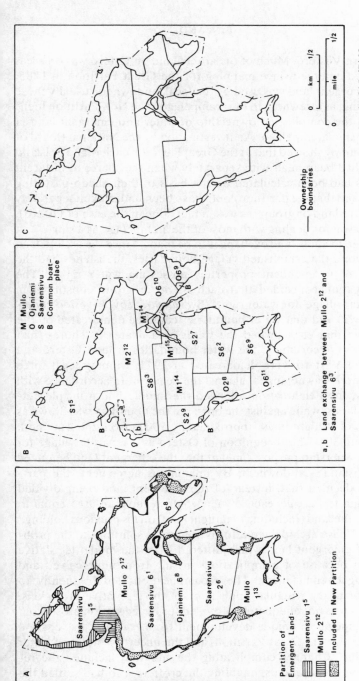

Fig 40   The Partition of Emergent Land and New Partition on Ulot, in the Maxmo archipelago: (A) Partition of Emergent Land, 1935; (B) New Partition of Emergent Land, 1937; (C) Landowner holdings, 1937. Numbers are property register numbers in each village.
SOURCE: National Board of Land Survey, Helsinki

northern Västerö. Much of the arable land on Österö was on areas that had emerged since mapping for the Great Partition in 1785. The emergent land was used by the local landowners, usually those adjoining, as elsewhere in the archipelago. The New Partition highlighted the complicated ownership of water and emergent land in the Maxmo archipelago. An investigation by the National Board of Land Survey showed that at the Great Partition each island or island group had been dealt with separately when the shares of different owners had been calculated on the basis of their sheep-pasturing rights, and that the partition could have been undertaken separately for each island or group (as was in fact done in the case of Österö). The reason for dealing with most of the archipelago as a single unit had been to allow land exchanges to be made. Since the archipelago lay beyond the established village boundaries, the islands had the nature of independent properties possessing water rights. The investigation concluded that each island or group constituted a separate 'village' for water rights (Sw *vattenrättsby*, Fi *vesioikeudellinen kylä*) and that water boundaries could be demarcated on the principle that each owned the water area nearer its shores than another's. Accordingly, the water boundaries around Österö and northern Västerö were demarcated in 1971, winning legal force when there was no appeal against the decision. In accordance with the law, the demarcation followed the middle-line principle between islands, while against the open sea the boundary was drawn as a series of straight lines, approximately 500 m from the 2 m depth limit (Fig 39). The recognition of Österö as a separate village for water-ownership purposes meant that the emergent land belonged to the island's landowners. By unanimous agreement, the part-owners decided that, instead of the emergent land being divided according to *mantal*, each owner would receive an area equal in value to the land (including emergent land) on his previous holding.

The Vaasa archipelago affords numerous solutions to the problems of emergent land which differed from the model legislative solution because of complications arising from unperceived and changing circumstances. These complications led frequently to errors or to the irregular application of the legislative provisions. Local factors not adequately provided for by legislation arose from the archipelago's unique development from *erämark*, its separate treatment at the Great Partition, and the uncertain status of water ownership. Changes complicating the situation included the redemption of leaseholds, enabling the crofters who had settled the archipelago in the eighteenth and nineteenth centuries to purchase their holdings, but leaving the status of water even less clear than before. Many of the land-survey operations involving the archipelago simply allotted the emergent land to adjoining holdings without any attempt at partition, and this, although not always in accordance with the law, was often the simplest solution. Conflicting interpretations regarding water-ownership rights have resulted in archipelago holdings sometimes being included in land-survey operations involving the mainland villages and sometimes being treated independently of the mainland. The Vaasa archipelago also provides examples of solutions dependent on local conventions functioning as alternatives to the model solution. The informal division of emergent land on Österö in 1837 took the unusual form of a division among tenants. Generally in the archipelago, the convention has been followed that the adjoining landowner has the right to use emergent land. This has had the consequence that adjoining owners have in many cases gained ownership through legally ratified land-survey operations, even although the procedure was irregular.

The Vaasa area shows the wide diversity in time and space of the human responses to land emergence. Local variations are produced by historical and geographical differences. At the same time, certain broad similarities are evident throughout the area as a result of the cultural and legal tradition to which it belongs. In the whole region, traditional responses are undergoing reassessment as a result of rapidly changing social and economic requirements. The special human landscape of the emerging coastlands is the final result of the complex interaction of all these factors.

8

Emergent Land and Recreation

The Transition from Agricultural to Recreational Uses of Emergent Land

THE SOCIAL CHANGES occurring in the wake of Finland's progressing industrialization, especially increasing urbanization, rising standards of living and shorter working hours, have led to new recreational needs and to new pressures on shore areas to satisfy these needs. While traditional uses of shores, such as pasture and meadow, have declined, new recreational uses have given shore areas a steadily rising value. Recreational development is not limited to the growing numbers of summer cottages. Expanding leisure-time activities such as boating, swimming and camping demand access to shores and the construction of facilities. In addition to the traditional role played by the village community in regulating emergent land, commune administrations are showing increasing interest in recreational development, both as a result of their role as the authorities granting building permits and because of the potential income for the commune from recreational activities and tourism.

The changing use of emergent land is illustrated in Figs 41 and 42 which show a wide emergent belt belonging to Maxmo village on the Kyrönjoki estuary. The southern part has mostly emerged since 1795, and was surrendered to the village at the Partition of Emergent Land earlier this century by the adjoining Church holding, which had no rights to emergent land. The northern section, adjoining Tottesund's land, is narrower, having emerged since the 1845 Partition of Emergent Land; the Maxmo villagers came to own the water here after the separation of Tottesund's fishing-waters from the rest of the village's in 1887, but Tottesund occupied the emergent land until the estate's boundaries were demarcated in 1916. The minutes of the Maxmo village meetings after this date allow the sequence of uses to be traced in detail. The meeting elected each year two villagers to take care of leasing pasture rights on the emergent land. Income also came from sales of sand and timber and from rent auctions of fishing-waters. The lease of part of the shore to a timber company as a collecting and sorting point for timber floated down the Kyrönjoki, besides providing local employment, led to a substantial increase in the village income. The village meeting decided each year whether or not to share out the income; between 1916 and 1941, it was shared out sixteen times, being divided into 450 equal shares, landowners with a larger *mantal* receiving more shares. The income ceased to be divided after 1941, providing instead the impetus for two co-operative undertakings by the villagers: a threshing co-operative and a short-lived cement-making enterprise, the latter on the emergent land to use the sand there. Interest in the emergent land for recreation began in the 1930s, when an area was leased for a children's summer camp. The first summer cottages appeared after World War II. Rented summer-cottage plots on the emergent land increased from four in 1959 to twenty in 1967. The shore has become popular for bathing, picnicking and camping, and the local youth club has a dance pavilion there. Recreational pressures have helped traditional uses to decline: whereas the whole shore was let as pasture in the inter-war period, by 1968 only part of the shore adjacent to Tottesund continued to be leased for grazing by the adjoining smallholdings.

Land use along Maxmo's western shore reflects developments on shore areas in general, emphasized by the retention of a comparatively extensive emergent area in common ownership. The adjoining landowners have no rights to the emergent land, and this prevents its integration into the adjoining land-tenure pattern, although integration of land use occurs where the Tottesund owners lease the emergent land. Their attempts to obtain ownership have been unsuccessful. In 1925, when the holdings newly redeemed by the crofters from the Tottesund estate were being marked out, compulsory exchange of the emergent land for land elsewhere was rejected because it would offer only a temporary solution to the problem, since land was emerging continuously. In 1959, the National Board of Forestry, which at that time looked after Tottesund Park, unsuccessfully requested the compulsory exchange or purchase of the northernmost section of the emergent land for

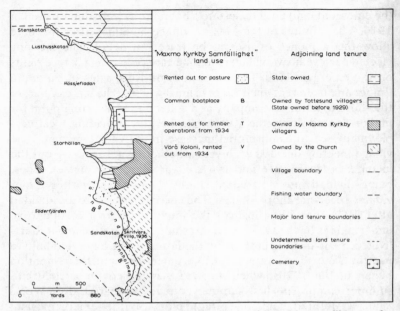

Fig 41   Inter-war land use on common land belonging to Maxmo village on the
western shore of the Maxmo peninsula. 'Maxmo Kyrkby Samfällighet' = Maxmo
village's common land. 'Vörå Koloni' = children's summer camp

development as a camping-area in accordance with the principle of
maintaining 'the historical park for public use'. The following year,
the Tottesund smallholders adjoining the emergent land requested
its compulsory purchase under a law of 1958 which allowed the
redemption of certain leased areas in rural communes. Some of the
former crofts had leased the emergent land since 1929 for supplementary pasture and watering their cattle as well as for mooring
their boats. Some had mink houses on the emergent land, while one
croft cultivated part of it. The requests were rejected, however, as
the leaseholds were not built on nor required for building and were
hence not redeemable under the 1958 law.

Within Tottesund, rights of harvesting hay and grazing cattle and
sheep on its own emergent land continued until 1962, to be
auctioned each year at the Twentieth-Day Council. Other uses were
subject to the agreement of the village meeting. At the end of the
war, when petrol was almost unobtainable, a local bus company
leased an area of the emergent land to establish a charcoal-burner
for the manufacture of charcoal gas as a petrol substitute. Rights to
use the village's shore, jetty and water for floating and loading

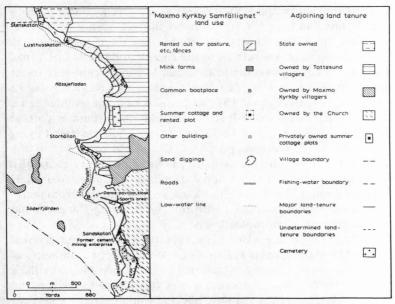

Fig 42 Present land use on common land belonging to Maxmo village on the western shore of the Maxmo peninsula. 'Maxmo Kyrkby Samfällighet' = Maxmo village's common land: (1) pasture unrented after 1961; (2) pasture unrented after 1963; (3) swimming and camping place; pasture unrented after 1961; timber operations ceased 1952, but rights leased to 1962; (4) pasture unrented after 1962; cement-mixing enterprise in operation 1947–54; first summer-cottage plots let in 1947; (5) used by Church estate.

timber for export were leased by a timber firm from 1935 to 1962. Two shore areas continued to be leased for grazing after 1962, but most of the emergent land has ceased to be important as natural pasture. The shores are, however, assuming increased significance for recreation; in 1964 one stretch of emergent land was declared a recreation area for swimming and camping.

Substantial changes are also evident in the skerry guard, where a steady improvement of communications in the form of new road links and better ferry services has occurred in the post-war period. Besides assisting the archipelago economically, improved accessibility has led to awakening interest in the skerry guard for recreation, and the sale of summer-cottage plots has provided an additional supplementary income for the archipelago's inhabitants. The development of communications in the Vaasa archipelago is illustrative. The first regular ferry service from the mainland to Replot began in 1952, and to Bergö ten years later. Road and bridge construction within the Replot skerry guard extended to Björköby in 1954 and Panike in 1962. In Maxmo, the reallocation of holdings on Österö provided the opportunity for new roads to be laid out. This development was related to the completion in 1965 of a road and bridges linking the middle and inner Maxmo archipelago to the mainland. Road and bridge construction in the Vaasa archipelago is continuing. Work began in 1972 to link Köklot to the mainland; it is expected that one result will be the stimulation of summer-cottage development on the island, and Vaasa corporation has been buying land there for recreational purposes. The recent construction of a forestry road from the mainland to the Sundom skerry guard also opens up this area for recreational dwellings. Roadless areas, particularly smaller islands close to Vaasa, are not immune from recreational pressures; associated with the rise in living-standards has been the purchase of motor boats.

In Björköby, changes due to the rapidly developing recreational demand for shore areas in the 1960s are evident from the minutes of the part-owners' meeting, which in 1959 replaced the old village meeting. In that year, the meeting was still willing to confirm the traditional right of owners to use hay and wood from the emergent land adjoining their property, and individual owners were even allowed to let summer-cottage plots on their emergent land for a maximum of five years. The right of villagers to let emergent land privately was rescinded in 1968, and existing contracts were regulated. A three-tier system of rents for summer-cottage plots was introduced, with resident village landowners paying the lowest rent, non-resident landowners paying a little more, and outsiders paying the highest rent. Rents were also introduced for the right of using emergent land next to privately owned cottage plots and for saunas built on emergent land. The village has followed a policy of refusing to sell emergent land for cottage plots, although land exchanges have been made with part-owners who wanted private access to shores adjoining their holdings. A request by the commune to purchase a stretch of shore for recreational development was also refused, although the commune was allowed to lease it. A plan was approved in 1971 to let another area of emergent land for private development as a camping-ground with holiday huts. The wide extent of the emergent land has allowed the village community some control over the location of recreational development. Half of the building permits granted for summer cottages in the period 1964-71 were for commonly owned land subject to regulation by the village part-owners' meeting. Only villagers are permitted to build summer cottages on the northern shores of the main island and in a large part of the archipelago, while in certain areas building is prohibited altogether; summer cottages belonging to outsiders are mainly concentrated on the southern shores of the island.

In parts of the Vaasa archipelago where water-ownership rights are unclear, a consequence of the new value of shore areas for recreation has been a series of ownership disputes concerning emergent land. During the late 1960s, a number of summer cottages were built without building permits on emergent land in Mickel-sörarna, the outer islands of Maxmo; retroactive permission could not be granted until ownership rights to the emergent land had been clarified. It transpired that landowners selling parts of their holdings in Mickelsörarna had also mistakenly sold rights of occupation to emergent islands long used by their families as sheep pasture (in one case for 130 years). The commune refused building permits on the grounds that the emergent areas were not private land but commonly owned, and therefore could not be sold without the agreement of all the part-owners. At least one person was compelled to move his cottage as a result. Uncertainty over ownership rights to emergent land in the Maxmo archipelago has complicated the planning of shore areas for recreation. In 1969, when Maxmo built a swimming-hut and camping facilities on emergent land at Sandska-tan, on the island of Pirklot, a dispute arose with Bertby village in Vörå, in which the adjoining holding was registered. The newly established part-owners' meeting in Bertby considered that all emergent land adjacent to the village's holdings was in their common ownership. The county council found that Maxmo commune was not the legal owners of the area nor had it leased it, and the commune was compelled to remove the buildings.

A final solution of such disputes requires a definitive settlement of the archipelago's water ownership, left unclear by the Great Partition and later land-survey operations. The question has assumed new relevance with the establishment by the mainland villages of formal administrations to take care of common property. Most mainland inhabitants last used their archipelago holdings for sheep pasture in the 1920s and 1930s, since when the holdings have been largely sold to the archipelago inhabitants. Little awareness of the villages' archipelago holdings was shown again until recently, when interest was renewed in the use of the archipelago for recreation. When Tuckur village set up a formal administration in 1968, some 260 holdings registered in the village possessed shares in common property, including holdings on the mainland and in the archipelago; all were considered to own shares in the emergent land and water adjoining the archipelago holdings. The village's main interest has focused on Lövsund, the former crofter settlement which grew up at Lövholmen on the land allotted to Tuckur owners at the Great Partition, whose holdings continued to be registered in Tuckur after they were redeemed by their tenants. The fishing-water boundaries around Lövholmen are clearly demarcated, and smaller emergent islands were used by local inhabitants as sheep pasture for several generations; in 1969, when the new administrative organ in Tuckur drew up leases for summer cottages built on one of the emergent islands, it was decided that part of the island was to be retained for the use of Tuckur villagers for swimming and recreation. Another emergent island was allowed rent-free to a Lövsund smallholder, who used it for pasture, in return for providing a car park and boatplace on his land for Tuckur villagers who wished to come to Lövsund 'to enjoy the archipelago, fish or sunbathe on the village's commonly owned land'.

Land-surveyors and lawyers are faced with the necessity of deciding between alternative interpretations regarding the ownership of water and emergent land in the archipelago. Tuckur, Bertby and other mainland villages in Vörå, which have begun to show an interest in their archipelago holdings, claim rights to emergent land according to the conventional interpretation that the village owns the fishing-waters offshore from the village's holdings. The possibility that the islands constitute separate 'villages' for water ownership has not been considered. For historical reasons, the legal situation is unclear, with the result that responses to land emergence have varied according to different interpretations. It is likely that the question will be ultimately solved in connection with a partition of water and emergent land requested by one of the disputants in Mickelsörarna, since a partition cannot be undertaken without deciding who are the part-owners of the archipelago waters. If the interpretation is accepted that the islands or island groups constitute separate units for water ownership, this would mean that only farms owning land in the archipelago at the time of the Great Partition could claim shares in water and emergent land; it would then be necessary to decide whether water ownership was included in the land exchanges. If this is assumed to be the case, as most consistent with the actual situation, the next problem is what should be the basis of partition. Since the archipelago holdings did not have their own *mantal* at the Great Partition, this cannot be the basis of partition. The *mantal* of the present archipelago holdings only indicates their value in relation to the parent holdings, not in relation to each other. It has been seen that shares to different islands were generally, although not in all cases, determined at the Great Partition on the basis of the number of sheep each owner had the right to graze. This, however, cannot provide a basis of partition where land exchanges were undertaken, as the value of each unit of sheep pasture varied on different islands, and so the exchanges were undertaken by converting each owner's sheep pasture into absolute values, which were then exchanged with each other. The values of the holdings on each island in relation to the total value of the island at the Great Partition seem to provide the logical basis of partition for the water and emergent land belonging to the island. The final problem that arises is whether the mainland farms that have sold their archipelago holdings, for example to crofters, still retain water-ownership rights. If no other agreement was made concerning water rights, the archipelago holdings should share water ownership with the parent holdings on the basis of *mantal*. Once the part-owners have been identified, disputes over summer cottages and recreational facilities built on emergent land will be more easily solved, and it will also be possible to determine which interests are responsible for regulating emergent land and other common property in the archipelago under the 1940 Act on Common Area, and also who receives the income from purchases of emergent land by adjoining owners.

In practice, the ownership of emergent land in the Vaasa archipelago will be settled by the decisions of land-surveyors in individual cases and by court cases where these decisions are challenged. The way in which emergent land has been dealt with where complications have arisen in the past has generally been left to the land-surveyor's judgement. Usually, the landowners have been satisfied, and there has been no appeal against the land-survey operation. If the law had been strictly interpreted in every case, a more complicated land-tenure pattern may have arisen than actually occurred when local conventions were followed, or unorthodox land-survey operations were undertaken. While it is possible to reverse a ratified land-survey operation found to be faulty, this is not common because of the high legal costs usually involved in relation to the value of the land. The increasing value of emergent land at the present time, however, has helped to make land-surveyors more aware of the special problems of ownership in the Vaasa archipelago. The solutions require thorough investigations of the historical development of land and water ownership in the archipelago, on which a firm case in law can be grounded.

The ownership of one area of emergent land in the Vaasa archipelago came before the Supreme Court in 1969. The case concerned the island of Teilot, the southern end of which is a holding registered in the village of Perkiö in Vähäkyrö. The adjoining waters belong partly to Petsmo and partly to Västerhankmo villages. When Petsmo's boundaries were demarcated in 1963 in connection with the New Partition, 1.75 ha of emergent land on southern Teilot was marked off as belonging to Petsmo on the assumption that the holding on the island was *urfjäll*. When the owner of the holding lodged an appeal, the land-partition court judged that southern Teilot was not *urfjäll* and was therefore entitled to the offshore waters and emergent land. The court's verdict was based on the interpretation that southern Teilot had been allocated to Perkiö village when the commonly owned land and archipelago possessions of Vähäkyrö had been partitioned at a Great Partition Complement in 1892, and that the area had been subsequently allotted to Hakala farm at a land reallocation completed in Perkiö in 1919; if southern Teilot had belonged in common to the parish before 1892, it could not be regarded as *urfjäll*, which by definition must originate as the possession of an individual farm in a village other than the one in which it is situated. Petsmo appealed against the verdict to the Supreme Court. The land-surveyor undertaking the New Partition submitted evidence that southern Teilot had never belonged in common to the parish or Perkiö village, nor had the holding originated as an independent archipelago property possessing water rights. Documents going back to the eighteenth century indicated that the area had always belonged privately to Hakala farm. On these grounds, it should be regarded as *urfjäll*. The Supreme Court judged in Petsmo's favour and quashed the verdict of the land-partition court. The owner of southern Teilot has subsequently made a request to purchase the emergent land under the 1961 law. The Teilot case does not afford a precedent for other parts of the archipelago, however, since most of the archipelago holdings registered in mainland villages differ from southern Teilot in two important respects. There is documentary evidence that the mainland owners' holdings were regarded as independent *utjordar*, and for the most part the holdings lie outside the demarcated fishing-water boundaries of the old-established villages. Only in certain individual instances can it be established that such holdings have the status of *urfjäll*. Each particular case has to be decided on its own merits.

Uncertain water ownership is not the only cause of difficulties arising from recreational development on emergent land. In the Jakobstad archipelago, the continued existence of customary tenure from the nineteenth century complicated a New Partition which began in the villages of Larsmo and Eugmo in 1954. The New Partition was necessary to overcome problems arising from fragmented and intermixed farm holdings, the result of a long series of informal subdivisions, and to regulate tenure conditions on emergent land, which accounted for 2,341 ha or $17 \cdot 6$ per cent of the two villages' total area of 13,300 ha. According to custom, the emergent land was held in general by the owners of the adjoining holdings, and included 53 ha which had been brought into cultivation. The situation of the islands within easy reach of both Jakobstad and Kokkola resulted in the leasing or sale by private landowners of a large number of summer-cottage plots to inhabitants of the two towns. By 1968, there were nearly 800 recreational dwellings, of which the majority were situated on emergent land. Although private landowners were not entitled to sell emergent land, which remained legally in common ownership, account had to be taken of tenure customs extending back more than a century. Holdings adjoining the shore had extended their boundaries as the sea receded, and the emergent land had automatically been included when holdings had been informally subdivided. Consequently, the benefit of the emergent land's enhanced value had fallen haphazardly to individual landowners instead of being distributed according to their legal shares. At the New Partition, it was necessary to find a solution that safeguarded both the rights of the owners of summer-cottage plots, whose purchase deeds were not entirely satisfactory from a legal point of view, and the rights of landowners who had not benefited from the sale of plots. According to the reallocation proposal, a holding that had sold emergent land had its share in the total emergent land reduced by an amount equal to the value of the area sold. A holding that had sold more emergent land than its share entitled surrendered an equivalent amount of its own land. Each holding was also allotted a shore length according to its *mantal*. Owners who had sold shore plots had their shores reduced accordingly. Financial compensation is payable by owners who had sold more shore than they were entitled to.

The convention that landowners have full rights to use the land emerging next to their holdings has produced problems elsewhere in the Jakobstad area. In 1961, the part-owners' meeting in Pedersöre kyrkoby requested a demarcation of their commonly owned emergent land. A number of circumstances rendered it difficult to determine where the boundary should run: the eighteenth-century maps of the Great Partition had been destroyed in Vaasa's fire of 1852; a partition of 55 ha of emergent land (mainly meadow) in the 1860s had embraced only part of the village's emergent land; many of the subdivisions of holdings since that time had incorporated adjoining emergent land, although in certain cases it had been excluded. An attempted demarcation of the land that had emerged since the 1860s met with protests from some of the part-owners, who would have been dispossessed of land allotted to their holdings by legally ratified farm subdivisions (one owner would have lost as much as 1·2 ha); furthermore, it was found that a large number of summer-cottage plots, which had been purchased from private landowners and entered without dispute in the land register as independent holdings, were partly or wholly on the wrong side of the demarcation line. The land-partition court ruled in 1968 that since there were so many uncertainties surrounding the true extent of the emergent land, while the incorporation of substantial parts of it into private holdings had passed unchallenged, the demarcation should be amended to follow the shorelines and boundaries marked on the most recent legally ratified land-survey maps.

The transition from traditional agricultural uses of emergent land to modern recreational uses has several significant consequences: the authority of the traditional village community, represented by its landowners, has been reasserted by the responsibility of the part-owners' meeting to regulate the use of the village's commonly owned emergent shores; a stimulus has been provided for the unravelling in archipelago waters and shore areas of ancient and complex tenure patterns, a process initiated on land by the Great Partition in the eighteenth century; customary tenures, often survivals of older patterns of activity, are being replaced by land-tenure patterns better suited to present-day needs and less amenable to dispute. Accompanying these developments has been the application of new land-survey operations, introduced to overcome the difficulties which traditional methods of partitioning emergent land have encountered as a result of the appearance of summer cottages and other forms of shore recreation.

New Solutions for the Parcelling of Emergent Land

The difficulties of bringing about a rational land-tenure pattern while partitioning emergent land on the basis of *mantal* were met by the 1961 amendment of the Land Partition Act: for the partition of emergent land among part-owners according to *mantal* was substituted the purchase of emergent land by adjoining landowners, if this was the only rational way in which the land could be used. One of the first villages in Finland where this procedure was adopted was Gerby, on the north side of Vaasa. Gerby is in the process of partitioning 63·16 ha of emergent land, together with 24 ha of other commonly owned land, in conjunction with a division of fishing-waters between Gerby and Vaasa. Owing to the town's proximity, 523 holdings lie on 76 km of mainland and archipelago shores; about 400 are summer-cottage plots, many not owning shares in the emergent land, initial mapping of which was completed in 1967. On the mainland, the area consisted mainly of what had emerged since mapping was undertaken in 1915 for a Partition of Emergent Land. In the archipelago, the emergent land had not been partitioned since the map used for the Great Partition was drawn in 1757. The old shorelines were marked on the new maps as accurately as possible, with levelling of the calculated height of the old shore in cases of uncertainty. Grading of the emergent land has now been carried out by a minus-points system. Each area has been given points according to its position, suitability for building summer cottages or saunas, type of land and wind direction. The best location according to each criterion received no points, the worst five or eight points. Emergent land receiving no points in all criteria will be subject to the maximum purchase price per square metre, the price being reduced in proportion to the number of points received. Land not suitable for recreational dwellings will be sold as forest land per hectare. Generally speaking, landowners will purchase the emergent land adjacent to their holdings whether they own shares or not, and disposal of the income will be decided by the part-owners' meeting. If it is decided to divided the income, each part-owner will receive a share proportional to his share in the emergent land. Part-owners with property adjoining the shore would thus be able to offset at least part of the purchase price. Many part-owners, however, would be entitled only to insignificant sums because of their small shares in the emergent land.

The Gerby case has proceeded sufficiently far to serve as a practical precedent for subsequent cases. As far as possible, the boundaries of existing holdings are simply extended to the shore, and the owners are obliged to purchase the emergent land falling within their extended boundaries. This principle is deviated from where special circumstances warrant it, for example to give an owner next to shallow water access to a boatplace on other emergent land nearby. The village can retain emergent land in common ownership, and Gerby has decided to retain a strip of shore by the village's harbour as a recreation area; the village will also retain plots of emergent land which have been leased for summer cottages. Purchase only operates where the emergent land disturbs the adjoining owner's use of his holding or if it is the best way of disposing of the emergent land. It does not apply to emergent islands or to other areas specifically left in common by earlier land-survey operations. In these cases, adjoining owners must negotiate separately with the village. Owners who have themselves artificially reclaimed land adjacent to their holdings are obliged to purchase the additional area. Owners of *urfjäll* are under the same compulsion as other owners to purchase adjoining emergent land. The procedure also allows rectification of mistakes made at earlier land-survey operations; a holding which at a boundary demarcation was allotted less land than it was entitled to is to be compensated by the parent holding purchasing on its behalf part of the adjoining emergent land. Vaasa's share of Gerby's water has been marked out in accordance with the *mantal* of the holdings owned by the town in Gerby. Adjoining landowners are here unable to purchase the emergent land, which the town has set aside as a public area. In all cases, the new procedure leaves the main responsibility with the land-surveyor to decide how the emergent land can best be disposed of regarding its rational use, subject to the right of owners to appeal to the land-partition court against the land-surveyor's decisions.

A second example of the new procedure is provided by Replot village, where it was instituted in 1969. In that year, 387 holdings owned shares in about 207 ha of emergent land which had emerged since the mapping was completed in 1906 for the previous Partition of Emergent Land. Bordering the shore were 312 holdings, of which 35 were summer-cottage plots. Since the majority of shore holdings are part-owners, the procedure in this case was comparatively simple. Each holding comes into possession of the adjoining emergent land by an extension of its boundaries, so that it receives a length of the present shore equivalent to what it owned of the old shore. Holdings which receive more than their due shares of the value of the emergent land will compensate those which receive less or nothing. The only exceptions are areas left in common at the request of the village. An interesting procedural problem arose in connection with a small island which is *urfjäll* registered in Norra Jungsund village, although it is now an independent holding used for a summer cottage. At the 1910 Partition of Emergent Land in

Replot, the emergent land surrounding the island was allotted to a farm which through subsequent subdivision had thirty-two part-owners in 1969. The emergent land remains in common, and the owners regulate it through their own part-owners' meeting and an elected administrative officer. They have recently requested, however, a partition of their common property — two similar partitions occurred in Replot in 1957 among other part-owners of emergent land adjoining *urfjäll* and left in common by its owners on the subdivision of their farms. Land which has emerged around the island since the 1910 partition belongs in common to Replot village; thus the original *urfjäll* island is now surrounded by two successive rings of emergent land belonging to two different groups of owners. The owner of the *urfjäll* has taken the precaution of purchasing from one of the part-owners of the inner ring a share in commonly owned land and water. This share, expressed as a fraction of a *mantal*, has not been demarcated on the ground but gives its owner a small voice in decisions concerning the use and disposal of the emergent land. In the normal way, the group of part-owners owning the inner ring, constituting the immediately adjoining holding, will purchase the outer ring of emergent land. They will then be entitled to partition all their common property, the owner of the *urfjäll* receiving his due share. Since this share is too small to entitle him to all of the emergent land surrounding the *urfjäll*, he has instead requested the right to purchase both rings of emergent land under the 1961 amendment allowing individual owners to purchase emergent land which can only be reasonably used by the adjoining holding. The procedure to be adopted lies in the hands of the land-surveyor, who can determine whether purchase by the *urfjäll's* owner is a more practical solution than arranging a land exchange which would consolidate the emergent land in a compact parcel on one part of the island.

The second amendment of 1961, allowing individual holdings to request the purchase of emergent land which cannot be reasonably used otherwise and where a land exchange is not possible, has begun to be exercised by summer-cottage owners in the Vaasa and Jakob-stad areas. The purchase price has generally been fixed as a compromise between the market values of recreational and forest land. In the Maxmo archipelago, the owner of a summer-cottage plot of 0·17 ha, situated on a former islet, purchased in 1972 an area of 0·20 ha of sandy alder woodland and periodically inundated natural meadow which cut his plot off from the shore. Since uncertainty surrounds the exact ownership of the emergent land in this area, the purchase sum was deposited with Vaasa County Council for safe keeping, as the sum was so little in relation to the legal costs of unravelling its correct ownership. In Iskmo village, where a summer-cottage owner has purchased 0·04 ha of emergent land, an administrative officer has been appointed to take care of the income until the villagers establish a formal part-owners' assembly.

The 1961 law also affords a convenient procedure for dealing with emergent land at a New Partition, as the increasing number of landowners, the proliferation of summer cottages, and the growing complexity of land tenure render the allocation of shares in emergent land on the basis of *mantal* an ever more laborious undertaking. In 1972, in connection with the revision of the New Partition in Petsmo, the sixty holdings bordering the shore purchased a total of 17·63 ha of emergent land which had emerged since the original map for the New Partition was completed in 1921. The emergent land was classified into three categories: the first was land suitable for recreational development, and fetched the highest price; the second category was forest land; and the third category, with the lowest value, was swampy shoreland. The income was paid into the village account, to be disposed of for general purposes or to be shared out according to the decision of the part-owners' meeting. In Sundom, incorporated in Vaasa at the beginning of 1973, there are numerous recreational dwellings which must be taken into consideration in the New Partition that began there in 1956. A total of 98 ha emerged along the 14 km-long mainland coast between 1900 and 1956, and the summer-cottage owners will probably purchase the emergent land in connection with the repartition. The emergent land has been demarcated and excluded from the area undergoing reallocation; once the new boundaries of the holdings are fixed, the purchase of the emergent land by the adjoining holdings will be the most practical solution. A request to deal in the same way with emergent land in the Sundom skerry guard, which is not included in the New Partition, has also been made. The New Partition has been delayed while awaiting the construction of a road bank and bridge to Vaskiluoto, considerably shortening the route to the centre of Vaasa, since the land cannot be graded until it is known how a direct road link to the centre of the town will affect land values. Meanwhile, Vaasa Corporation has been buying land in Sundom opposite Vaskiluoto in order to secure control over the future use of the area, which the town plans to reserve for expanding harbour facilities, industry and dwellings. The town bought more than 400 ha of land in Sundom from 1966 to the beginning of 1972, including 50 ha of emergent land purchased from the village in 1966 and 1967. The income from the sales, as from the leasing of summer cottages on the emergent land, has been shared at intervals among the part-owners in Sundom. They have been careful not to include rights to a share in the village's common fishing-waters in the sales. Instead, the town has purchased the water area immediately adjoining its purchases of emergent land. The future of summer cottages leased on the purchased emergent land is uncertain.

Thus, to sum up, the determining factor for allocating emergent land to holdings under the 1961 amendments to the Land Partition Act is its rational use. Subject to the owners' right of appeal, the land-surveyor has responsibility for choosing the most practical solution. The loss by individual owners of part of their ownership rights is compensated financially. The aim of the traditional Parti-tion of Emergent Land to maintain strict rights of ownership by division according to *mantal* had become increasingly incompatible with the aim of integrating the emergent land into the existing land-tenure pattern; the most common result was the inefficient parcelling of emergent land into numerous small lots, which often produced practical problems of use. The model legislative solution was becoming less attainable as time went on, with the result that it became necessary to introduce legislative changes to improve the model solution. The 1961 amendments strengthened the provisions designed to bring about rational land tenure. The legislative model has been given greater flexibility, and consequently the actual solu-tions have a greater chance of satisfying the aims of the legislation.

The physical phenomenon of land uplift continually interacts with cultural, social and economic factors to produce distinctive geographical patterns. Owing to special geographical and historical circumstances, the Vaasa area affords a deeper view than other areas of the contemporary problems which, as a result of land emergence, face farmers and townspeople, as well as professional people such as land-surveyors. Human activity is affected by land emergence along the length of the Bothnian coast, on both the Finnish and Swedish shores. Human responses from place to place show both similarities and differences; such responses have varied in the past, and new ones are likely to appear in the future. The pattern of future land emergence is indicated by the marine con-tours on the sea charts published by the Finnish and Swedish Boards of Navigation, and new problems can arise as islands emerge in outer territorial waters. A study of past and present solutions can contribute to finding solutions in the future.

Notes and References

Chapter 1 *Finland, Daughter of the Sea*
1   Vita-Finzi, C. 'Early man and environment', in Cooke, R. U., and Johnson, J. H. (eds) *Trends in Geography* (Oxford, 1969), 102.
2   Lambert, A. M. *The Making of the Dutch Landscape* (1971).
3   Andrews, J. T. *A geomorphological study of post-glacial uplift with particular reference to Arctic Canada*, Institute of British Geographers, Special Publication, 2 (1970), xxi, 8.
4   Bell, R. 'Proofs of the rising of the land around Hudson Bay', *American Journal of Science*, 151 (1896), 219–28.
5   Smeds. H. 'Finland', in Sømme, A. (ed) *A Geography of Norden* (Oslo, new edition, 1968), 155.
6   Renqvist, H. 'Finlands sekulära arealtillväxt', *Beretning om det 18. Skandinaviske Naturforskerm de i København 26–31 August 1929* (1929), 466–7.
7   Topelius, Z. *En resa i Finland* (Helsingfors, 1873), 5.
8   Lönnrot, E. *Kalevala. The land of heroes*, I (1907), 6–8 (translated by W. F. Kirby); original in Finnish (Helsinki, 1838–49). Topelius's father, Zachris Topelius sr, collected and published Finnish folk poems of the *Kalevala* type before Lönnrot's work first appeared.
9   Smeds, H. 'The Replot skerry guard: emerging islands in the northern Baltic', *Geographical Review*, 40 (1950), 103–33; 'Den österbottniska skärgårds- och tillandningskusten', *Svensk Geografisk Årsbok 1950* (Lund, 1950), 119–34

Chapter 2 *The Physical Phenomenon*
1   Erici, E. *Postilla eli ulgostoimitus nijnen evangeliumitten päälle cuin ymbäri aiastaian saarnaten Jumalan seuracunassa*, I (Stockholm, 1621), 40.
2   Jutikkala, E. 'Kirjallinen ja kansanomainen traditio Hämeessä v. 1605 tapahtuneesta luonnonmullistuksesta', *Historiallinen Arkisto*, 46 (1939), 9–25.
3   Ehnholm, G. 'Fisket under 1400- och 1500-talen i Kvarkens skärgård', *Budkavlen*, 23 (Åbo, 1944), 123.
4   Ström, H. 'Korsholms kungsgård 1556–1622', *Historiallinen Arkisto*, 39:3 (1932), 40.
5   Högbom, A. G. 'Nivåförändringarna i Norden. Ett kapital ur den svenska naturforskningens historia', *Göteborgs Kungl. Vetenskaps- och Vitterhets-Samhälles Handlingar*, fjärde följden, 21–22 (1920).

6 Hiärne, U. *Den korta anledningen til åthskillige malm och jordeslags etc. efterspörjande och angifwande, beswarad och förklarad jämte deras natur, födelse och i jorden tilwerdande, samt uplösning och anatomie, i gjörligaste måtto beskrifwan. Första flock om watn* (Stockholm, 1702); *Den beswarad och förklarade anledningens andra flock om jorden och landskap i gemeen* (Stockholm, 1706).

7 Swedberg, E. *Om watnens högd och förra werldens starcka ebb och flod, bewjs utur Swerige* (Stockholm, 1719); Celsius, A. 'Anmärkning om vatnets förminskande, så i Östersiön som i Vesterhafvet', *Kongl Svenska Wetenskaps Academiens Handlingar*, 4 (1743), 33–50; Linné, C. von. *De terrae habitabilis incremento* (Uppsala, 1743).

8 Runeberg, E. O. 'Anmärkning om några förändringar på jord-ytan i allmänhet och under det kalla climat i synnerhet', *K. Svenska Vetensk-Akad Handl*, 26 (1765), 81–115.

9 Mead, W. R. 'Zachris Topelius', *Norsk Geografisk Tidsskrift*, 22 (1968), 93; Jones, M. 'Landhöjningen i Zachris Topelius ögon', *Österbotten 1971* (Vasa, 1971), 205–32.

10 Moberg, A. 'Om finska kustens höjning under åren 1858–72', *Öfversikt af Finska Vetenskaps-Societetens Förhandlingar*, 15 (1873), 118–20.

11 Sieger, R. 'Seenschwankungen und Strandvershiebungen in Skandinavien', *Zeitschrift der Gesellschaft für Erdkunde zu Berlin*, 28 (1893), 395–488.

12 Kääriäinen, E. 'On the recent uplift of the Earth's crust in Finland', *Fennia*, 77:2 (1953), 12.

13 Witting, R. 'Hafsytan, geoidytan och landhöjningen utmed Baltiska hafvet och vid Nordsjön', *Fennia*, 39:5 (1918).

14 Lisitzin, E. 'Contribution to the knowledge of land uplift along the Finnish coast', *Fennia*, 89:4 (1964), 7, 14.

15 Sirén, A. 'On computing the land uplift from the lake water level records in Finland', *Fennia*, 73:5 (1951).

16 Kääriäinen, E. *Fennia* (1953); 'Land uplift in Finland computed by the aid of precise levellings', *Fennia*, 89:1 (1963), 15–18.

17 Hyyppä, E. 'The Late-Quaternary land uplift in the Baltic sphere and the relation diagram of the raised and tilted shore levels', *Annales Academiae Scientiarum Fennicae*, Series A III, 90 (1966), 153–68.

18 Kääriäinen, E. 'The Second Levelling of Finland in 1935–1955', *Veröffentlichungen des Finnischen Geodätischen Institutes*, 61 (1966), 47–8.

19 Ibid, 9.

20 The methods of calculation are explained by Kääriäinen, *Fennia* (1953), 36–61 and *Veröff Finn Geod Inst* (1966), 40–3.

21 Kääriäinen, *Fennia* (1953), 28.

22 Hela, I. 'A study of land upheaval at the Finnish coast', *Fennia*, 76:5 (1953), 29: Lisitzin, *Fennia* (1964), 19; Andrews, J. T. *A geomorphological study* (1970), 124.

23 Lamb, H. H. *The Changing Climate. Selected papers* (1966), 2, 13, 58–9, 118–19, 170, 197–200.

24 Hela, *Fennia* (1953), 29.

25 Kääriäinen, *Veröff Finn Geod Inst* (1966), 41.

26 Kukkamäki, T. J. 'Report of the work of the Fennoscandian Sub-Commission', *Problems of recent crustal movements. Third International Symposium. Leningrad, U.S.S.R., 1968* (Moscow, 1969), 49–54.

27 Kääriäinen, *Fennia* (1953), 29.

28 Jamieson, T. F. 'On the history of the last geological changes in Scotland', *Quarterly Journal of the Geological Society of London*, 21 (1865), 178.

29 Sauramo, M. 'The Quaternary geology of Finland', *Bulletin de la Commission Géologique de Finlande*, 86 (1929); 'The mode of the land upheaval in Fennoscandia during Late-Quaternary time', *Fennia*, 66:2 (1939); *Suomen luonnon kehitys jääkaudesta nykyaikaan* (Helsinki, 1940); 'Die Geschichte der Ostsee', *Annls Acad Sci Fenn*, Series A III, 51 (1958).

30 De Geer, G. 'Om Skandinaviens nivåförändringar under qvartär-perioden', *Geologiska Föreningens i Stockholm Förhandlingar*, 10 (1888), 366–79, and 12 (1890), 61–110.

31 Witting, R. *Fennia* (1918); 'La soulèvement récent de la Fennoscan-die. Quelques mots à propos de l'article de M. Rune dans ces Annales', *Geografiska Annaler*, 4 (1922), 458–87; 'Landhöjningen utmed Baltiska havet under åren 1898–1927', *Fennia*, 68:1 (1943).

32 Rune, G. A. 'Quelques remarques au mémoire de M. Witting sur la surface de la mer, la surface géoidïque et l'élevation Fennoscandinave', *Geogr Annlr*, 4 (1922), 194.

33 Lisitzin, *Fennia* 1964), 8–9.

34 Witting, *Fennia* (1918), 299; Härme, M. 'On the sheer zones and fault lines in Finnish Pre-Cambrian strata', *Fennia*, 89:1 (1963), 29–31; Paarma, H. 'On the tectonic structure of the Finnish basement, especially in the light of geophysical maps', *Fennia*, 89:1 (1963), 33.

35 Nikolayev, N. I. 'Late-stage neotectonic movements in Scandinavia, Karelia and the Kola peninsula', *Doklady of the Academy of Sciences of the U.S.S.R. (Doklady Akademii Nauk SSSR) Earth Science Section*, 167:1–6 (Washington, 1966), 60–2; Nikolayev, N. I., Babak, V. I., and Medyantsev, A. I. 'Some neotectonic problems of the Baltic Shield and the Norwegian Caledonides', *Baltica*, 3 (Vilnius, 1967), 183–202.

36 Stille, H. 'Recent deformations of the Earth's crust in the light of those of earlier epochs', in Poldervaart, A. (ed) *Crust of the Earth (a symposium)*, Geological Society of America, Special Paper, 62 (1955), 173; Innes, M. J. S., and Weston, A. A. 'Crustal uplift of the Canadian Shield and its relation to the gravity field', *Annls Acad Sci Fenn*, Series A III, 90 (1966), 175; Lyustikh, E. N., and Magnitskii, V. A. 'Vertical movements of the Earth's crust, changes in the gravity field in time, and displacement of sub-crustal masses', in Gerasimov, I. P. (ed) *Recent Crustal Movements. Collection of articles no. 1* (Jerusalem, 1967), 31; Andrews, A. *Geomorphological Study*, (1970), 124.

37 Honkasalo, T. 'Gravity and land upheaval in Fennoscandia', *Annls Acad Sci Fenn*, Series A III, 90 (1966), 139–41; Lyustikh and Magnitskii, *Recent Crustal Movements* (1967), 30–3.

38 Seppälä, M. 'Onko maankohoamisen syynä jääisostasia?', *Terra*, 81 (1969), 241–6; Aario, L. 'Landhebung und Eisisostasie in Finnland', *Abhandlungen des 1. Geographischen Instituts der Freien Universität Berlin*, 13 (1970), 55–68.

39   Ramsay, W. 'On relations between crustal movements and variations of sea-level during Late Quaternary time, especially in Fennoscandia', *Fennia*, 44:5 (1924).

40   Donner, J. J. 'The Quaternary of Finland', in Rankama, K. (ed) *The Geologic Systems. The Quaternary*, I (New York, 1965), 258; Lundqvist, J. 'The Quaternary of Sweden', in Rankama (ed) *The Geologic Systems* (1965), 180–1.

41   Okko, M. 'The relation between raised shores and present land uplift in Finland during the past 8000 years', *Annls Acad Sci Fenn*, Series A III, 93 (1967).

42   Sauramo, *Bull Commn Géol Finl* (1929), *Suomen luonnon kehitys* (1940), and *Annls Acad Sci Fenn* (1958).

43   Helle, R. 'Strandwallbildungen im Gebiet am Unterlauf des Flusses Siikajoki', *Fennia*, 95:1 (1965); Jones, M. 'Raised beaches and land tenure in the Siikajoki area, Finland', *Terra*, 85 (1973), 210–16.

44   Mead, W. R. 'Finland', in *An Advanced Geography of Northern and Western Europe* (1967), 54.

45   Sauramo, *Bull Commn Géol Finl* (1929), 91–2.

46   Saarnisto, M. 'The Late Weichselian and Flandrian history of the Saimaa lake complex', *Commentationes Physico-Mathematicae*, 37 (1970); 'The upper limit of the Flandrian transgression of Lake Päijänne', *Commentat Physico-Math*, 41 (1971), 149–70; 'The history of Finnish lakes and Lake Ladoga', *Commentat Physico-Math*, 41 (1971), 371–88.

47   Blomqvist, E. 'Vattenståndsförändringar och strandförskjutningar i Pälkänevesi, Joutenselkä, Längelmävesi och Vesijärvi sjöar sedan början av 1600-talet', *Svenska Tekniska Vetenskapsakademien i Finland, Acta*, 4 (1926), 72–9.

48   Palmén, E. G. 'Äldre och nyare sjöfällningar och sjöfallningsförsök i Finland', *Fennia*, 20:7 (1902–3), 28–37.

49   Ibid, 22–3, 65–88.

50   Sauramo, M., and Auer, V. 'On the development of Lake Höytiäinen in Carelia and its ancient flora', *Bull Commn Géol Finl*, 81 (1928), 6.

51   Mead, W. R. *An Economic Geography of the Scandinavian States and Finland* (1958), 37 fn.

52   Saarnisto, M. 'The Flandrian history of Lake Höytiäinen, eastern Finland', *Bulletin of the Geological Society of Finland*, 40 (1968), 90.

53   Auer, V. 'Peat lands', in Suomi, a general handbook on the geography of Finland, *Fennia*, 72 (1952), 248–9.

54   Backman, A. L. 'Torvmarksundersökningar i mellersta Österbotten', *Acta Forestalia Fennica*, 12 (1919).

55   Huikari, O. *Primäärisen soistumisen osuudesta Suomen soiden synnyssä* (Helsinki, 1956).

56   Smeds, *Svensk Geogr Årsb* (1950), 125.

57   Renqvist, *Beretning* (1929).

58   Kääriäinen, *Fennia* (1953).

59   Kukkamäki, T. J. 'Korkeusmittausten lähtökorkeus', *Terra*, 68 (1956), 120.

60   Smeds, H. 'Geografisk översikt av de nuvarande svenskbygderna', in Sommerschield, F. E. (ed) *Den svenska folkstammen i Finland* (Helsingfors, 1940), 59.

61   Ylinen, M., and Matala, H. *Maankohoamisen merkitys Suur-Oulun kaavoitukselle* (Oulu, 1968); 'The significance of land uplift for the drawing of a town plan for Suur-Oulu', *Oulujärvi-Seuran Julkaisuja*, 4 (Oulu, 1971).
62   Rosberg, J. E. *Bottenvikens finska delta* (Helsingfors, 1895).
63   Säntti, A. A. 'Die rezente Entwicklung des Kokemäenjoki-Deltas', *Turun Yliopiston Maantieteellisen Laitoksen Julkaisuja*, 29 (1954), 5–16.
64   Rosberg, *Bottenvikens finska deltan* (1895), 246.
65   Varjo, U. 'Über finnische Küsten und ihre Entstehung unter besonderer Berücksichtigung der Bildungen ihrer trockenen Zone', *Fennia*, 91:2 (1964).
66   Jurva, R. 'Seas', in Suomi, a general handbook on the geography of Finland, *Fennia*, 72 (1952), 148.
67   Smeds, *Geogrl Rev* (1950), 116–17, and *Svensk Geogr Årsb* (1950), 122–3.
68   Hustich, I. 'Finlands kust i omvandling', *Terra*, 76 (1964), 189–200.
69   Brunberg-Schwanck, B., and Bärlund, U. 'Vegetation och landhöjning', *Skärgårdsboken* (Helsingfors, 1948), 257–91; Palomäki, M. 'Über den Einfluss der Landhebung als ökologischer Faktor in der Flora flacher Inseln', *Fennia*, 88:2 (1963).
70   Appelroth, E. 'Några av landhöjningen betingade skogliga särdrag inom den österbottniska skärgården', *Skärgårdsboken* (1948), 292–304.

Chapter 3   *The Human Problem*

1   Mead, *An Economic Geography* (1958), 36.
2   The dates in this chapter are according to the chronology revised on the basis of radiocarbon measurements by Siiriäinen, A. 'Über die Chronologie der steinzeitlichen Küstenwohnplätze Finnlands im Lichte der Uferverschiebung', *Suomen Museo*, 76 (1969), 68–9; 'A gradient/time curve for dating Stone Age shorelines in Finland', *Suom Mus*, 79 (1972), 10; 'Studies relating to shore displacement and Stone Age chronology in Finland', *Finskt Museum*, 80 (1973), 6–9, 11, 14; and personal communication.
3   Siiriäinen, A. 'Archeological background of ancient Lake Päijänne and geological dating of the Meso-Neolithic boundary in Finland', *Bull Geol Soc Finl*, 42 (1970), 119–27; Saarnisto, *Commentat Physico-Math* (1970).
4   Meinander, C. F. 'Förutsättningarna för den förhistoriska bebyggelsen i södra Österbotten', *Nordenskiöld-Samfundets Tidskrift*, 6 (1946), 79–81; Äyräpää, A. 'The settlement of prehistoric age', in Suomi, a general handbook on the geography of Finland, *Fennia*, 72 (1952), 292–3; Kivikoski, E. *Finland*, Ancient Peoples and Places series (1967), 47–52.
5   Äyräpää, A. 'Den yngre stenålderns kronologi i Finland och Sverige', *Finskt Mus*, 62 (1955), 11, 15; Meinander, C. F. 'Kolsvidja', *Finska Fornminnesföreningens Tidskrift*, 58 (1957), 203–4; Kivikoski, *Finland* (1967), 54–5.
6   Kivikoski, *Finland* (1967), 56–8.
7   Meinander, C. F. 'Dåvits. En essä om förromersk järnålder', *Finskt Mus*, 76 (1969), 27–69.

8   Meinander, *Nordenskiöld-Samf Tidskr* (1946), 89–100; Äyräpää, *Fennia (1952)*, 295–8; Kivikoski, *Finland* (1967), 69–134.

9   Kerkkonen, G. *Västnyländsk kustbebyggelse under medeltiden* (Helsingfors, 1945), 269–77; Luukko, A. *Etelä-Pohjanmaan historia*, II (Helsinki, 1950), 74–81; Ahlbäck, O. 'Medeltida utmarksrätt i Finland', *Saga och sed. Kungl. Gustav Adolfs Akademiens årbok 1962* (Uppsala, 1962), 22–3.

10   Luukko, A. 'Erämark', in *Kulturhistoriskt lexikon för nordisk medeltid från vikingatid till reformationstid*, IV (Helsingfors, 1959), 39–45.

11   Ahlbäck, O. *Saga och sed* (1962), 24–6.

12   Luukko, *Etelä-Pohjanmaan historia* (1950), 78; Ahlbäck, O. *Saga och sed* (1962), 24.

13   Ahlbäck, R. 'Rätten till fiske i Skärgårdshavet', *Historisk Tidskrift för Finland*, 36 (1951), 2–5; Ahlbäck, O. *Saga och sed* (1962), 27–32.

14   Hiärne, *Den beswarad och förklarad anledningens andra flock* (1706), 286–7.

15   Hiärne, *Den beswarad och förklarad anledningens andra flock* (1706), 289.

16   1 Swedish mile = 10 km.

17   Celsius, K. *Svenska Wetensk Acad Handl* (1743), 36–44.

18   Runeberg, K. *Svenska Vetensk-Akad Handl* (1765), 102–3.

19   Smeds, H. 'Skärgårdens kulturlandskap', *Skärgårdsboken* (1948), 551.

20   Birck, E. L. 'Om jordbruket med binäringar i 1700-talets Österbottcn', *Österbotten 1971* (1971), 160–2.

21   Vilkuna, K. 'Gränsen mellan Sverige och Finland i etnologisk belysning', *Rig*, 34 (Stockholm, 1951), 41–6.

22   Smeds, H. *Malaxbygden* (Helsingfors, 1935), 152–4.

23   Wikman, K. R. V. 'En beskrivning över Vörå socken år 1825', *Budkavlen*, 7 (Åbo, 1928), 122.

24   Cajanus, E. *Historisk och oeconomisk beskrifning öfver Cronoby Sokn uti Österbotn* (Åbo, 1755 and Helsingfors, 1956), 33.

25   Ehnholm, G. 'Fisket i Helsingby åminne jämte angränsande byvatten från 1500-talet intill nutiden', *Brage Årsskrift*, 41–42 (Vasa, 1948), 79–86.

26   Smeds, *Malaxbygden* (1935), 236, 292–4, 296–9, 302–3, 305–7.

27   Jones, *Österbotten* (1971).

28   Mead, *An Economic Geography* (1958), 40.

29   Mead, *An Advanced Geography of Northern and Western Europe* (1967), 63.

30   Gardberg, C. J. 'Turku — ancient capital of Finland', *Introduction to Finland 1963* (Porvoo, 1963), 19.

31   Säntti, A. A. 'Die Häfen an der Kokemäenjoki-Mündung', *Fennia*, 74:3 (1951).

32   Aspelin, H. E. *Wasa stads historia* (Nikolaistad, 1892), 67–9, 694–703; Smeds, H. *Svenska Österbotten. Vasatraktens kust- och skärgårdskommuner* (Helsingfors, 1953), 11–20; Hoving, V. *Vasa 1852–1952. En krönika om Vasa och vasabor under hundra år* (Vasa, 1956), 22–7, 267–71.

33   Wichmann, V. K. E. *Nykarleby stad 1620–1920* (Helsingfors, 1920), 9–14, 31–3, 75–8.

34 Söderhjelm, A. *Jakobstads historia*, I (Helsingfors, 1907), 14–15, 133; III (Helsingfors, 1914), 135, 424.
35 Mickwitz, A., and Möller, S. *Gamlakarleby stads historia*, I (Åbo, 1951), 1–19.
36 Mead, W. R. *Farming in Finland* (1953), 177.
37 Air photos in Smeds, *Skärgårdsboken* (1948), 536–7, and *Geogrl Rev* (1950), 123.
38 Mead, *An Economic Geography* (1958), 44.
39 Palmén, *Fennia* (1902–3), 18–20; Jutikkala, *Historiallinen Arkisto* (1939), 9–13.
40 Åkerblom, K. V. *Korsholms historia*, I (Vasa, 1941), 72–8; Nikander, G. 'By och bonde i Svenskösterbotten', *Folklivsstudier*, V (Borgå, 1959), 82–5; Åkerblom, B. *Vörå sockens historia* I (Vasa, second edition, 1962), 217.
41 Åkerblom, K. V. *Korsholms historia*, II (Vasa, 1956), 42–7.
42 Hellström, F. E. *Undersökningar om det inflytande nivåförändringen i Bottniska Viken utöfvat på Gamla Carleby stadsplans hygieniska förhållanden* (Helsingfors, 1895), 19–24, 36–9, 43–4, 76–7.
43 Åkerblom, K. V. *Replot historia* (Vasa, 1958), 103.
44 Paulaharju, S. *Kuvauksia Hailuodosta. 'Vanhan väen muistelmain mukaan* (Helsinki, 1914), 62–6; Paasivirta, P. 'Piirteitä Hailuodon kulttuurimaantieteestä', *Terra*, 48 (1936), 82–4.
45 Smeds, H. 'Fäbodbebyggelse och fäboddrift i södra Österbotten', *Hem och Hembygd*, 6 (Helsingfors, 1929), 15–49; *Malaxbygden* (1935), 281–3; 'Fäbodbebyggelsen i Finland. En historisk-geografisk översikt', *Geographica*, 15 (1944), 192–232.
46 Smeds, *Malaxbygden* (1935), 17–19, 162, 172–5.
47 Smeds, *Svenska Österbotten* (1953), 53.
48 Ibid, 80–1.
49 Smeds, *Malaxbygden* (1935).
50 Mead, *Farming in Finland* (1953), 77.
51 Åkerblom, B. *Maxmo sockens historia* (Vasa, 1968), 36.
52 Säntti, A. A. 'Merestä kohoavan maan käyttö Etelä-Satakunnan rannikolla', *Terra*, 72 (1960), 84–6.
53 Illustrated with maps by Mead, *Farming in Finland* (1953), 78, 175.
54 Säntti, *Terra* (1960), 84–6.
55 Runeberg, *K. Svenska Vetensk-Akad Handl* (1765), 98.
56 Smeds, *Svensk Geogr Årsb* (1950), 130-1; Backholm, B. 'Från sumpmark till åkerjord', *Österbottnisk Årsbok 1958* (Vasa, 1958), 72–99.
57 Hustich, *Terra* (1964), 193–5.
58 Ibid, 196.
59 Ylinen and Matala, *Maankohoamisen merkitys* (1968), and *Oulujärvi-Seuran Julkaisuja* (1971).
60 Pölönen, H. F. 'Vesijätön jaosta', *Suomen Maanmittariyhdistyksen Aikakauskirja*, 48 (1939), 81.
61 Celsius, *K. Svenska Wetensk Acad Handl* (1743), 40.
62 Runeberg, *K. Svenska Vetensk-Akad Handl* (1765), 82.
63 'Rättsfall 12. Tvist om giltighet af en emellan stadsboar och byamän träffad förlikning, hvarigenom stadens innevänare till byamännen afstått mark som uppkommit genom tillandning af staden tillhöriga notvarp',

Tidskrift, utgifven af Juridiska Föreningen i Finland, 30 (1894), 265–7; Söderhjelm, *Jakobstads historia*, II (Helsingfors, 1909), 282–7.
64 Mead, *An Economic Geography* (1958), 40–2.
65 Ibid, 1

Chapter 4 *The Institutional Framework: Finnish Land-tenure Principles and Legislation*

1 Jutikkala, E. *Bonden i Finland genom tiderna* (Helsingfors, 1963), 76–89.
2 Helmfrid, S. 'The *storskifte, enskifte* and *laga skifte* in Sweden — general features', *Geogr Annlr*, 43 (1961), 115–18.
3 The provisions of the Great Partition are discussed in detail by Lagus, K. F. *Om jordaskiften enligt svensk-finsk lagstiftning* (Helsingfors, 1857), 52–155, and Moring, K. A. *Finlands skiftesrätt*, I (Helsingfors, 1922), 111–90.
4 Thulin, G. *Om mantalet*, I (Stockholm, 1890), 1–2, 12, 41; Jutikkala, *Bonden i Finland* (1963), 71–4, 111–12.
5 Helmfrid, S. ' "Storskifte" und "laga skifte" in Väveresunda. Ein Beispiel des kulturlandschaftsformenden Planungs- und Beschlussprozesses', *Geographische Zeitschrift*, 56 (1968), 194–212.
6 Jutikkala, *Bonden i Finland* (1963), 370, 387.
7 Ibid, 331, 388.
8 Ibid, 389.
9 Smeds, *Malaxbygden* (1935), 324–5.
10 Full details of the provisions of the New Partition are given by Moring, *Finlands skiftesrätt* (1922), 344–65.
11 Viiala, A. 'Den nya skifteslagen', *Tidskrift för Lantmän*, 33 (Helsingfors, 1951), 147.
12 Gylling, E. *Suomen torpparinlaitoksen kehityksen pääpiirteet ruotsinvallan aikana* (Helsinki, 1909), appendices, 76; Gebhard, H. *Subkomitén för den obesuttna befolkningen. Statistisk undersökning af socialekonomiska förhållanden i Finlands landskommuner år 1901*, III (Helsingfors, 1908), table appendices, 350–1, and I (Helsingfors, 1913), 93–7.
13 'Tilastollisia katsauksia — Statistical data', *Asustustoimikunnan Aikakauskirja*, 17:1 (Helsinki, 1964), 11–12.
14 Smeds, H. *A Geography of Norden* (1968), 173.
15 Kemppinen, V. and Linkojoki, P. 'Loma-asutus Suomessa 1960-luvun lopulla', *Valtakunnansuunnittelutoimiston Julkaisusarja*, A:26 (Helsinki, 1972), 20.
16 Smeds, *A Geography of Norden* (1968), 167; *Official Statistics of Finland*, XIV A, 69 (1973), 46.

Chapter 5 *The Legal Status of Emergent Land*

1 'Då genom behörigt skifte fiskevattnet under ett hemmans enskilda land tillfallit annan fastighet, men vattnet uttorkar och tillandning uppstår, hvilkendera lägenheten skall denna mark rätteligen tillhör?', *Juridiska Föreningens i Finland Tidskrift*, 3 (1868), 200.

2 Holmbäck, Å., and Wessén, E. 'Östgötalagan', *Svenska landskaps-lagar tolkade och förklarade för nutidens svenskar,* I (Uppsala, 1933), 241-2 fn 137.
3 Ahlbäck, O. *Saga och sed* (1962), 27-30; cf Luukko, *Etelä-Pohjan-maan historia* (1950), 120-1.
4 Lang, J. N. *Om eganderätten till Finlands vatten* (Helsingfors, 1905), 56.
5 Ibid, 46.
6 Jutikkala, *Bonden i Finland* (1963), 47.
7 Lang, *Om eganderätten* (1905), 56-7.
8 Ibid, 60.
9 Ibid, 60-1.
10 Haataja, K. *Jord- och vattenrätten samt skogs- och lantbrukslagstift-ningen* (Helsingfors, 1947), 134.
11 Lang, *Om eganderätten* (1905), 61.
12 Moring, *Finlands skiftesrätt,* III (Helsingfors, 1927), 812-15.
13 Ibid, 818; Haataja, *Jord- och vattenrätten* (1947), 132.
14 Fuller treatment by Moring, *Finlands skiftesrätt* (1927), 721-9.
15 Moring, *Finlands skiftesrätt* (1927), 722.
16 Ibid (1922), 103, (1927), 722.
17 Ibid (1922), 101.
18 Ibid (1922), 102-3, (1927), 726-7; Haataja, *Jord- och vattenrätten* (1947), 133.
19 Haataja, *Jord- och vattenrätten* (1947), 133.
20 Lang, *Om eganderätten* (1905), 58-9.
21 Serlachius, J. *Finsk vattenrätt allmäntfattlight framställd* (Helsingfors, 1909), 4; Lang, *Om eganderätten* (1905), 65.
22 Lang, *Om eganderätten* (1905), 59-60.
23 Moring, *Finlands skiftesrätt* (1927), 815.
24 Ibid
25 Ibid, 728
26 Ibid, 727.
27 Åkerblom, K. V. *Vassor bys historia* (Vasa, 1943), 55, 97.
28 Åkerblom, K. V. *Replot historia* (1958), 99-101.
29 Moring, *Finlands skiftesrätt* (1922), 275-7; cf Pölönen, *Suomen Maanmittyhd Aikak* (1939), 86.
30 Serlachius, *Finsk vattenrätt* (1909), 9-10; Haataja, *Jord- och vatten-rätten* (1957), 33-4.
31 Pölönen, *Suomen Maanmittyhd Aikak* (1939), 87.
32 Moring, *Finlands skiftesrätt* (1927), 739-40.

Chapter 6 *The Regulation of Emergent Land*
1 Haataja, *Jord- och vattenrätten* (1947), 138.
2 Åkerblom, B. *Vörå* (1962), 215.
3 Smeds, *Malaxbygden* (1935), 24 fn; Åkerblom, B. *Vörå* (1962), 215.
4 Åkerblom, K. V. *Korsholms historia* (1941), 33.
5 Åkerblom, K. V. *Lappfjärds historia,* II (Vasa, 1952), 14.
6 Åkerblom, B. *Vörå* (1962), 215.
7 Åkerblom, B. *Kvevlax historia* (1962), 30.
8 Åkerblom, B. *Vörå* (1962), 215-16.

9 Cf Lagus, *Om jordaskiften* (1857), appendix IV.
10 Åkerblom, K. V. *Korsholms historia* (1941), 182–3; Åkerblom, B. *Vörå* (1962), 227.
11 Suomaa, V. *Jakolainsäädäntö selityksineen* (Porvoo, second edition, 1971), 224.
12 Jutikkala, *Bonden i Finland* (1963), 24.
13 Nikander, *Folklivsstudier* (1959), 86.
14 Ibid, 104.
15 Jutikkala, *Bonden i Finland* (1963), 25.
16 Luukko, *Etelä-Pohjanmaan historia* (1950), 119–22.
17 Jutikkala, *Bonden i Finland* (1963), 25–6.
18 Nikander, *Folklivsstudier* (1959), 62, 127–8; Jutikkala, *Bonden i Finland* (1963), 26–30.
19 Nikander, *Folklivsstudier* (1959), 62, 104.
20 Ibid, 107–11.
21 Ibid, 111–13.
22 Ibid, 113–21.
23 Smeds, *Skärgårdsboken* (1948), 543; Gustafsson, E. 'Strömmingsfisket och livet i fiskelägena i Björkö för 50 år sedan', *Brage Årsskrift*, 43–52 (Vasa, 1958), 73–83; Nikander, *Folklivsstudier* (1959), 88–9,94–5.
24 Gardberg, J. 'Samfällda näringsfång i havsbandet', *Svenska Litteratursällskapets Folkloristiska och Etnografiska Studier*, 4 (Helsingfors, 1931), 128–33.
25 Nikander, *Folklivsstudier* (1959), 87.
26 Jutikkala, *Bonden i Finland* (1963), 263–7; Ahlbäck, R. 'De österbottniska byordningarna och deras bakgrund', *Västerbotten 1967* (Umeå, 1967), 199–206; 'Socklots byrätts protokoll 1751–1761', *Folklivsstudier*, VIII (Helsingfors, 1971), 7–10.
27 Jutikkala, *Bonden i Finland* (1963), 262–3; Ahlbäck, R. *Västerbotten* (1967), 206.
28 Wahlroos, A. 'Bidrag till kännedom om hafsstrandens förskjutning vid en del af Finlands vestkust', *Fennia*, 12:9 (1896), 12.
29 Haataja, *Jord- och vattenrätten* (1947), 168–72.
30 Ibid, 172–3.
31 Eyre, S. R., and Jones, G. R., 'Introduction', in *Geography as Human Ecology* (1966), 16.
32 Legal opinions and legal literature have a considerable creative influence on legislation, however.
33 In a sense, *urfjäll* are anomalies, since it was intended that as far as possible they should be exchanged at the Great Partition. cf Lang, *Om eganderätten* (1905), 76.
34 Helmfrid, *Geogr Z* (1968).
35 Jones, M. 'A model of human response to land emergence in the Vaasa area, Finland', *Terra*, 82 (1970), 1–9.

Chapter 7 *The Ownership and Use of Emergent Land in Practice: Examples from the Vaasa Area*

1 Luukko, *Etelä-Pohjanmaan historia* (1950), 68, 72.
2 Karsten, T. E. *Svensk bygd i Österbotten, nu och fordom. En namnundersökning*, I (Helsingfors, 1921), 561–3; Thors, C.-E. 'En österbottnisk

skärgårds förflutna i ortnamnens spegel', *Namn och bygd*, 56 (Lund, 1968), 20–1.

3 Luukko, *Etelä-Pohjanmaan historia* (1950), 76–7; Thors, *Namn och bygd* (1968).

4 Wallén, H. *Språkgränsen och minoriteterna i Finlands svenskbygder omkr. 1600–1865* (Åbo, 1932), 45.

5 Luukko, *Etelä-Pohjanmaan historia* (1950), 80, 113–15, 186; Huldén, L. 'Namnet Vörå', *Budkavlen*, 36 (Åbo, 1957), 2–3, 48; Åkerblom, B. *Vörå* (1962), 49, 59, 134, 149–50; Thors, *Namn och bygd* (1968), 21.

6 Cf Wallén, *Språkgränsen* (1932), 48–9; Luukko, *Etelä-Pohjanmaan historia* (1950), 186–7.

7 Åkerblom, B. *Vörå* (1962), 49–50; cf *Atlas of Finnish history* (Porvoo, second edition, 1963), 18–19.

8 Lamb, *The Changing Climate* (1966), 148.

9 Wikman, *Budkavlen* (1928), 50, 58.

10 Smeds, *Svenska Österbotten* (1953), 36; Huldén, *Budkavlen* (1957), 47–8.

11 Jones, M. 'Landhöjning och bebyggelse i Maxmonejden intill 1700-talet', *Hist Tidskr Finl*, 56 (1971), 145–58.

12 Smeds, *Malaxbygden* (1935), 43–4, and *Skärgårdsboken* (1948), 530.

13 Åkerblom, B. *Maxmo sockens historia* (1968), 14–16.

14 Luukko, *Etelä-Pohjanmaan historia* (1950), 116.

15 Cf Luukko, *Kulturhistoriskt lexikon* (1959); Kerkkonen, G. 'Obygderämark-nybygd. Kolonisatorisk bondeföretagsomhet i Norden', *Historiallinen Arkisto*, 60 (1966), 11–12.

16 Ehnholm, G. 'Michelsöarna, en gammal fiskeplats i Vasa skärgård', *Svenskbygden*, 1930 (Helsingfors, 1930), 112–15, 147–9; *Budkavlen* (1944), 116–32.

17 Smeds, *Svenska Österbotten* (1953), 34–8, 52–3, 66–7.

18 Smeds, *Skärgårdsboken* (1948), 530–1.

19 Cf Åkerblom, K. V. 'I Kvevlaks skärgård. Köklot ös historia', *Kalender utgiven af Svenska Folkskolans Vänner*, 34 (Helsingfors, 1919), 122–4.

20 Smeds, *Skärgårdsboken* (1948), 534.

21 Smeds, H. 'Tvenne 1700-talsnybyggen i Vasa skärgård', *Brage Årsskrift*, 41–2 (Vasa, 1948), 60.

22 Birck, *Österbotten* (1971), 35.

23 Wikman, *Budkavlen* (1928), 85.

24 Birck, *Österbotten* (1971), 50.

25 Smeds, *Svenska Österbotten* (1953), 36.

26 Åkerblom, K. V. *Vassor bys historia* (1943), 84, 87.

27 Lang, *Om eganderätten* (1905), 76; Moring, *Finlands skiftesrätt* (1922), 105–6.

28 Lang, *Om eganderätten* (1905), 76–7; Moring, *Finlands skiftesrätt* (1927), 736.

29 Noted by Smeds, *Svensk Geogr Årsb* (1950), 126, and illustrated by Mead, *Farming in Finland* (1953), 175–7.

30 Åkerblom, K. V. 'Blad ur Replot sockens historia', *Kalender utgifven av Svenska Folkskolans Vänner*, 9 (Helsingfors, 1904), 165.

31 Smeds, *Skärgårdsboken* (1948), 551, 553.

32   Ahlbäck, R. *Folklivsstudier* (1971), 20.
33   Åkerblom, K. V. *Korsholms historia* (1941), 61.
34   Wikman, *Budkavlen* (1928), 55.
35   Åkerblom, K. V. *Replot historia* (1958), 111.
36   Wahlstedt, E. 'Västerhankmo', *Den österbottniska byn, En samling minnesbilder* (Helsingfors, 1943), 337.
37   Ibid, 336.
38   Smeds, *Georgrl Rev* (1950), 127–8.
39   Åkerblom, K. V. *Replot historia* (1958), 111.
40   Åkerblom, B. *Maxmo sockens historia* (1968), 114.
41   Åkerblom, K. V. *Replot historia* (1958), 91.
42   Moring, *Finlands skiftesrätt* (1921), 728.
43   Alm, G. *Fångstmän. Noveller* (Helsingfors, 1924), 54–5.

Index

Following Swedish and Finnish practice, å, ä and ö are placed at the end of the alphabet.

Figures in *italics* refer to a map or diagram on the specified page.

240